Middle School 3-2
기말고사 완벽대비

적중100

영어 기출 문제집

중3

천재 | 정사열

Best Collection

KB087730

구성과 특징

교과서의 주요 학습 내용을 중심으로 학습 영역별 특성에 맞춰 단계별로 다양한 학습 기회를 제공하여
단원별 학습능력 평가는 물론 중간 및 기말고사 시험 등에 완벽하게 대비할 수 있도록 내용을 구성

Words & Expressions

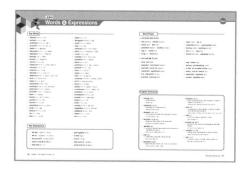

Step1	Key Words 단원별 핵심 단어 설명 및 풀이
	Key Expression 단원별 핵심 숙어 및 관용어 설명
	Word Power 반대 또는 비슷한 뜻 단어 배우기
	English Dictionary 영어로 배우는 영어 단어
Step2	실력평가 단원별 수시평가 대비 주관식, 객관식 문제풀이
Step3	서술형 대비 학업성취도 및 수행능력평가 대비 서술형 문제풀이

Conversation

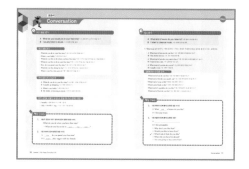

Step1	핵심 의사소통 소통에 필요한 주요 표현 방법 요약
	핵심 Check 기본적인 표현 방법 및 활용능력 확인
Step2	대화문 익히기 교과서 대화문 심층 분석 및 확인
Step3	교과서 확인학습 빈칸 채우기를 통한 문장 완성 능력 확인
Step4	기본평가 시험대비 기초 학습 능력 평가
Step5	실력평가 단원별 수시평가 대비 주관식, 객관식 문제풀이
Step6	서술형 대비 학업성취도 및 수행능력평가 대비 서술형 문제풀이

Grammar

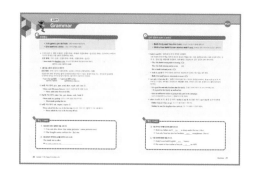

Step1	주요 문법 단원별 주요 문법 사항과 예문을 알기 쉽게 설명
	핵심 Check 기본 문법사항에 대한 이해 여부 확인
Step2	기본평가 시험대비 기초 학습 능력 평가
Step3	실력평가 단원별 수시평가 대비 주관식, 객관식 문제풀이
Step4	서술형 대비 학업성취도 및 수행능력평가 대비 서술형 문제풀이

Reading

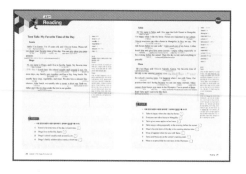

Step1	구문 분석 단원별로 제시된 문장에 대한 구문별 분석과 내용 설명
	확인문제 문장에 대한 기본적인 이해와 인지능력 확인
Step2	확인학습A 빈칸 채우기를 통한 문장 완성 능력 확인
Step3	확인학습B 제시된 우리말을 영어로 완성하여 작문 능력 키우기
Step4	실력평가 단원별 수시평가 대비 주관식, 객관식 문제풀이
Step5	서술형 대비 학업성취도 및 수행능력평가 대비 서술형 문제풀이
	교과서 구석구석 교과서에 나오는 기타 문장까지 완벽 학습

Composition

|영역별 핵심문제|
단어 및 어휘, 대화문, 문법, 독해 등 각 영역별 기출문제의 출제 유형을 분석하여 실전에 대비하고 연습할 수 있도록 문제를 배열

|단원별 예상문제|
기출문제를 분석한 후 새로운 시험 출제 경향을 더하여 새롭게 출제될 수 있는 문제를 포함하여 시험에 완벽하게 대비할 수 있도록 준비

|서술형 실전 및 창의사고력 문제|
학교 시험에서 점차 늘어나는 서술형 시험에 집중 대비하고 고득점을 취득하는데 만전을 기하기 위한 학습 코너

|단원별 모의고사|
영역별, 단계별 학습을 모두 마친 후 실전 연습을 위한 모의고사

교과서 파헤치기

- **단어Test1~3** 영어 단어 우리말 쓰기, 우리말을 영어 단어로 쓰기, 영영풀이에 해당하는 단어와 우리말 쓰기
- **대화문Test1~2** 대화문 빈칸 완성 및 전체 대화문 쓰기
- **본문Test1~5** 빈칸 완성, 우리말 쓰기, 문장 배열연습, 영어 작문하기 복습 등 단계별 반복 학습을 통해 교과서 지문에 대한 완벽한 습득
- **구석구석지문Test1~2** 지문 빈칸 완성 및 전문 영어로 쓰기

Lesson 7

Fact, Opinion, or Fake

 의사소통 기능

- 의견 묻기
  How do you feel about this drama?
- 이의 제기하기
  I don't agree (with you).

 언어 형식

- 간접화법
  Garcia-Fuller **said** she was teaching her students how to tell fake news from real news.
- 명사절을 이끄는 접속사 if
  You also have to check **if** they are based on facts.

Words & Expressions

Key Words

- **actually** [ǽktʃuəli] ⓟ 실제로, 사실
- **appear** [əpíər] ⑧ ~인 것 같다
- **artwork** [άːrtwərk] ⑲ 예술 작품
- **attack** [ətǽk] ⑧ 공격하다
- **boring** [bɔ́ːriŋ] ⑱ 지루한
- **check** [tʃek] ⑧ 확인하다
- **cheer** [tʃíər] ⑧ 환호하다
- **cleaner** [klíːnər] ⑲ 세제, 청소기
- **clown** [klaun] ⑲ 광대
- **comfortable** [kʌ́mfərtəbl] ⑱ 편안한
- **complete** [kəmplíːt] ⑱ 완전한
- **cool** [kuːl] ⑱ 멋있는, 시원한
- **critically** [krítikəli] ⑟ 비판적으로
- **cute** [kjuːt] ⑱ 귀여운
- **evidence** [évədəns] ⑲ 증거
- **false** [fɔːls] ⑱ 거짓의, 잘못된
- **friendly** [fréndli] ⑱ 친절한
- **funny** [fʌ́ni] ⑱ 우스운
- **healthy** [hélθi] ⑱ 건강한
- **information** [ìnfərméiʃən] ⑲ 정보
- **light** [lait] ⑱ 가벼운
- **major** [méidʒər] ⑱ 주요한, 주된
- **octopus** [άktəpəs] ⑲ 문어
- **offer** [ɔ́ːfər] ⑧ 제공하다
- **perfect** [pə́ːrfikt] ⑱ 완벽한

- **performance** [pərfɔ́ːrməns] ⑲ 공연, 수행
- **prefer** [prifə́ːr] ⑧ 선호하다
- **provide** [prəváid] ⑧ 제공하다
- **recently** [ríːsntli] ⑟ 최근에
- **save** [seiv] ⑧ 구하다
- **scared** [skɛərd] ⑱ 겁먹은
- **scary** [skɛ́əri] ⑱ 무서운
- **search** [səːrtʃ] ⑧ 찾다, 검색하다
- **seem** [siːm] ⑧ ~인 것 같다
- **sink** [siŋk] ⑧ 가라앉다
- **site** [sait] ⑲ 장소
- **skill** [skil] ⑲ 기술, 실력
- **smart** [smɑːrt] ⑱ 똑똑한
- **snake** [sneik] ⑲ 뱀
- **source** [sɔːrs] ⑲ 근원, 출처
- **spread** [spred] ⑱ 퍼진 ⑧ 퍼지다
- **support** [səpɔ́ːrt] ⑧ 지지하다, 후원하다
- **tooth** [tuːθ] ⑲ 이, 치아
- **totally** [tóutəli] ⑟ 전적으로
- **touching** [tʌ́tʃiŋ] ⑱ 감동적인
- **unclear** [ənklíər] ⑱ 불확실한
- **unique** [juːníːk] ⑱ 독특한
- **untrue** [əntrúː] ⑱ 사실이 아닌
- **wear** [wɛər] ⑧ 착용하다

Key Expressions

- **along with** ~와 함께
- **be based on** ~에 바탕을 두다
- **be made out of** ~로부터 만들어지다
- **by the way** 그런데
- **get along well with** ~와 잘 지내다
- **get scared** 겁먹다
- **give up** 포기하다
- **laugh out loud** 큰 소리로 웃다
- **look like** ~처럼 보이다

- **made up** 꾸며낸, 지어낸
- **make sense** 의미가 통하다
- **pass away** 돌아가시다
- **pay attention to** ~에 주의를 기울이다
- **slow down** 속도를 줄이다
- **take a break** 휴식을 취하다
- **tell A from B** A와 B를 구별하다
- **too good to be true** 너무 좋아서 믿어지지 않는
- **turn out** 판명되다

Word Power

※ 서로 비슷한 뜻을 가진 어휘

- □ **appear** ~인 것 같다 – **seem** ~인 것 같다
- □ **attack** 공격하다 – **strike** 치다, 공격하다
- □ **evidence** 증거 – **proof** 증거
- □ **major** 주요한, 주된 – **principal** 주된
- □ **recently** 최근에 – **lately** 최근에
- □ **totally** 전적으로 – **wholly** 전적으로

- □ **artwork** 예술 작품 – **craft** 공예품
- □ **check** 확인하다 – **examine** 조사하다
- □ **false** 거짓의, 잘못된 – **fake** 거짓의
- □ **offer** 제공하다 – **provide** 제공하다, **supply** 공급하다
- □ **search** 찾다 – **investigate** 조사하다
- □ **unclear** 불확실한 – **uncertain** 불확실한

※ 서로 반대의 뜻을 가진 어휘

- □ **attack** 공격하다 ↔ **defend** 방어하다
- □ **comfortable** 편안한 ↔ **uncomfortable** 불편한
- □ **false** 거짓의 ↔ **true** 진실인
- □ **light** 가벼운 ↔ **heavy** 무거운
- □ **perfect** 완벽한 ↔ **imperfect** 불완전한
- □ **untrue** 사실이 아닌 ↔ **true** 사실인

- □ **boring** 지루한 ↔ **exciting** 흥미로운
- □ **complete** 완전한 ↔ **incomplete** 불완전한
- □ **friendly** 친절한 ↔ **unfriendly** 불친절한
- □ **major** 주요한, 주된 ↔ **minor** 사소한
- □ **sink** 가라앉다 ↔ **float** 떠오르다

※ 명사 – 형용사

- □ **comfort** 편안함 – **comfortable** 편안한
- □ **health** 건강 – **healthy** 건강한

- □ **evidence** 증거 – **evident** 명백한
- □ **skill** 기술, 실력 – **skillful** 능숙한

※ 동사 – 명사

- □ **inform** 알려주다 – **information** 정보

- □ **perform** 공연하다 – **performance** 공연, 수행

English Dictionary

□ **attack** 공격하다
→ to try to hurt or damage someone or something using physical violence
물리적인 폭력을 사용하여 다치게 하거나 손상을 주려고 하다

□ **clown** 광대
→ a performer in a circus who wears funny clothes and bright make-up, and does silly things in order to make people laugh
서커스에서 우스운 옷을 입고 밝은 화장을 하고 사람들을 웃게 하려고 어리석은 행동을 하는 공연자

□ **critically** 비판적으로
→ in a way that expresses disapproval
불찬성을 표현하는 방식으로

□ **evidence** 증거
→ anything that causes you to believe that something is true
당신이 어떤 것이 사실이라고 믿도록 만드는 어떤 것

□ **false** 거짓의, 잘못된
→ incorrect, untrue, or mistaken
정확하지 않거나 사실이 아닌, 또는 잘못된

□ **lie** 거짓말
→ an untrue statement
사실이 아닌 진술

□ **major** 주된, 주요한
→ very important and serious
매우 중요하고 진지한

□ **octopus** 문어
→ a soft sea creature with eight long arms
여덟 개의 긴 다리를 가진 연한 바다 생물

□ **opinion** 의견
→ what you think or believe about something
무엇에 관하여 생각하거나 믿고 있는 것

□ **sink** 가라앉다
→ to disappear below the surface of the water
수면 아래로 사라지다

□ **spread** 퍼지다
→ to open it out or arrange it over a place or surface
한 장소나 표면 위에 펼치거나 배열하다

□ **support** 지지하다
→ to give assistance, approval, comfort, or encouragement to someone
어떤 사람에게 도움, 동의, 위로, 격려 등을 주다

□ **totally** 전적으로
→ completely, absolutely
완전하게, 절대적으로

서답형

01 다음 문장의 빈칸에 〈영어 설명〉에 맞게 한 단어로 쓰시오.

> In my _____, English is the most difficult subject.
> 〈영어 설명〉 a thought or belief about something or someone

02 다음 빈칸에 공통으로 들어갈 말로 가장 적절한 것은?

> • This new trend _____s to be continuing for a while.
> • A new vending machine will _____ at a subway station in Tokyo.

① check   ② spread
③ report   ④ appear
⑤ provide

03 다음 빈칸에 들어갈 말이 알맞게 짝지어진 것은?

> (A) My teacher got upset because my homework wasn't _____.
> (B) We must find the _____ of the information first.

① false – source
② complete – resource
③ critical – impressed
④ complex – resource
⑤ complete – source

[04~05] 다음 설명에 해당하는 단어를 고르시오.

04

> to try to hurt or damage someone or something using physical violence

① save   ② attack
③ support   ④ search
⑤ offer

05

> a performer in a circus who wears funny clothes and bright make-up, and does silly things in order to make people

① snake   ② octopus
③ clown   ④ source
⑤ crown

06 짝지어진 단어의 관계가 나머지 넷과 <u>다른</u> 것은?

① inform – information
② evidence – evident
③ comfort – comfortable
④ skill – skillful
⑤ health – healthy

서답형

07 다음 우리말에 맞게 주어진 단어를 이용하여 두 단어로 쓰시오.

> 그의 이야기는 거짓으로 밝혀졌다. (turn)

➡ His story _____ to be a lie.

서답형

08 다음 짝지어진 단어의 관계가 같도록 알맞은 말을 쓰시오.

> evidence – proof : fake – _____

01 〈보기〉에서 알맞은 단어를 선택하여 문장의 빈칸을 완성하시오. (필요하면 변형하여 쓰시오.)

┌─ 보기 ─┐
critical   scare   spread   sink
└─────┘

(1) The story quickly _____ to everyone.
(2) The workers must think _____ to solve problems.
(3) The little boy is _____ of monsters.
(4) If a boat has a hole in it, the boat will _____.

02 대화의 빈칸에 〈영영풀이〉에 해당하는 단어를 주어진 철자로 쓰시오.

┌─────────────────────┐
G: How do you feel about this drama?
B: I think it's very t_____. The boy gave up his life to save his sister.
└─────────────────────┘

┌─────────────────────┐
<영영풀이> making you feel pity, sympathy, sadness, etc.
└─────────────────────┘

➡ _____

03 다음 우리말과 같은 표현이 되도록 문장의 빈칸을 채우시오.

(1) 모든 승객들은 지하철에서 편안한 시간을 가질 권리가 있습니다.
  ➡ All passengers have a right to have a c_____ time in the subway.
(2) 매일 같은 것을 연습하는 것은 지루한 일입니다.
  ➡ Practicing the same thing every day is b_____.

(3) 온실가스 배출은 지구 온난화의 주요한 원인들 중 하나입니다.
  ➡ Greenhouse gas emission is one of the m_____ causes of global warming.
(4) 신호등이 노란색으로 바뀌는 것을 볼 때는 속도를 낮춰라.
  ➡ S_____ down when you see the traffic light turn yellow.

04 영영풀이에 해당하는 단어를 〈보기〉에서 찾아 첫 번째 빈칸에 쓰고, 두 번째 빈칸에는 우리말 뜻을 쓰시오.

┌─ 보기 ─┐
sink   support   octopus   spread
└─────┘

(1) _____: to give assistance, approval, comfort, or encouragement to someone: _____
(2) _____: to open it out or arrange it over a place or surface: _____
(3) _____: to disappear below the surface of the water: _____
(4) _____: a soft sea creature with eight long arms: _____

05 다음 문장의 빈칸에 들어갈 말을 〈보기〉의 단어를 이용하여 완성하시오.

┌─ 보기 ─┐
attention   tell   make up
└─────┘

(1) Students should _____ their teacher.
(2) His parents taught him how to _____ right _____ wrong.
(3) The story about the pink horse was _____.

Conversation

① 의견 묻기

• **How do you feel about this drama?** 이 드라마에 대해서 어떻게 생각하니?

■ 'How do you feel about ~?'은 '~을[~에 대해] 어떻게 생각해?'라는 의미로 상대방에게 어떤 대상에 대한 의견을 물을 때 사용하는 표현이다. 'What do you think about ~?(~에 대하여 어떻게 생각하니?)', 'What's your opinion about ~?(~에 대한 의견이 무엇이니?)', 'What do you say about ~?(~에 대하여 어떻게 생각하십니까?)'와 같은 표현을 사용하여 의견을 물어볼 수 있다. 'How do you like ~?'는 '~가 마음에 드니?'의 의미로 상대방이 만족하는지 등의 의견을 물어보는 표현이다.

■ 경험한 일을 바탕으로 하여 상대방의 의견이나 감정을 물을 때는 'Do you find it ~?(너는 ~하다고 생각하니?)'를 사용할 수 있다. 주로 가목적어 it을 사용하여 'find it+형용사+to부정사'의 형태가 되고 목적격보어로 쓰이는 다양한 형용사 다음에 진목적어인 to부정사가 따라온다.

■ 상대방의 의견을 물어보는 표현으로 'Would you find it easy/hard to ~ if you had the chance to ~?(만약 네가 ~할 기회가 있다면 너는 ~하는 것이 쉽다고/어렵다고 생각하니?)'를 사용할 수 있고, think를 사용하여 'Do you think it is easy/hard to ~?(너는 ~하는 것이 쉽다고/어렵다고 생각하니?)'와 같이 물어볼 수 있다.

상대방의 의견 묻기

• How do you feel about ~? ~에 대하여 어떻게 생각하니?

• What do you think about ~? ~에 대하여 어떻게 생각하니?

• What's your opinion about ~? ~에 대한 의견이 무엇이니?

• What do you say about ~? ~에 대하여 어떻게 생각하십니까?

• Do you find it ~? 너는 ~하다고 생각하니?

• Do you think it is easy/hard to ~? 너는 ~을 쉽다고/어렵다고 생각하니?

핵심 Check

1. 다음 우리말을 주어진 단어를 포함하여 영작하시오.

   G: Look at those shoes the girl is wearing. I think they're great. 그것에 대하여 어떻게 생각하니? (feel, how)

   B: I think they look light and comfortable.

   G: Right. I want to buy them for the school field trip.

   ➡ _____

② **이의 제기하기**

> • I don't agree (with you). 저는 동의하지 않아요.

- 'I don't agree with you.(나는 동의하지 않아요.)'는 상대와 의견이 달라서 동의하지 않고 상대의 의견에 이의를 제기하는 말이다. 'I have a different idea.(나는 생각이 달라.)', 'I don't think so.(나는 그렇게 생각하지 않아.)', 'I don't believe so.(그렇게 생각하지 않습니다.)', 'I disagree with you.(저는 반대합니다.)'도 이의를 제기하는 표현이다.

- 상대방의 말이나 의견에 동의할 때는 'You can say that again.'이라고 한다. 'I agree with you.'라고 할 수도 있다. 상대방에게 자신의 말에 대하여 동의를 구할 때 간단하게는 부가의문문을 덧붙여서 나타낼 수 있고, 구체적으로 'Don't you agree (with me)?'라고 하거나 '제 생각에 동의하지 않으세요?'의 의미로 'Don't you think so?'라고 할 수도 있다.

- 상대방의 표현에 동의할 때는 '나도 그래.'의 의미로 'Me, too.' 또는 'So+동사+주어.'의 형태를 쓴다. 이때 사용하는 동사는 be동사, do, does, did를 포함하는 조동사들이다. 부정문에 이어지는 경우에는 so 대신 neither를 사용하여 'Neither+동사+주어.'라고 하거나 'Me neither.'라고 할 수 있다.

이의 제기하기

- I don't agree with you. 나는 동의하지 않아.
- I don't think so. 나는 그렇게 생각하지 않아.
- I disagree with you. 저는 반대합니다.
- I have a different idea. 나는 생각이 달라.
- I don't believe so. 저는 그렇게 생각하지 않습니다.

동의하기

- You can say that again. 네 말이 맞아.
- So am/do I. 나도 마찬가지야.
- Me, neither. 나도 그래. (부정의 대답)
- I agree with you. 네 말에 동의해
- Me, too. 나도 그래. (긍정의 대답)

핵심 Check

2. 다음 대화의 내용으로 보아, 밑줄 친 말 대신 쓰기에 <u>어색한</u> 것은?

G: I like the coat the boy is wearing. I think it's warm and light.

B: Well, I don't agree with you. Actually, I bought one last week. It's not so warm, and it's much heavier than it looks.

G: Really? I don't believe it.

① I don't think so.
② I have a different idea.
③ You can say that again.
④ I don't believe so.
⑤ I disagree with you.

Conversation 교과서 대화문 익히기

Step UP - Real-life Scene

Alex: Big Mouth's show is really cool. ❶How do you feel about it?

Somi: Well, ❷I don't think it's that great.

Alex: Come on. I love Mr. Big Mouth. He always ❸makes me laugh out loud.

Somi: He's funny, but ❹don't believe everything he says.

Alex: All right. Oh, look at his photo of an octopus. ❺He said it lives in a tree.

Somi: It doesn't make sense.

Alex: He took the photo when it was climbing the tree. I don't think he's lying. It's a great photo.

Somi: ❻I don't agree with you. It's a fake photo. An octopus can't live out of the sea.

Alex: Big Mouth 쇼는 정말 굉장해. 너는 어떻게 생각하니?

소미: 글쎄, 나는 그렇게 대단한 것 같지 않아.

Alex: 왜 그래. 나는 Big Mouth 씨를 진짜 좋아해. 그는 언제나 나를 큰 소리로 웃게 해 줘.

소미: 웃기긴 하지만, 그가 하는 모든 말을 믿지는 마.

Alex: 알았어. 오, 그가 찍은 문어 사진을 봐. 그가 말하기를 그건 나무에 산대.

소미: 말도 안 돼.

Alex: 그는 문어가 나무에 기어 올라갈 때 사진을 찍었대. 그가 거짓말하고 있는 것 같지는 않아. 대단한 사진이야.

소미: 나는 네 말에 동의하지 않아. 그건 가짜 사진이야. 문어는 바다 밖에서는 살 수 없다고.

❶ 'How do you feel about ~?(~에 대해 어떻게 생각하니?)'의 뜻으로 상대방의 의견이나 느낌을 묻는 표현이다.
❷ 'I don't think (that)+주어+동사 ~.'는 '~하지 않다고 생각해.'라는 의미로 목적어를 이끄는 접속사 'that'이 생략되어 있다.
❸ 'make'는 사역동사로 'make+목적어(me)+목적격보어(동사원형: laugh)' 형태를 가진다. '~가 …하도록 하게 하다[시키다]'로 해석한다. 'out loud'는 '큰 소리로'의 뜻으로 'aloud'로 바꾸어 사용할 수 있다.
❹ '~하지 마'라는 의미로 명령문을 부정할 때 'Don't'나 'Never'를 사용한다. 'everything'과 'he says' 사이에는 목적격 관계대명사 'that'이 생략되어 있다.
❺ 동사 'said' 뒤에는 목적어를 이끄는 접속사 'that'이 생략되어 있다.
❻ 상대방의 말에 동의하지 않을 때 사용하는 표현으로 'I don't think so.'로 바꾸어 표현할 수 있다.

Check(√) True or False

(1) Alex thinks that Mr. Big Mouth's photo is real. T ☐ F ☐

(2) Alex said the octopus in the photo lives in a tree. T ☐ F ☐

 ### Start Off - Listen & Talk A 1

G: ❶Look at those shoes the girl is wearing. I think they're great. How do you feel about them?

B: I think they ❷look light and comfortable.

G: Right. I ❸want to buy them for the school field trip.

G: 저 여자애가 신고 있는 신발 좀 봐. 멋있는 것 같아. 너는 저 신발을 어떻게 생각해?

B: 가볍고 편안해 보여.

G: 맞아. 난 학교 체험 학습 때 신으려고 저걸 사고 싶어.

❶ 'the girl is wearing'은 선행사 'those shoes'를 수식하는 목적격 관계대명사절로 관계대명사 'that' 또는 'which'가 생략되어 있다.
❷ 'look+형용사' 형태로 '~하게 보인다'라는 의미이다.
❸ 'want'는 목적어로 to부정사를 취하는 동사이다.

Check(√) True or False

(3) The girl thinks those shoes the girl is wearing are great. T ☐ F ☐

(4) The boy agrees with the girl. T ☐ F ☐

Get Ready 2

(1) **G:** ❶There's no monkey like this in the world. Its nose is too big. I think it's fake.

B: I don't agree. I saw that kind of monkey on TV. It's real.

(2) **G:** This animal has a long nose and two long, sharp teeth. ❷What do you think of it? Is it real?

B: Well, let's search the Internet and check it together.

G: That's a good idea.

(3) **B:** What do you think of this animal?

G: It doesn't have legs, but it doesn't ❸look like a snake. It's very strange.

B: I think so, too.

(4) **B:** This monkey is very small. Is it real?

G: I don't know. Let's visit some animal fact sites and check it together.

B: That's a good idea.

❶ 'There is+단수명사'로 '~가 있다'는 의미이고, 'no'는 'not ~ any'의 의미로 명사를 부정할 때 사용한다.

❷ What do you think of[about] ~?: '~에 대해 어떻게 생각하니?'의 의미로 상대방의 생각을 물어볼 때 사용한다.

❸ 'look like+명사'는 '~처럼 보인다'라는 의미이다.

Start Off - Listen & Talk A 2

G: I like the coat the boy is wearing. I think it's warm and light.

B: Well, I don't agree with you. ❷Actually, I bought one last week. It's not so warm, and it's ❸much heavier than it looks.

G: Really? I don't believe it.

❶ 'the coat'와 'the boy' 사이에 목적격 관계대명사 'that/which'가 생략되어 있다.

❷ 'Actually'는 앞 문장의 말에 대해 강조하여 말할 때 사용하는 부사로 '사실'의 뜻이다.

❸ 'much'는 비교급을 강조하는 말로 '훨씬, 한층'의 의미로 해석한다. 'much' 대신에 'still, even, far, a lot'을 사용할 수 있다.

Start Off - Listen & Talk B

G: ❶How do you feel about this drama?

B: I think it's very touching. The boy gave up his life to save his sister. It's the best drama of this year.

G: I don't agree. It's not a good drama.

B: Come on. ❷Why do you think so?

G: It doesn't ❸seem real. And it's ❹a little boring.

❶ How do you feel about ~?: '~에 대해 어떻게 생각하니?'의 뜻으로 상대방의 의견이나 느낌을 묻는 표현이다.

❷ '왜 그렇게 생각하니?'의 의미로 'What makes you think so?'와 같은 표현이다.

❸ 'seem+형용사' 형태로 '~하게 보이다'로 해석한다.

❹ 'a little'은 부사구로 형용사 'boring'을 수식하고 '약간, 조금'의 뜻이다.

Start Off - Speak Up

A: How do you feel about this ad?

B: I think it's great. ❶It shows the phone is strong.

A: I don't agree. We should not believe every ad.

❶ 동사 'shows' 뒤에는 목적절을 이끄는 접속사 'that'이 생략되어 있다.

Start Off - Express Yourself A

1. **G:** How do you feel about these animals?

   B: They are very cute, but ❶I think cats don't get along well with dogs.

   G: I don't agree. And these two are good friends. They are enjoying the trip together.

2. **G:** How do you feel about this kid here?

   B: I think she is very pretty. ❷By the way, why did she cut her hair?

   G: Can you guess?

   B: Well, girls these days prefer short hair.

   G: I don't agree with that. Most girls like long hair better than short hair. And this kid here is not a girl. In fact, he is a boy.

   B: Really?

   G: Yes. He grew his hair ❸to help sick children.

3. **G:** How do you feel about the teddy bears?

   B: They are cute. Is there ❹anything special about them?

   G: They were made out of a police officer's uniform.

   B: Oh, I see.

   G: This police officer made them for the kids. Their dad was a police officer, and he ❺ passed away recently.

   B: That's very touching.

❶ 동사 'think' 뒤에는 목적절을 이끄는 접속사 'that'이 생략되어 있다. 'get along with ~'는 '~와 사이좋게 지내다, 잘 지내다'라는 뜻이다.

❷ 'By the way'는 대화나 글의 화제를 전환할 때 사용하는 표현으로 '그런데'의 의미이다.

❸ 'to help'는 부정사의 부사적 용법의 '목적'으로 '~하기 위해'의 의미다. 'so as to'나 'in order to'로 바꾸어 쓸 수 있다.

❹ 부정대명사 'anything'은 형용사가 뒤에서 수식을 한다. '-thing, -one, -body'로 끝나는 부정대명사는 형용사가 반드시 뒤에서 수식을 해야 한다.

❺ 'pass away'는 '돌아가시다'라는 의미이다.

Conversation **13**

● 다음 우리말과 일치하도록 빈칸에 알맞은 말을 쓰시오.

Get Ready 2

(1) G: There's no monkey _____ this in the world. Its nose is too big. _____ _____ it's _____.

B: I don't _____. I saw that _____ of monkey on TV. It's _____.

(2) G: This animal has a long nose and two long, _____ _____. _____ _____ _____ _____ _____ _____ it? Is it _____?

B: Well, let's _____ the Internet and _____ it together.

G: That's a good idea.

(3) B: _____ do you think of this animal?

G: It doesn't have legs, but it doesn't _____ _____ a snake. It's very _____.

B: I think so, _____.

(4) B: _____ monkey is very small. Is it _____?

G: I don't know. _____ visit some animal _____ sites and check it together.

B: That's a good idea.

Start Off - Listen & Talk A

1. G: Look at those shoes the girl is wearing. I think they're great. _____ _____ _____ _____ _____ them?

B: I think they look _____ and _____.

G: Right. I want _____ _____ them for the _____ _____ _____.

2. G: I like the coat the boy _____ _____. I think it's warm and light.

B: Well, I don't _____ _____ you. _____, I bought one last week. It's not so warm, and it's _____ _____ than it looks.

G: Really? I don't _____ it.

Start Off - Listen & Talk B

G: _____ do you _____ about this drama?

B: I think it's very _____. The boy _____ _____ his life _____ _____ his sister. It's the best drama of this year.

G: I don't agree. It's not a good drama.

B: Come on. _____ do you think so?

G: It doesn't _____ _____. And it's _____ _____ _____ _____.

(1) G: 세상에 이런 원숭이는 없어. 코가 너무 크잖아. 나는 그것이 가짜라고 생각해.

B: 나는 동의하지 않아. 저런 종류의 원숭이를 TV에서 본 적이 있어. 그건 진짜야.

(2) G: 이 동물은 긴 코와 두 개의 길고 날카로운 이빨을 가지고 있어. 그것을 어떻게 생각해? 진짜일까?

B: 음, 인터넷을 찾아보고 함께 확인해 보자.

G: 좋은 생각이야.

(3) B: 이 동물을 어떻게 생각해?

G: 그것은 다리가 없지만 뱀처럼 보이지는 않아. 정말 이상하네.

B: 나도 그렇게 생각해.

(4) B: 이 원숭이는 정말 작아. 진짜일까?

G: 모르겠어. 동물 사실 확인 사이트를 방문해서 함께 확인해 보자.

B: 좋은 생각이야.

1. G: 저 여자애가 신고 있는 신발 좀 봐. 멋있는 것 같아. 너는 저 신발을 어떻게 생각해?

B: 가볍고 편안해 보여.

G: 맞아. 난 학교 체험 학습 때 신으려고 저걸 사고 싶어.

2. G: 저 남자애가 입고 있는 코트가 마음에 들어. 따뜻하고 가벼울 것 같아.

B: 글쎄, 나는 동의하지 않아. 사실 나는 지난주에 저것을 샀어. 그렇게 따뜻하지도 않고 보기보다 훨씬 더 무거워.

G: 정말로? 믿을 수가 없어.

G: 이 드라마를 어떻게 생각하니?

B: 난 아주 감동적이라고 생각해. 소년이 그의 여동생을 구하기 위해 자신의 생명을 포기했잖아. 올해 최고의 드라마야.

G: 난 동의하지 않아. 그건 좋은 드라마가 아니야.

B: 이런. 왜 그렇게 생각해?

G: 현실적으로 보이지 않아. 그리고 약간 지루해.

Start Off - Speak Up

A: _____ do you feel _____ this _____?

B: I think it's great. It _____ the phone is strong.

A: I don't agree. We _____ _____ believe every ad.

Step Up - Real-life Scene

Alex: Big Mouth's show is really _____. _____ _____ _____ _____ _____ it?

Somi: Well, I don't think it's _____ great.

Alex: Come on. I love Mr. Big Mouth. He always _____ me _____ out _____.

Somi: He's funny, but don't believe everything he says.

Alex: All right. Oh, look at his photo of an _____. He said it lives in a tree.

Somi: It doesn't _____ _____.

Alex: He took the photo _____ it was _____ the tree. I don't think he's _____. It's a great photo.

Somi: I don't _____ you. It's a _____ photo. An octopus can't live _____ _____ the sea.

Express Yourself A

1. G: _____ do you feel _____ these animals?
   B: They are very cute, but I think cats don't _____ _____ well _____ dogs.
   G: I don't agree. And _____ _____ are good friends. They are _____ the trip _____.

2. G: How do you feel about this kid here?
   B: I think she is very pretty. _____ _____ _____, why did she cut her hair?
   G: Can you _____?
   B: Well, girls these days _____ short hair.
   G: I don't agree _____ that. Most girls like long hair _____ _____ short hair. And this kid here is not a girl. _____ _____, he is a boy.
   B: Really?
   G: Yes. He grew his hair _____ _____ sick children.

3. G: How do you _____ _____ the teddy bears?
   B: They are cute. Is there _____ _____ about them?
   G: They _____ _____ out of a police officer's _____.
   B: Oh, I see.
   G: This police officer made them for the kids. Their dad was a police officer, and he _____ _____ recently.
   B: That's very _____.

해석

A: 이 광고를 어떻게 생각하니?

B: 굉장하다고 생각해. 그건 그 전화기가 튼튼하다는 것을 보여주고 있어.

A: 나는 동의하지 않아. 우리는 모든 광고를 믿어서는 안 돼.

Alex: Big Mouth 쇼는 정말 굉장해. 너는 어떻게 생각하니?

소미: 글쎄, 나는 그렇게 대단한 것 같지 않아.

Alex: 왜 그래. 나는 Big Mouth 씨를 진짜 좋아해. 그는 언제나 나를 큰 소리로 웃게 해 줘.

소미: 웃기긴 하지만, 그가 하는 모든 말을 믿지는 마.

Alex: 알았어. 오, 그가 찍은 문어 사진을 봐. 그가 말하기를 그건 나무에 산대.

소미: 말도 안 돼.

Alex: 그는 문어가 나무에 기어 올라갈 때 사진을 찍었어. 그가 거짓말하고 있는 것 같지는 않아. 대단한 사진이야.

소미: 나는 네 말에 동의하지 않아. 그건 가짜 사진이야. 문어는 바다 밖에서는 살 수 없다고.

1. G: 이 동물들을 어떻게 생각해?
   B: 아주 귀엽지만, 고양이는 개와 잘 어울리지 못한다고 생각해.
   G: 나는 동의하지 않아. 그리고 이 둘은 좋은 친구야. 그들은 함께 즐겁게 여행하고 있어.

2. G: 여기 이 아이를 어떻게 생각해?
   B: 매우 예쁘다고 생각해. 그런데 그녀는 왜 머리카락을 잘랐니?
   G: 짐작할 수 있어?
   B: 음, 요새 여자아이들은 짧은 머리를 더 좋아하더라.
   G: 난 그것에 동의하지 않아. 대부분의 여자아이는 짧은 머리보다 긴 머리를 좋아해. 그리고 여기 이 아이는 여자아이가 아니야. 사실, 이 아이는 남자아이야.
   B: 정말이니?
   G: 응. 그는 아픈 아이들을 돕기 위해 머리를 길렀어.

3. G: 곰 인형들을 어떻게 생각해?
   B: 귀여워. 뭔가 특별한 점이 있니?
   G: 그것들은 한 경찰관의 제복으로 만들어졌어.
   B: 아, 그렇구나.
   G: 이 경찰이 아이들을 위해 그것들을 만들어 줬어. 그들의 아빠는 경찰관이었고, 최근에 세상을 떠나셨어.
   B: 아주 감동적이야.

01 우리말에 맞도록 주어진 단어를 활용하여 빈칸을 채우시오.

> 이 동물을 어떻게 생각해? (think)

➡ _____ do you _____ _____ this animal?

02 다음 대화의 빈칸에 들어갈 말로 <u>어색한</u> 것은?

> A: _____ classical music?
> B: I love it. It makes me calm down and feel happy.

① How do you feel about
② What do you think about
③ What do you say about
④ What do you know about
⑤ What's your opinion about

03 다음 대화의 빈칸에 들어갈 말로 알맞지 <u>않은</u> 것은?

> A: What do you think of listening to music while studying math?
> B: I think it's very helpful.
> A: _____

① I agree with you.
② I don't think so.
③ I've never done that.
④ I couldn't agree more.
⑤ I can't agree with you more.

04 다음 대화의 밑줄 친 말의 의도로 알맞은 것은?

> G: I like the coat the boy is wearing. I think it's warm and light.
> B: <u>Well, I don't agree with you.</u> Actually, I bought one last week. It's not so warm, and it's much heavier than it looks.

① 관심 표현하기   ② 이의 제기하기
③ 동의하기   ④ 의견 표현하기
⑤ 의도 표현하기

[01~02] 다음 대화를 읽고 물음에 답하시오.

G: How do you feel about this drama?

B: I think it's very (a)(touch). The boy gave up his life to save his sister. It's the best drama of this year.

G: _____(A)_____ It's not a good drama.

B: Come on. Why do you think so?

G: It doesn't seem real. And it's a little (b)(bore).

01 위 대화의 빈칸 (A)에 들어갈 말로 알맞은 것은?

① I couldn't agree more.

② I think so, too.

③ I can't agree with you more.

④ I don't agree.

⑤ You can say that again.

02 위 대화의 (a)와 (b)의 단어를 알맞은 형태로 고쳐 쓰시오.

(a) _____ (b) _____

[03~04] 다음 대화를 읽고 물음에 답하시오.

Alex: Big Mouth's show is really cool. How do you feel about it?

Somi: Well, I don't think it's that great.

Alex: Come on. I love Mr. Big Mouth. He always makes me laugh out loud.

Somi: He's funny, but don't believe everything he says.

Alex: All right. Oh, look at his photo of (a)an octopus. He said (b)it lives in a tree.

Somi: (c)It doesn't make sense.

Alex: He took the photo when (d)it was climbing the tree. I don't think he's lying. It's a great photo.

Somi: I don't agree with you. It's a fake photo. (e)It can't live out of the sea.

03 위 대화를 읽고 답할 수 없는 질문은?

① What are they talking about?

② What are they watching now?

③ Why does Alex like Mr. Big Mouth?

④ Does Somi agree with Alex about the photo?

⑤ Does Alex know a lot about an octopus?

04 위 대화의 (a)~(e) 중 가리키는 대상이 다른 하나는?

① (a)   ② (b)   ③ (c)   ④ (d)   ⑤ (e)

[05~06] 다음 대화를 읽고 물음에 답하시오.

G: I like the coat the boy is wearing. I think it's warm and light.

B: Well, I don't agree with you. ___(A)___, I bought one last week. It's not so warm, and it's ___(B)___ heavier than it looks.

G: Really? I don't believe it.

05 위 대화의 빈칸 (A)에 들어갈 말로 알맞은 것은?

① Therefore   ② For example

③ Actually   ④ However

⑤ On the other hand

06 위 대화의 흐름상 (B)에 들어갈 말로 알맞지 <u>않은</u> 것은?

① much   ② very

③ even   ④ still

⑤ a lot

서답형

07 다음 대화의 빈칸에 들어갈 단어를 주어진 영영풀이를 보고
3 단어로 쓰시오.

> G: How do you feel about these animals?
> B: They are very cute, but I think cats don't _____ _____ well _____ dogs.
> G: I don't agree. And these two are good friends. They are enjoying the trip together.

> <영영풀이> If two or more people get along, they have a friendly relationship.

➡ _____

[08~09] 다음 대화를 읽고 물음에 답하시오.

> G: (A)How do you feel about this kid here?
> B: I think she is very pretty. By the way, why did she cut her hair?
> G: Can you guess?
> B: Well, girls these days prefer short hair.
> G: I don't agree with that. Most girls like long hair better than short hair. And this kid here is not a girl. In fact, he is a boy.
> B: Really?
> G: Yes. He grew his hair to help sick children.

08 위 대화의 밑줄 친 (A)와 바꾸어 쓸 수 있는 말은?

① What do you know about this kid here?
② Have you ever met this kid here?
③ Why do you think so about this kid here?
④ What did you say to this kid here?
⑤ What's your opinion about this kid here?

중요
09 위 대화를 읽고 Fact에 해당하는 문장을 고르시오.

① Girls these days prefer short hair.
② This kid is very pretty.
③ Every girl likes long hair better than short hair.
④ This kid grew his hair to help sick children.
⑤ This kid here is a girl.

[10~11] 다음 대화를 읽고 물음에 답하시오.

> (1) G: This animal has a long nose and two long, sharp teeth. _____(A)_____ it? Is it _____(a)_____?
> B: Well, let's search the Internet and check it together.
> G: That's a good idea.
> (2) B: _____(A)_____ this animal?
> G: It doesn't have legs, but it doesn't look like a snake. It's very _____(b)_____.
> B: I think so, too.

10 위 대화의 빈칸 (A)에 공통으로 들어갈 말은?

① What do you think of
② Have you ever heard of
③ How did you like
④ How about seeing
⑤ Why did you feel so about

중요
11 위 대화의 흐름상 빈칸 (a)와 (b)에 들어갈 말로 알맞은 것은?

① fake – real
② interesting – real
③ real – strange
④ real – boring
⑤ fake – disappointing

[01~02] 다음 대화를 읽고 물음에 답하시오.

Alex: (A)Big Mouth's show is really cool.
_____(A)_____

Somi: Well, I don't think it's that great.

Alex: Come on. I love Mr. Big Mouth. He always makes me laugh out loud.

Somi: He's funny, but don't believe everything he says.

Alex: All right. Oh, look at his photo of an octopus. He said it lives in a tree.

Somi: It doesn't make sense.

Alex: He took the photo when it was climbing the tree. I don't think he's lying. It's a great photo.

Somi: _____(B)_____ It's a fake photo. An octopus can't live out of the sea.

01 위 대화의 빈칸 (A)와 (B)에 들어갈 말을 〈조건〉에 맞게 영어로 쓰시오.

┤ 조건 ├
(A) • Big Mouth's show에 대한 의견을 묻는 표현을 사용할 것.
 • 'feel'과 'it'을 사용할 것.
(B) • 'agree'를 이용하여 상대방의 의견에 동의하지 않는 표현을 사용할 것. (5 words)

(A) _____

(B) _____

02 위 대화를 읽고 다음 물음에 영어로 답하시오. (Because를 사용할 것.)

Q: Why does Alex like Mr. Big Mouth?

➡ _____

03 다음 대화의 빈칸 (A)와 (B)에 아래의 〈조건〉에 맞게 알맞은 표현을 쓰시오.

B: _____(A)_____ these animals?

G: They are very cute, but ___(B)___.

B: I don't agree. And these two are good friends. They are enjoying the trip together.

┤ 조건 ├
(A) 'about', 'think'를 이용하여 상대방의 의견을 묻는 표현을 쓸 것.
(B) '고양이는 개와 잘 어울리지 못한다고 생각해.'라는 의견을 말하는 표현을 쓸 것.

(A) _____

(B) _____

04 대화의 흐름상 빈칸 (A)에 들어갈 말을 〈조건〉에 맞게 쓰시오.

G: I like the coat the boy is wearing. I think it's warm and light.

B: Well, ___(A)___. Actually, I bought one last week. It's not so warm, and it's much heavier than it looks.

G: Really? I don't believe it.

┤ 조건 ├
'agree'를 이용할 것 (5 words)

➡ _____

Grammar

① 간접화법

• Garcia-Fuller **said** she was teaching her students how to tell fake news from real news.

Garcia-Fuller는 그녀가 자신의 학생들에게 가짜 뉴스와 진짜 뉴스를 구분하는 방법을 가르치고 있다고 말했다.

■ 직접화법: 다른 사람의 말을 따옴표(" ")로 묶어 그대로 되풀이하여 전달한다.

　직접화법: 따옴표 없이 전하는 이의 입장에서 시제나 인칭을 바꿔 내용을 전달한다.

■ 직접화법의 간접화법으로의 전환

　(1) 평서문
　　• 전달동사를 바꾼다. say → say, say to 사람 → tell 사람
　　• 전달하는 내용의 콤마(,)와 따옴표(" ")를 없애고 접속사 'that'을 넣는다. (단, 생략 가능)
　　• 전달동사가 현재이면 시제를 그대로 사용하고 전달동사가 과거라면, 시제의 일치 법칙에 맞게 시제를 바꾼다. (현재 → 과거, 현재완료 또는 과거 → 과거완료)
　※ 시제의 일치의 예외: 전할 말이 전하는 시점에서도 여전히 사실일 경우에는 현재 시제를 과거로 바꾸는 것이 필수적인 것은 아니며, 현재 시제를 그대로 사용할 수도 있다. 또한 전할 말이 역사적인 사실일 경우 과거시제를 유지한다.
　　• 인칭대명사를 전달자의 입장에 맞게 바꾼다.
　　　ex) 따옴표 속 'I'는 문장의 주어, 따옴표 속 'you'는 듣는 이로 바꾼다.
　　• 지시대명사와 부사를 전달자의 입장에 맞게 바꾼다.
　　　here → there　　this → that　　now → then　　today → that day
　　　tonight → that night　　　　yesterday → the day before, the previous day
　　　tomorrow → the next day, the following day
　(2) 의문문
　　• 전달동사를 바꾼다. say 또는 say to → ask
　　• 전달하는 내용의 콤마(,)와 따옴표(" ")를 없애고 간접의문문으로 전환한다. 물음표(?)는 마침표로 바꾼다.
　　• 시제, 인칭대명사, 지시대명사, 부사 등을 적절하게 바꾼다.
　(3) 명령문
　　• 전달동사를 어조에 따라 tell, ask, order, advise 등으로 바꾼다.
　　• 명령문의 동사원형을 긍정은 to부정사로, 부정은 not to 또는 never to부정사로 바꾼다.

핵심 Check

1. 다음 괄호 안에서 알맞은 것을 고르시오.

　(1) Tom (said to / told) her that he wanted to play soccer then.

　(2) My mom said that dinner (is / was) ready.

② 명사절을 이끄는 접속사 if

> • You also have to check **if** they are based on facts.
> 여러분은 그것들이 사실에 기반을 둔 것인지를 확인해 보아야 합니다.

- 형태: if 주어+동사
  의미: ~인지 아닌지

- 명사절을 이끌며 주로 동사의 목적어로 쓰인다.
  - I don't know **if** she works for the company. 나는 그녀가 그 회사에서 일하는지 아닌지 모르겠다.

- 명사절을 이끄는 접속사 'if'는 좀 더 격식을 갖춘 표현인 'whether'로 대체할 수 있다. 단, 'whether'는 주어, 보어, 동사의 목적어, 전치사의 목적어 자리에 모두 쓰일 수 있고, 'if'는 동사의 목적어 자리에 주로 쓰인다.
  - He asked **if** I could speak English. = He asked **whether** I could speak English.
    그는 내가 영어를 말할 수 있는지 물었다.
  - **If** it will snow or not doesn't matter. (×) → **Whether** it will snow or not doesn't matter. (○)
    눈이 올지 안 올지는 중요하지 않다.

- 'if'는 'or not'을 함께 사용할 때 문장 끝에만 사용 가능하며, 'whether'는 바로 다음이나 문장 끝에 'or not'을 붙여 쓸 수도 있다.
  - Tell me **if** or not she is married. (×)
  - Tell me **if** she is married or not. (○)
  - Tell me **whether** or not she is married. (○)
  - Tell me **whether** she is married or not. (○)

- '만일 ~라면'의 뜻으로 쓰인 'if'는 조건을 나타내는 부사절의 접속사이고 미래시제를 현재시제로 나타내는 반면, 명사절의 'if'는 정해진 시제를 그대로 쓴다.
  - **If** you do well on the next exam, I will buy you the latest smart phone.
    만일 다음 시험을 잘 본다면, 나는 너에게 최신식 스마트폰을 사줄 거야.
  - I'm not sure **if** you will do well on the next exam. 나는 네가 다음 시험을 잘 볼지 확신하지 못한다.

핵심 Check

2. 다음 괄호 안에서 알맞은 것을 고르시오.

(1) (If / Whether) you succeed or fail depends on your effort.

(2) I'm not sure (if / whether) or not he will come.

01 〈보기〉를 참고하여 A의 질문에 대한 B의 응답을 따옴표 안에 주어진 문장을 사용하여 빈칸에 알맞은 형태로 써 넣으시오.

┤ 보기 ├

"You have blue eyes like me."

A: What did the man say to his sister?

B: He told her that <u>she had blue eyes like him.</u>

(1) "You are very tall."

　A: What did the woman say to her brother?

　B: She told him that ＿＿＿＿＿＿＿＿＿＿＿＿＿＿.

(2) "I'm very happy to meet you."

　A: What did the woman say to her brother?

　B: She told him that ＿＿＿＿＿＿＿＿＿＿＿＿＿＿.

(3) "I'm not crying."

　A: What did the woman say to her brother?

　B: She told him that ＿＿＿＿＿＿＿＿＿＿＿＿＿＿.

(4) "You look great."

　A: What did the man say to his sister?

　B: He told her that ＿＿＿＿＿＿＿＿＿＿＿＿＿＿.

02 다음 문장에서 어법상 어색한 부분을 바르게 고쳐 쓰시오.

(1) I wonder that she will like my present.

　➡ ＿＿＿＿＿＿＿＿＿＿＿＿＿＿＿＿＿＿

(2) I don't know if or not he will give me flowers.

　➡ ＿＿＿＿＿＿＿＿＿＿＿＿＿＿＿＿＿＿

(3) I want to know if will he throw the ball.

　➡ ＿＿＿＿＿＿＿＿＿＿＿＿＿＿＿＿＿＿

(4) The question is if they believe what I said or not.

　➡ ＿＿＿＿＿＿＿＿＿＿＿＿＿＿＿＿＿＿

01 다음 중 간접화법으로의 전환이 올바르지 <u>않은</u> 것을 고르시오.

① Sarah said, "I am so happy."
= Sarah said that she was so happy.

② Suji said, "I will be back in ten minutes."
= Suji said that she would be back in ten minutes.

③ Minsu said to her, "You look tired today."
= Minsu told her that she looked tired that day.

④ Jason said to me, "I ate lunch."
= Jason told me that he has eaten lunch.

⑤ She said to him, "You are very tall."
= She told him that he was very tall.

서답형

02 다음 괄호 안에 주어진 어구를 바르게 배열하여 문장을 완성하시오.

(if, will, I, he, my ball, wonder, catch).

➡ _____

03 다음 중 밑줄 친 if의 뜻이 나머지 넷과 <u>다른</u> 것은?

① I'm not sure <u>if</u> he is single.

② I don't know <u>if</u> he will come back from his long journey.

③ Mom doesn't remember <u>if</u> she turned off the gas or not.

④ What he has to do is to see <u>if</u> anyone is in the building.

⑤ You can see the animal <u>if</u> it is in a good mood.

04 다음 중 내용상 어색한 문장을 고르시오.

① He told me that he wanted to help me.

② She told me that she had gone on a picnic the day before.

③ He told me that my mom would come.

④ Jaeho said that he would be busy tomorrow.

⑤ Jenny said that she had already read that book.

05 다음 빈칸에 들어갈 말로 적절한 것을 고르시오.

He asked me _____ or not I could help him.

① if   ② what   ③ that
④ whether   ⑤ how

서답형

06 다음 직접화법을 간접화법으로 바꾼 문장에서 어법상 어색한 것을 바르게 고쳐 다시 쓰시오.

(1) I said to Amy, "I want to play with you now."
➡ I told Amy that I wanted to play with her now.
➡ _____

(2) Mom said to me, "Are you finished with your homework?"
➡ Mom told me if I was finished with my homework.
➡ _____

07 다음 중 빈칸에 들어갈 단어가 <u>다른</u> 하나를 고르시오.

① _____ you aren't busy, we will watch the TV show.

② Do you know _____ the news is true?

③ I knew _____ it rained yesterday as the road was wet this morning.

④ I can help you _____ you want.

⑤ He wondered _____ he could get the diamond ring.

08 다음 주어진 화법 전환에서 <u>어색한</u> 부분을 바르게 고친 것은?

> She said to me, "What do you want to buy?"
> → She ①said to me ②what ③I ④wanted ⑤to buy.

① said to → asked

② what → that

③ I → she

④ wanted → did I want

⑤ to buy → buy

09 빈칸에 들어갈 말을 순서대로 바르게 연결한 것은?

> • I wonder _____ you made this reusable tote bag.
> • What I want to know is _____ she remembers my name.

① that – if   ② that – whether

③ if – whether   ④ whether – if

⑤ if – that

10 다음 괄호 안에 주어진 어구를 바르게 배열하여 문장을 완성하시오.

> I am (if, do, on, not, I, well, the test, sure)

➡ _____

11 다음 문장과 같은 뜻을 가진 것은?

> She said to him, "I want to stay with you forever."

① She said to him that she wanted to stay with me forever.

② She asked him that she wanted to stay with him forever.

③ She told him that she wanted to stay with him forever.

④ She said to him that she wanted to stay with you forever.

⑤ She told him that I wanted to stay with you forever.

12 다음 두 문장을 접속사를 사용하여 한 문장으로 연결하시오.

> • Will they give me a big hand?
> • I'm not sure.

➡ _____
_____

13 주어진 어휘를 이용하여 다음 우리말을 영어로 쓰시오.

> 나의 언니는 내가 그 시험에서 부정행위를 했는지 안했는지 의심한다. (if, doubt, cheat, the test)

➡ _____

14 다음 중 어법상 <u>어색한</u> 문장을 고르시오.

① Tom says that he likes Amy.
② My sister told me that she meets Tom by chance the day before.
③ She told me that she had received the gift that day.
④ She advised me to take the medicine regularly.
⑤ My brother asked me where I had put his glasses.

15 빈칸에 들어갈 말을 순서대로 바르게 연결한 것은?

- _____ he will come or not is another matter.
- The detective must find out _____ the document is fake or not.

① That – if
② Whether – that
③ If – whether
④ That – whether
⑤ Whether – if

16 다음 빈칸에 들어갈 수 <u>없는</u> 것은?

The old lady _____ me to keep an eye on her dog.

① asked
② told
③ ordered
④ begged
⑤ made

17 다음 우리말을 영어로 바르게 옮긴 것은?

그녀가 지금 회의 중인지 내가 확인할게.

① Let me check that she's in the meeting now.
② Let me check if she's in the meeting now.
③ Let me to check if she's in the meeting now.
④ Let me check if or not she's in the meeting now.
⑤ Let me check that she's in the meeting or not now.

18 다음 중 어법상 <u>어색한</u> 문장의 개수로 알맞은 것은?

a. Mom ordered me to brush my teeth before breakfast.
b. She told that she was not ready for the race.
c. The doctor said me that I should take a rest for a few days.
d. I told my father to not smoke indoors.
e. They wanted to know if I was satisfied with the result.

① 1개 ② 2개 ③ 3개 ④ 4개 ⑤ 5개

서답형

19 다음 괄호 안에서 알맞은 말을 고르시오.

(1) She (said to / asked) me where I was going.
(2) John (says / says to) that he has a dream of being a musical actor.
(3) My teacher asked me (if / that) I could lend him a pen.
(4) Tom said that he (feels / felt) sick that day.
(5) Our science teacher said that the Earth (is / was) round.

Grammar 25

 명사절의 접속사(if, whether, that)를 사용하여 두 문장을 한 문장으로 쓰시오.

(1) • I wonder.
   • Did the plane arrive on time?
   ➡ _____

(2) • I asked.
   • Was she married?
   ➡ _____

(3) • Is the meeting ready?
   • The question is this.
   ➡ _____

(4) • I think.
   • He is very honest.
   ➡ _____

(5) • Will she attend the audition?
   • It depends on her physical condition.
   ➡ _____
   _____

02 다음 문장을 간접화법으로 바꾸어 쓰시오.

(1) He said to me, "I really appreciate your help."
   ➡ _____

(2) My roommate said to me, "I will be late tonight."
   ➡ _____
   _____

03 다음 빈칸에 알맞은 말을 쓰시오.

(1) He said, "I know the answer."
   ➡ He said that _____ _____ the answer.

(2) Jane said, "_____ _____ to be a teacher."
   ➡ Jane said that she wanted to be a teacher.

(3) He said to me, "I will help you."
   ➡ He told me that _____ _____ _____ _____.

04 잘못된 부분을 바르게 고쳐 문장을 다시 쓰시오.

(1) John said Mary, "I love you."
   ➡ _____

(2) She told him that she is sorry.
   ➡ _____

(3) I told my dad that I would call you later.
   ➡ _____

(4) Mr. Brown said me that he wanted me to study more.
   ➡ _____

(5) My mom said this dish tasted good.
   ➡ _____

05 다음 두 문장을 간접화법을 이용하여 하나의 문장으로 바꾸어 쓰시오.

> • He said to her.
> • What is the weather like in New York today?

➡ _____

_____

06 다음 문장을 어법에 맞게 고쳐 쓰시오.

(1) I understand if you don't want to talk about it.

➡ _____

(2) Whether you are a boy or a girl make no difference to me.

➡ _____

_____

(3) If you will succeed or not depends on your efforts.

➡ _____

_____

(4) I am not sure that there is life on other planets.

➡ _____

_____

(5) Tell me that you have any plans for your future.

➡ _____

_____

07 〈보기〉에 주어진 문장과 접속사 'if, that, whether'를 각각 한번만 써서 문장의 빈칸을 완성하시오.

> ┤ 보기 ├
> • He had lied to his family.
> • She will have a garage sale in her backyard.
> • We have enough money to buy the new car.

(1) Our question is _____

_____.

(2) He admitted _____.

(3) I asked my grandmother _____

_____.

08 다음 그림 속 내용을 다른 사람에게 전달하는 문장으로 완성하시오.

(1)

> Are you hungry?
>
> Why does she look angry?

| The man asked if the cat _____ and he wondered _____. |

(2)

> You are very cute.
>
> Does she like this food?

| The man said the cat _____ and he wondered _____. |

Reading

How to Be a Smart News Reader

In October 2016, stories about scary clowns shook schools across the
Washington area, but Danina Garcia-Fuller's students didn't believe
them a bit.

"Some people were getting scared because they saw things on social
media," said Patricia Visoso, one of Garcia-Fuller's students. "But
they never checked up on who was saying this." The stories were
actually made by teenagers, not by major newspapers or TV stations.
They offered no hard evidence that clowns really were trying to attack
students. The story turned out to be a complete lie.

"I think a lot of people just look at one thing and believe it's true,"
Patricia's classmate Ivy-Brooks said. "It's really important to look at
the right sources and to pay attention to what is real and what is fake."

Like Garcia-Fuller's students, many teenagers in America are
learning to think critically about information they're seeing in the news
and on the Internet. This skill is getting more important these days as
stories can spread very fast, and anyone can make a website full of
false information.

Vocabulary:
- scary 무서운
- clown 광대
- area 지역, 구역
- a bit 조금, 약간
- scared 무서워하는
- social media 소셜 미디어
- check up on ~을 확인하다
- major 주요한, 중대한
- hard 명백한
- evidence 증거
- attack 공격하다
- turn out ~인 것으로 드러나다, 밝혀지다
- complete 완벽한, 완전한
- lie 거짓말
- source 자료, 출처
- pay attention to ~에 주목하다, 유의하다
- critically 비판적으로
- spread 퍼지다
- false 틀린, 거짓의

 확인문제

- 다음 문장이 본문의 내용과 일치하면 T, 일치하지 <u>않으면</u> F를 쓰시오.

1 Danina Garcia-Fuller's students didn't believe stories about scary clowns a bit. ☐

2 The stories about scary clowns were actually made by major newspapers or TV stations. ☐

3 Ivy-Brooks said a lot of people just looked at one thing and believed it was true. ☐

4 These days, anyone can make a website full of true information. ☐

Garcia-Fuller said she was teaching her students how to tell fake news from real news.
직접화법: Garcia-Fuller said. "I am teaching my students how to tell fake news from real news."

"One of the first steps is to slow down. If a story or a photo seems too good to be true, stop and think: Is there any evidence that supports what the writer says? And where is this coming from?"
one of+복수명사: '~ 중 하나'라는 뜻   to slow down: to부정사의 명사적 용법
If: '만약 ~한다면'이라는 조건의 의미를 지니는 부사절을 이끎.
너무 좋아서 믿어지지 않는. too+형용사/부사+to부정사: 너무 …해서 ~할 수 없다   주격 관계대명사
what: 선행사를 포함한 관계대명사. '~한 것'

Garcia-Fuller's students also learn how to tell fact from opinion in the news. "Opinions are good to read," said 15-year-old McKenzie Campbell, "but you also have to check if they are based on facts."
how+to부정사: ~하는 방법   tell A from B: A와 B를 구분하다
형용사 'good'을 수식하는 to부정사의 부사적 용법
= whether. if: ~인지 아닌지 (명사절을 이끎)

Garcia-Fuller also said sometimes it can be very hard to be a smart news reader. She tests her students with a website that appears to provide information on an animal called a tree octopus. The site is full of information on this animal, along with a few unclear photos of octopuses in trees. But like the story of scary clowns, it's totally made up.
said 다음에 접속사 'that' 생략   가주어   진주어
주격 관계대명사(= which)
appear to+동사원형: ~인 것 같다   'an animal' 뒤에 'which is' 생략
~와 함께

The lesson, Garcia-Fuller tells her students, is to "check the information you're seeing once more carefully" and to "question everything, even things that I say."
to부정사의 명사적 용법
rmation' 다음에 목적격 관계대명사 'that[which]' 생략
to부정사의 명사적 용법
목적격 관계대명사, 생략가능.

tell … from ~ …를 ~와 구분하다
slow down (속도, 활동)을 늦추다
support 지지하다, 지원하다
be based on ~에 기초하다, 근거하다
appear 나타나다, ~인 것 같다
octopus 문어
site 사이트, 현장, 위치
unclear 불확실한, 불분명한
totally 완전히
be made up ~로 꾸며지다
question 의심하다, 의문을 갖다

확인문제

● 다음 문장이 본문의 내용과 일치하면 T, 일치하지 않으면 F를 쓰시오.

1   Garcia-Fuller said she was teaching her students how to distinguish fake news from real news. ☐

2   Garcia-Fuller's students also learn how to tell fake news from opinion in the news. ☐

3   Garcia-Fuller said sometimes it can be very hard to be a smart news reader. ☐

4   Unlike the story of scary clowns, the information on a tree octopus is true. ☐

● 우리말을 참고하여 빈칸에 알맞은 말을 쓰시오.

1 How to Be a _____ _____ _____

2 In October 2016, stories about scary clowns _____ _____ across the Washington area, but Danina Garcia-Fuller's students _____ _____ them _____ _____ .

3 "Some people were _____ _____ because they saw things on social media," said Patricia Visoso, one of Garcia-Fuller's students.

4 "But they never _____ _____ _____ who was saying this."

5 The stories _____ _____ _____ by teenagers, not by major newspapers or TV stations.

6 They offered _____ _____ _____ that clowns really were trying to attack students.

7 The story _____ _____ _____ _____ a complete lie.

8 "I think a lot of people _____ _____ _____ _____ _____ and believe it's true," Patricia's classmate Ivy-Brooks said.

9 "It's really important _____ _____ _____ _____ and to pay attention to _____ _____ _____ and _____ _____ _____ ."

10 _____ Garcia-Fuller's students, many teenagers in America are learning _____ _____ _____ about information they're seeing in the news and _____ _____ _____ .

11 This skill is _____ _____ _____ these days as stories can spread very fast, and anyone can make a website full of false information.

우리말
1 현명한 뉴스 독자가 되는 방법
2 2016년 10월, 무서운 광대들에 관한 이야기가 워싱턴 지역 전역의 학교에 충격을 안겼지만, Danina Garcia-Fuller의 학생들은 조금도 그 이야기들을 믿지 않았다.
3 "몇몇 사람들은 그들이 소셜 미디어에 올라온 것들을 봤기 때문에 무서워했어요."라고 Garcia-Fuller의 학생 중 한 명인 Patricia Visoso가 말했다.
4 "하지만 그들은 이것을 누가 말하고 있는지를 전혀 확인하지 않았어요."
5 그 이야기들은 실제로 주요 신문사나 TV 방송국이 아닌 10대들이 지어냈다.
6 그들은 광대들이 정말로 학생들을 공격하려고 한다는 명백한 증거를 하나도 제공하지 않았다.
7 그 이야기는 결국 완벽한 거짓말인 것으로 드러났다.
8 "많은 사람이 단지 한 가지만을 보고 그것이 사실이라고 믿는 것 같아요.라고 Patricia의 반 친구인 Ivy-Brooks가 말했다.
9 올바른 출처를 살펴보고, 무엇이 진짜이고 무엇이 가짜인지에 주의를 기울이는 것은 정말 중요해요."
10 Garcia-Fuller의 학생들처럼, 많은 미국의 10대들은 뉴스 속 그리고 인터넷상에서 보고 있는 정보에 관해 비판적으로 생각하는 것을 배워 나가고 있다.
11 이 기능은 최근 더 중요해지고 있는데, 이야기들은 아주 빠른 속도로 퍼져 나갈 수 있고 누구나 허위 정보로 가득 찬 웹사이트를 만들어 낼 수 있기 때문이다.

12 Garcia-Fuller said she was teaching her students _____ _____ _____ fake news _____ real news.

13 "_____ _____ _____ _____ _____ is to slow down.

14 If a story or a photo seems _____ _____ _____ _____ _____, stop and think.

15 Is there any evidence that supports _____ _____ _____?

16 And where is this _____ _____?"

17 Garcia-Fuller's students also learn _____ _____ fact _____ opinion in the news.

18 "Opinions are good to read," said 15-year-old McKenzie Campbell, "but you also have to check _____ they _____ _____ _____ facts."

19 Garcia-Fuller also said sometimes it can be very hard to be _____ _____ _____ _____.

20 She tests her students with a website that _____ _____ _____ information on an animal called a tree octopus.

21 The site is full of information on this animal, _____ _____ a few unclear photos of octopuses in trees.

22 But _____ the story of scary clowns, it's totally _____ _____.

23 The lesson, Garcia-Fuller tells her students, is to "check the information you're seeing _____ _____ _____" and to "_____ _____, even things that I say."

---

12 Garcia-Fuller는 그녀가 자신의 학생들에게 가짜 뉴스를 진짜 뉴스로부터 구분하는 방법을 가르치고 있다고 말했다.

13 "첫 단계 중 하나는 속도를 늦추는 것(천천히 생각하는 것)입니다.

14 만약 어떤 이야기나 어떤 사진이 진짜라고 하기엔 너무 좋아 보인다면, 멈춰서 생각해 보세요.

15 글쓴이가 말하고 있는 것을 뒷받침하는 어떠한 증거라도 있나요?

16 그리고 이 정보가 어디서 온 것인가요?"

17 Garcia-Fuller의 학생들은 또한 뉴스에서 사실을 의견과 구분하는 방법에 대해서도 배운다.

18 "의견들은 읽을 만한 가치가 있습니다,"라고 15살인 McKenzie Campbell이 말했다. "하지만 여러분은 그것들이 사실에 기반을 둔 것인지를 확인해 보아야 합니다."

19 Garcia-Fuller는 또한 때때로 현명한 뉴스 독자가 되는 것이 아주 어려울 수도 있다고 말했다.

20 그녀는 자신의 학생들을 '나무 문어'라는 이름의 동물에 대한 정보를 제공하는 것처럼 보이는 웹사이트로 시험한다.

21 그 사이트는 나무 위에 있는 문어들의 몇몇 불확실한 사진과 함께, 이 동물에 대한 정보로 가득 차 있다.

22 하지만 무서운 광대들의 이야기와 마찬가지로, 그것은 완전히 꾸며진 것이다.

23 Garcia-Fuller가 그녀의 학생들에게 말하는 교훈은 '당신이 보고 있는 정보를 한 번만 더 신중하게 확인해 보라'는 것과 '모든 것, 심지어 내가 말하는 것에도 의문을 가져 보라'는 것이다.

● 우리말을 참고하여 본문을 영작하시오.

1 현명한 뉴스 독자가 되는 방법

➡ _____

2 2016년 10월, 무서운 광대들에 관한 이야기가 워싱턴 지역 전역의 학교에 충격을 안겼지만,
Danina Garcia-Fuller의 학생들은 조금도 그 이야기들을 믿지 않았다.

➡ _____

_____

3 "몇몇 사람들은 그들이 소셜 미디어에 올라온 것들을 봤기 때문에 무서워했어요."라고 Garcia-Fuller의
학생 중 한 명인 Patricia Visoso가 말했다.

➡ _____

_____

4 "하지만 그들은 이것을 누가 말하고 있는지를 전혀 확인하지 않았어요."

➡ _____

5 그 이야기들은 실제로 주요 신문사나 TV 방송국이 아닌 10대들이 지어냈다.

➡ _____

6 그들은 광대들이 정말로 학생들을 공격하려고 한다는 명백한 증거를 하나도 제공하지 않았다.

➡ _____

7 그 이야기는 결국 완벽한 거짓말인 것으로 드러났다.

➡ _____

8 "많은 사람이 단지 한 가지만을 보고 그것이 사실이라고 믿는 것 같아요."라고 Patricia의
반 친구인 Ivy-Brooks가 말했다.

➡ _____

_____

9 "올바른 출처를 살펴보고, 무엇이 진짜이고 무엇이 가짜인지에 주의를 기울이는 것은 정말 중요해요."

➡ _____

_____

10 Garcia-Fuller의 학생들처럼, 많은 미국의 10대들은 뉴스 속 그리고 인터넷상에서 보고 있는 정보에 관해
비판적으로 생각하는 것을 배워 나가고 있다.

➡ _____

_____

11 이 기능은 최근 더 중요해지고 있는데, 이야기들은 아주 빠른 속도로 퍼져 나갈 수 있고 누구나 허위 정보로
가득 찬 웹사이트를 만들어 낼 수 있기 때문이다.

➡ _____

_____

12 Garcia-Fuller는 그녀가 자신의 학생들에게 가짜 뉴스를 진짜 뉴스로부터 구분하는 방법을 가르치고 있다고 말했다.

➡ _____

13 "첫 단계 중 하나는 속도를 늦추는 것(천천히 생각하는 것)입니다.

➡ _____

14 만약 어떤 이야기나 어떤 사진이 진짜라고 하기엔 너무 좋아 보인다면, 멈춰서 생각해 보세요.

➡ _____

15 글쓴이가 말하고 있는 것을 뒷받침하는 어떠한 증거라도 있나요?

➡ _____

16 그리고 이 정보가 어디서 온 것인가요?"

➡ _____

17 Garcia-Fuller의 학생들은 또한 뉴스에서 사실을 의견과 구분하는 방법에 대해서도 배운다.

➡ _____

18 "의견들은 읽을 만한 가치가 있습니다."라고 15살인 McKenzie Campbell이 말했다. "하지만 여러분은 그것들이 사실에 기반을 둔 것인지를 확인해 보아아 합니다."

➡ _____

_____

19 Garcia-Fuller는 또한 때때로 현명한 뉴스 독자가 되는 것이 아주 어려울 수도 있다고 말했다.

➡ _____

20 그녀는 자신의 학생들을 '나무 문어'라는 이름의 동물에 대한 정보를 제공하는 것처럼 보이는 웹사이트로 시험한다.

➡ _____

_____

21 그 사이트는 나무 위에 있는 문어들의 몇몇 불확실한 사진과 함께, 이 동물에 대한 정보로 가득 차 있다.

➡ _____

_____

22 하지만 무서운 광대들의 이야기와 마찬가지로, 그것은 완전히 꾸며진 것이다.

➡ _____

23 Garcia-Fuller가 그녀의 학생들에게 말하는 교훈은 '당신이 보고 있는 정보를 한 번만 더 신중하게 확인해 보라'는 것과 '모든 것, 심지어 내가 말하는 것에도 의문을 가져 보라'는 것이다.

➡ _____

_____

[01~03] 다음 글을 읽고 물음에 답하시오.

In October 2016, stories about scary clowns shook schools across the Washington area, but Danina Garcia-Fuller's students didn't believe them a bit.

"Some people were getting scared because they saw things ___ⓐ___ social media," said Patricia Visoso, one of Garcia-Fuller's students. "But they never checked up ___ⓑ___ who was saying this." The stories were actually made by teenagers, not by major newspapers or TV stations. ⓒThey offered no hard evidence that clowns really were trying to attack students. The story turned out to be a complete lie.

01 위 글의 빈칸 ⓐ와 ⓑ에 들어갈 전치사가 바르게 짝지어진 것은?

ⓐ	ⓑ		ⓐ	ⓑ
① to	– on		② on	– in
③ to	– in		④ in	– to
⑤ on	– on			

서답형

02 위 글의 밑줄 친 ⓒThey가 가리키는 것을 본문에서 찾아 쓰시오.

➡ _____

중요

03 According to the passage, which is NOT true?

① In October 2016, schools across the Washington area were shocked at stories about scary clowns.

② Danina Garcia-Fuller's students didn't believe the stories about scary clowns a bit.

③ Some people who were getting scared because they saw things on social media never found out who was saying this.

④ The stories about scary clowns were not made by teenagers but by major newspapers or TV stations.

⑤ The story about scary clowns proved to be a complete lie.

[04~06] 다음 글을 읽고 물음에 답하시오.

"I think a lot of people just look at one thing and believe it's true," Patricia's classmate Ivy-Brooks said. "It's really important to look at the right (A)[sources / resources] and to pay attention to what is real and what is fake."

(B)[Alike / Like] Garcia-Fuller's students, many teenagers in America are learning to think ___ⓐ___ about information they're seeing in the news and on the Internet. This skill is getting more important these days as stories can spread very fast, and anyone can make a website full of (C)[false / true] information.

04 위 글의 빈칸 ⓐ에 들어갈 알맞은 말을 고르시오.

① unquestioningly

② conformingly

③ adaptationally

④ critically

⑤ unconditionally

서답형

05 위 글의 괄호 (A)~(C)에서 문맥이나 어법상 알맞은 낱말을 골라 쓰시오.

➡ (A) _____ (B) _____ (C) _____

서답형

06 다음 문장에서 위 글의 내용과 <u>다른</u> 부분을 찾아서 고치시오.

Patricia's classmate Ivy-Brooks thinks many people look at everything and believe it's true.

_____ ➡ _____

[07~09] 다음 글을 읽고 물음에 답하시오.

Garcia-Fuller also said sometimes it can be very hard to be a smart news reader. ⓐ She tests her students with a website that is appeared to provide information on an animal called a tree octopus. The site is full of information on this animal, ⓑalong with a few unclear photos of octopuses in trees. But like the story of scary clowns, it's totally made up.

The lesson, Garcia-Fuller tells her students, is to "check the information you're seeing once more carefully" and to "question everything, even things that I say."

서답형

07 위 글의 밑줄 친 ⓐ에서 어법상 틀린 부분을 찾아 고치시오.

_____ ➡ _____

서답형

08 위 글의 밑줄 친 ⓑalong with와 바꿔 쓸 수 있는 단어를 쓰시오. (two words)

➡ _____

09 위 글을 읽고 알 수 <u>없는</u> 것을 고르시오.

① According to Garcia-Fuller, sometimes what can be very hard?

② Is it always easy to be a smart news reader?

③ What does the website with which Garcia-Fuller tests her students seem to provide?

④ What is the website with which Garcia-Fuller tests her students full of?

⑤ Who made up the information on the tree octopus?

[10~12] 다음 글을 읽고 물음에 답하시오.

Garcia-Fuller said she was teaching her students how to ⓐtell fake news from real news.

"One of the first steps is to slow down. If a story or a photo seems too good to be true, stop and think: Is there any evidence ⓑthat supports what the writer says? And where is this coming from?"

Garcia-Fuller's students also learn how to tell fact from opinion in the news. "Opinions are good to read," said 15-year-old McKenzie Campbell, "but you also have to check if they are based on facts."

10 위 글의 밑줄 친 ⓐtell과 바꿔 쓸 수 있는 말을 <u>모두</u> 고르시오.

① know　　　　② protect

③ talk　　　　④ distinguish

⑤ keep

11 위 글의 밑줄 친 ⓑthat과 문법적 쓰임이 같은 것을 <u>모두</u> 고르시오.

① She was so tired <u>that</u> she couldn't think properly.

② This is all <u>that</u> matters.

③ The rumor <u>that</u> he married Kate is not true.

④ She said <u>that</u> the story was true.

⑤ Where's the letter <u>that</u> came yesterday?

12 위 글의 주제로 알맞은 것을 고르시오.

① the best way to teach students the importance of real news

② the reason to stop and think when a story seems too good to be true

③ how to tell fake news from real news and fact from opinion in the news

④ how to find out the evidence that supports what the writer says

⑤ the opinions which are based on facts

[13~14] 다음 글을 읽고 물음에 답하시오.

"I think a lot of people just look at one thing and believe it's true," Patricia's classmate Ivy-Brooks said. "It's really important to look at the right sources and to pay attention to what is real and what is fake."

Like Garcia-Fuller's students, many teenagers in America are learning to think critically about information they're seeing in the news and on the Internet. This skill is getting more important these days as stories can spread very fast, and anyone can make a website ⓐfull of false information.

서답형

13 위 글의 밑줄 친 ⓐfull of false information 앞에 생략된 말을 쓰시오.

➡ _____

14 Which question CANNOT be answered after reading the passage?

① According to Ivy-Brooks, what do many people look at when they believe it's true?

② What are many teenagers in America learning?

③ Where are many teenagers in America seeing information?

④ Are many teenagers in America learning to think critically about information?

⑤ Why do people make a website full of false information?

[15~16] 다음 글을 읽고 물음에 답하시오.

Garcia-Fuller said she was teaching her students how to tell fake news from real news.

"One of the first steps is to slow down. If a story or a photo seems too good to be true, stop and think: ⓐ글쓴이가 말하고 있는 것을 뒷받침하는 어떠한 증거라도 있나요? And where is this coming from?"

Garcia-Fuller's students also learn how to tell fact from opinion in the news. "Opinions are good to read," said 15-year-old McKenzie Campbell, "but you also have to check if ⓑ they are based on facts."

서답형

15 위 글의 밑줄 친 ⓐ의 우리말에 맞게 주어진 어휘를 알맞게 배열하시오.

> the writer / that / there / supports / any evidence / is / says / what / ?

➡ _____

_____

서답형

16 위 글의 밑줄 친 ⓑthey가 가리키는 것을 본문에서 찾아 쓰시오.

➡ _____

[17~19] 다음 글을 읽고 물음에 답하시오.

In October 2016, stories about scary clowns shook schools across the Washington area, but Danina Garcia-Fuller's students didn't believe them a bit. (①)

"Some people were getting scared because they saw things on social media," said Patricia Visoso, one of Garcia-Fuller's students. (②) The stories were actually made by teenagers, not by major newspapers or TV stations. (③) They offered no hard evidence ⓐthat clowns really were trying to attack students. (④) The story turned out to be a complete lie. (⑤)

17 위 글의 흐름으로 보아, 주어진 문장이 들어가기에 가장 적절한 곳은?

> "But they never checked up on who was saying this."

①   ②   ③   ④   ⑤

18 위 글의 밑줄 친 ⓐthat과 문법적 쓰임이 같은 것을 모두 고르시오.

① There was no hope that she would recover her health.

② She said that the story was true.

③ No one can deny the fact that you are guilty.

④ It's true that we were a little late.

⑤ The trouble is that we are short of money.

19 위 글의 제목으로 알맞은 것을 고르시오.

① Scary Clowns Shook Schools across the Washington Area

② Danina Garcia-Fuller's Smart Students

③ Hey, Be Careful in Believing Things on Social Media!

④ Stories on Social Media Made by Teenagers

⑤ Why Don't You Believe Things on Social Media?

[20~21] 다음 글을 읽고 물음에 답하시오.

Garcia-Fuller also said sometimes it can be very hard to be a smart news reader. She tests her students with a website that appears to provide information on an animal ⓐ a tree octopus. The site is full of information on this animal, along with a few unclear photos of octopuses in trees. But like the story of scary clowns, it's totally made up.

The ⓑlesson, Garcia-Fuller tells her students, is to "check the information you're seeing once more carefully" and to "question everything, even things that I say."

서답형

20 위 글의 빈칸 ⓐ에 call을 알맞은 형태로 쓰시오.

➡ _____

21 위 글의 밑줄 친 ⓑlesson과 같은 의미로 쓰인 것을 고르시오.

① What did we do last lesson?

② Let her fate be a valuable lesson to you.

③ We studied lesson Five today.

④ She was preparing a lesson plan for a class she was teaching.

⑤ No talking was allowed during the lesson.

[01~04] 다음 글을 읽고 물음에 답하시오.

In October 2016, stories about scary clowns shook schools across the Washington area, but Danina Garcia-Fuller's students didn't believe them a bit.

ⓐ"Some people were getting scared because they saw things on social media," said Patricia Visoso, one of Garcia-Fuller's student. "But they never checked up on who was saying this." ⓑThe stories were actually made by teenagers, not by major newspapers or TV stations. They offered no hard evidence that clowns really were trying to attack students. ⓒThe story turned out to be a complete lie.

01 위 글의 밑줄 친 ⓐ에서 어법상 틀린 부분을 찾아 고치시오.

_____ ➡ _____

02 위 글의 밑줄 친 ⓑ를 다음과 같이 바꿔 쓸 때 빈칸에 들어갈 알맞은 단어를 쓰시오.

> The stories were actually made _____ by major newspapers or TV stations _____ by teenagers.

03 위 글의 밑줄 친 ⓒ를 복문으로 바꾸시오.

➡ _____

04 본문의 내용과 일치하도록 다음 빈칸 (A)와 (B)에 알맞은 단어를 쓰시오.

> Some people were getting scared of the stories about scary clowns because they saw things (A)_____ _____ _____, but they never checked up on who was saying the story, which turned out to be (B)_____ _____ _____ .

[05~07] 다음 글을 읽고 물음에 답하시오.

"I think a lot of people just look at one thing and believe it's true," Patricia's classmate Ivy-Brooks said. "It's really important to look at the right sources and to pay attention to what is real and what is fake."

Like Garcia-Fuller's students, many teenagers in America are learning to think critically about information they're seeing in the news and on the Internet. ⓐThis skill is getting more important these days as stories can spread very fast, and anyone can make a website ⓑfull of false information.

05 위 글의 밑줄 친 ⓐThis skill이 가리키는 것을 본문에서 찾아 쓰시오.

➡ _____

_____

06 위 글의 밑줄 친 ⓑfull of와 바꿔 쓸 수 있는 말을 쓰시오.

➡ _____

07 According to Patricia's classmate Ivy-Brooks, what is really important? Answer in English in a full sentence beginning with "It".

➡ _____

_____

_____

[08~11] 다음 글을 읽고 물음에 답하시오.

ⓐGarcia-Fuller said she was teaching her students how to tell fake news from real news.

"One of the first steps (A)[are / is] to slow down. If a story or a photo seems (B)[good enough / too good] to be true, stop and think: Is there any evidence that (C)[denies / supports] what the writer says? And where is this coming from?"

ⓑGarcia-Fuller's students also learn how to tell fact from opinion in the news. "Opinions are good to read," said 15-year-old McKenzie Campbell, "but you also have to check if they are based on facts."

08 위 글의 밑줄 친 ⓐ를 직접화법으로 고칠 때, 빈칸 (A)와 (B)에 들어갈 알맞은 말을 쓰시오.

Garcia-Fuller said, "(A)_____ _____ teaching (B)_____ students how to tell fake news from real news."

09 위 글의 괄호 (A)~(C)에서 문맥이나 어법상 알맞은 낱말을 골라 쓰시오.

➡ (A) _____ (B) _____ (C) _____

10 위 글의 밑줄 친 ⓑ를 다음과 같이 바꿔 쓸 때 빈칸에 들어갈 알맞은 말을 두 단어로 쓰시오.

Garcia-Fuller's students also learn how _____ _____ tell fact from opinion in the news.

11 What's one of the first steps to tell fake news from real news? Fill in the blanks (A)~(C) with suitable words.

It's to (A)_____ _____. When it seems that a story or a photo is so good that it can't be true, you must (B)_____ and think if there is (C)_____ _____ that supports the writer's word and the source of this.

[12~14] 다음 글을 읽고 물음에 답하시오.

Garcia-Fuller also said sometimes it can be very hard to be a smart news reader. She tests her students with a website that appears to provide information on an animal called a tree octopus. The site is full of information on ⓐthis animal, along with a few unclear photos of octopuses in trees. But like the story of scary clowns, it's totally made up.

The lesson, Garcia-Fuller tells her students, is to "check the information you're seeing once more carefully" and to "question everything, even ⓑthings that I say."

12 위 글의 밑줄 친 ⓐthis animal이 가리키는 것을 본문에서 찾아 쓰시오.

➡ _____

13 위 글의 밑줄 친 ⓑthings that과 바꿔 쓸 수 있는 한 단어를 쓰시오.

➡ _____

14 What is the lesson that Garcia-Fuller gives to her students? Fill in the blanks (A) and (B) with suitable words.

It's to "check the information you're seeing (A)_____ _____ _____" and to "(B)_____ _____, even things that she says."

해석

After You Read A

- In October 2016, stories about scary clowns shook schools across the
  in: 시간과 함께 쓰여 '(특정 기간)에'   about: 주제와 연관성의 의미로 '…에 관한'   across: 장소와 함께 쓰여 '∼에 걸쳐, 온 …에'
  Washington area.

  ↓ how+to부정사: '…하는 방법'
- Garcia-Fuller's students also learn how to tell fact from opinion in the news.
  tell A from B: A와 B를 구분하다

- The site is full of information on this animal, along with a few unclear
  be full of: ∼로 가득 차 있다   = together with
  photos of octopuses in trees.

구문해설 • scary: 무서운 • clown: 광대 • area: 지역, 구역 • tell … from ∼: …를 ∼와 구분하다
• site: 사이트, 현장, 위치 • unclear: 불확실한, 불분명한 • octopus: 문어

- 2016년 10월, 무서운 광대들에 관한 이야기가 워싱턴 지역 전역의 학교에 충격을 안겼다.
- Garcia-Fuller의 학생들은 또한 뉴스에서 사실을 의견과 구분하는 방법에 대해서도 배운다.
- 그 사이트는 나무 위에 있는 문어들의 몇몇 불확실한 사진과 함께, 이 동물에 대한 정보로 가득 차 있다.

Do It Yourself

Team NW danced on the stage during the school festival. They wondered if
전치사 '∼ 동안'   'wonder'의 목적어를 이끄는 접속사로 '∼인지 아닌지' = whether
the students and teachers would like their dancing. But they performed much
비교급 강조(훨씬)
better than any other team. A lot of students stood up and cheered loudly when
비교급 than any other+단수명사   = Many   부사로 동사 'cheered'를 수식
the team danced. Ms. Yu, the P.E. teacher, said it was the performance of the year.
Ms. Yu를 설명하는 동격어구

구문해설 • stage: 무대 • festival: 축제 • wonder: 궁금해 하다 • perform: 공연하다
• cheer: 환호하다 • performance: 공연

NW 팀은 학교 축제 기간에 무대에서 춤을 선보였다. 그들은 학생들과 선생님들이 그들의 춤을 좋아할지 확신이 서지 않았다. 하지만 그들은 다른 어떠한 팀보다 훨씬 더 멋지게 공연을 해냈다. 그 팀이 춤출 때 많은 학생이 일어서서 크게 환호했다. 체육 선생님인 유 선생님은 그해 최고의 공연이라고 말씀하셨다.

Link to the World

Fact

- This drawing, *Don Quixote*, is one of Picasso's works.
  one of 복수명사

- Picasso drew it in 1955 with black lines against a white background.

Opinion

- I don't know if the man on the horse is brave, but he looks very tired and
  ∼인지 아닌지
  hungry. I think he needs some food and water.

- I think this artwork shows the most interesting part of Cervantes' novel *Don*
  뒤에 접속사 that 생략
  Quixote.

구문해설 • drawing: 그림 • work: 작품 • artwork: 미술작품 • novel: 소설

사실
- 이 그림 '돈키호테'는 피카소의 작품 중 하나이다.
- 피카소는 이 그림을 1955년에 흰 배경과 대비를 이루는 검은 선들로 그렸다.
의견
- 말 위에 올라탄 남자가 용감한지는 잘 모르겠지만, 그는 매우 피곤하고 굶주려 보인다. 내 생각에는 그에게 약간의 음식과 물이 필요한 것 같다.
- 나는 이 미술품이 세르반테스의 소설인 '돈키호테'의 가장 흥미로운 부분을 보여 주고 있다고 생각한다.

Words & Expressions

01 다음 주어진 두 단어의 관계가 같도록 빈칸에 알맞은 단어를 쓰시오.

> boring – exciting : defend – _____

02 다음 문장의 빈칸 (a)와 (b)에 들어갈 단어로 바르게 짝지어진 것은?

> • This book _____ (a) _____ a true story.
> • The story about the pink horse _____ (b) _____ .

① gets along with – was slowed down
② gives up – was got over
③ is based on – was made up
④ stands up for – got scared
⑤ looks like – passed away

03 다음 밑줄 친 부분의 뜻이 잘못된 것은?

① You look pretty <u>cool</u> with that new haircut. (멋진)
② This sentence doesn't <u>make sense</u>. (타당하다, 말이 되다)
③ The roller coaster looked so <u>scary</u> that we didn't ride it. (무서운)
④ My teacher got upset because my homework wasn't <u>complete</u>. (완료하다)
⑤ The <u>major</u> roads in this city are always busy. (주요한)

[04~05] 다음 영영풀이에 해당하는 것을 고르시오.

04
> anything that causes you to believe that something is true

① performance   ② source
③ skill   ④ evidence
⑤ site

05
> in a way that expresses disapproval

① critically   ② friendly
③ totally   ④ recently
⑤ unclearly

06 다음 대화의 빈칸에 들어갈 말을 〈영영풀이〉를 참고하여 네 글자(four letters)로 된 한 단어를 쓰시오.

> G: There's no monkey like this in the world. Its nose is too big. I think it's _____.
> B: I don't agree. I saw that kind of monkey on TV. It's real.

> 〈영영풀이〉 not real, but made to look or seem real

➡ _____

Conversation

07 다음 대화의 밑줄 친 단어를 알맞은 형으로 고치시오.

> G: Look at those shoes the girl is wearing. I think they're great. How do you feel about them?
>
> B: I think they look light and <u>comfort</u>.

➡ _____

08 다음 대화의 빈칸에 'B'의 입장에서 할 말로 알맞은 것은?

> G: There's no monkey like this in the world. Its nose is too big. I think it's fake.
>
> B: I don't agree. I saw that kind of monkey on TV. It's _____.

① fake
② exciting
③ real
④ an opinion
⑤ a lie

09 다음 짝지어진 대화 중 어색한 것은?

① A: Let's take a lunch break. I want to eat some healthy food.
  B: Sounds great! I'm ready to eat anything.
② A: How do you feel about this bird?
  B: I think it looks clean. It's a perfect pet for us.
③ A: What do you think of this dog?
  B: I think it looks friendly.
④ A: This monkey is a perfect pet for us. Don't you agree?
  B: Yes, I agree.
⑤ A: How do you feel about this ad?
  B: I think it's great. We should not believe every ad.

[10~12] 다음 대화를 읽고 물음에 답하시오.

> Alex: Big Mouth's show is really cool. How do you feel about it?
>
> Somi: Well, (a)<u>I don't think it's that great.</u>
>
> Alex: Come on. I love Mr. Big Mouth. He always (b)<u>makes me laugh out loud.</u>
>
> Somi: He's funny, but (c)<u>don't believe everything he says.</u>
>
> Alex: All right. Oh, look at his photo of an octopus. He said it lives in a tree.
>
> Somi: (d)<u>It makes sense.</u>
>
> Alex: He took the photo when it was climbing the tree. I don't think he's lying. It's a great photo.
>
> Somi: (e)<u>I don't agree with you.</u> It's a fake photo. An octopus can't live out of the sea.

10 위 대화의 흐름상 밑줄 친 (a)~(e) 중 어휘의 쓰임이 어색한 것은?

① (a) ② (b) ③ (c) ④ (d) ⑤ (e)

11 위 대화의 제목으로 가장 적절한 것은?

① How to Make a Popular Show
② Big Mouth's Show: Real or Fake?
③ Truth Becoming Falsehood
④ Where an Octopus Lives
⑤ Big Mouth's Show Alex Really Likes

12 위 대화의 내용과 일치하지 <u>않는</u> 것을 고르시오.

① Alex and Somi are looking at a photo of an octopus.
② Alex likes Mr. Big Mouth because he makes him laugh out loud.
③ Somi warns Alex not to trust Mr. Big Mouth.
④ Alex doesn't think a picture of an octopus climbing a tree is real.
⑤ Somi doesn't agree with Alex because an octopus can't live out of the sea.

Grammar

13 주어진 문장의 밑줄 친 if와 용법이 같은 것은?

> This test tells <u>if</u> a student understands what she learned.

① You don't have to come <u>if</u> you don't want to.

② I am worrying <u>if</u> I can receive the support fund.

③ We will leave <u>if</u> everyone is ready.

④ You can see this movie <u>if</u> you are over 18 years old.

⑤ I won't go there <u>if</u> you don't come.

14 다음 글에서 어법상 어색한 부분을 찾아 바르게 고치시오.

> Opinion
> • I don't know ①that the man on the horse ②is brave, but he looks very ③<u>tired</u> and hungry. I think he ④<u>needs</u> some food and water.
> • I think this artwork shows ⑤the most interesting part of Cervantes' novel *Don Quixote*.

_____ ➡ _____

15 다음 두 문장이 같은 뜻이 되도록 빈칸에 들어갈 알맞은 것은?

> He said to me, "Who brought this gecko home?"
> = He asked me _____.

① who brought that gecko home

② who had brought this gecko home

③ who that gecko had brought home

④ who had brought that gecko home

⑤ who that gecko brought home

16 다음 중 어법상 <u>어색한</u> 문장의 개수로 알맞은 것은?

> a. Do you know if will it be rainy tomorrow?
> b. I am not sure that he can finish his project.
> c. Jenny told me that she was sleepy then.
> d. Tell me do you have the time.
> e. He asked me if I want something to eat.
> f. Mom asked me not to lose my umbrella again.

① 1개   ② 2개   ③ 3개   ④ 4개   ⑤ 5개

17 다음 두 문장이 같은 뜻이 되도록 빈칸에 들어갈 알맞은 것은?

> Mr. Hong said to me, "You can come to my house for dinner tomorrow."
> = Mr. Hong told me that _____.

① you could come to my house for dinner the following day

② he could come to my house for dinner the following day

③ I could come to his house for dinner the following day

④ I could come to his house for dinner the previous day

⑤ you could come to my house for dinner the previous day

18 다음 직접화법 문장들을 간접화법으로 바꿀 때 <u>잘못된</u> 곳을 바르게 고치시오.

(1) He asked her what she was doing there.

➡ He said to her, "What you are doing here?"

➡ _____

영역별 핵심문제 **43**

(2) She told him that she had met her sister the day before.

➡ She said to him, "I meet my sister yesterday."

➡ _____

(3) She said that she was very happy then.

➡ She said, "I am very happy then."

➡ _____

Reading

[19~21] 다음 글을 읽고 물음에 답하시오.

In October 2016, stories about scary clowns shook schools across the Washington area, but Danina Garcia-Fuller's students didn't believe them a bit.

"Some people were getting scared because they saw things on social media," said Patricia Visoso, one of Garcia-Fuller's students. "But they never checked up on who was saying (A)this." The stories were actually made by teenagers, not by major newspapers or TV stations. (B)그들은 광대들이 정말로 학생들을 공격하려고 한다는 명백한 증거를 하나도 제공하지 않았다. The story turned out to be ⓐ .

19 위 글의 빈칸 ⓐ에 들어갈 알맞은 말을 고르시오.

① a reliable rumor   ② a complete lie
③ a valid story   ④ a complete truth
⑤ a suspicious column

20 위 글의 밑줄 친 (A)가 가리키는 것을 우리말로 쓰시오.

➡ _____

21 위 글의 밑줄 친 (B)의 우리말에 맞게 주어진 어휘를 알맞게 배열하시오.

to attack / no / clowns / offered / trying / really / students / hard evidence / they / were / that

➡ _____

_____

[22~24] 다음 글을 읽고 물음에 답하시오.

"I think a lot of people just look at one thing and believe it's true," Patricia's classmate Ivy-Brooks said. "It's really important to look at the right sources and to pay attention to what is real and what is fake."

Like Garcia-Fuller's students, many teenagers in America are learning to think critically about information they're seeing in the news and on the Internet. This skill is getting more important these days ⓐas stories can spread very fast, and anyone can make a website full of false information.

22 위 글의 밑줄 친 ⓐas와 문법적 쓰임이 같은 것을 고르시오.

① Leave the papers as they are.
② As you know, Julia is leaving soon.
③ As we go up, the air grows colder.
④ As I was tired, I soon fell asleep.
⑤ He came up to me as I was speaking.

23 위 글의 주제로 알맞은 것을 고르시오.

① the situation where people look at just one thing and believe it's true
② the importance of thinking critically about information you're seeing in the news and on the Internet

③ how to look at the right sources

④ the way you can pay attention to what is real and what is fake

⑤ the skill to make a website full of false information

24 According to the passage, which is NOT true?

① Ivy-Brooks thinks many people just look at one thing and believe it's true.

② Ivy-Brooks said that it was really important to look at the right sources.

③ Many teenagers in America are learning to think critically about information they're seeing only on the SNS.

④ These days, stories can spread very fast.

⑤ These days, it is possible for anyone to make a website full of false information.

[25~26] 다음 글을 읽고 물음에 답하시오.

Garcia-Fuller also said sometimes it can be very hard to be a smart news reader. She tests her students with a website that appears to provide information on an animal called a tree octopus. The site is full of information on this animal, along with a few unclear photos of octopuses in trees. But like the story of scary clowns, it's totally ⓐmade up.

The lesson, Garcia-Fuller tells her students, is to "check the information you're seeing once more carefully" and to "question everything, even things that I say."

25 위 글의 밑줄 친 ⓐmade up과 같은 뜻을 가지는 단어를 철자 i로 시작하여 쓰시오.

➡ _____

26 위 글의 제목으로 알맞은 것을 고르시오.

① Who Is a Smart News Reader?

② To Test Students with a Website

③ Information on an Animal Called a Tree Octopus

④ Can You Believe the Information on the Tree Octopus?

⑤ To Check the Information Carefully and to Question Everything

[27~28] 다음 글을 읽고 물음에 답하시오.

The reporter says the ducks jumped down on the road by themselves. ⓐ , it's not a fact. ⓑA man took the ducks and put down them safely on the road one by one. I wonder if the reporter saw the scene himself.

27 위 글의 빈칸 ⓐ에 들어갈 알맞은 말을 고르시오.

① For example ② In addition

③ In other words ④ However

⑤ Therefore

28 위 글의 밑줄 친 ⓑ에서 어법상 틀린 부분을 찾아 고치시오.

➡ _____ ➡ _____

01 다음 짝지어진 단어의 관계가 같도록 빈칸에 알맞은 말을 쓰시오.

> information – inform : performance – _____

02 다음 영영풀이에 해당하는 단어는?

> very important and serious

① minor   ② noisy   ③ false
④ total   ⑤ major

[03~04] 다음 대화를 읽고 물음에 답하시오.

G: How do you feel about the teddy bears?
B: They are cute. (A)뭔가 특별한 점이 있니?
G: They were made out of a police officer's uniform.
B: Oh, I see.
G: This police officer made them for the kids. Their dad was a police officer, and he passed away recently.
B: That's very touching.

03 위 대화의 'Teddy Bears'에 관한 내용 중에서 'Fact'에 해당하는 문장을 모두 찾아 그대로 쓰시오.

➡ _____
_____

04 위 대화의 우리말 (A)에 맞게 주어진 단어를 알맞은 순서로 배열하시오.

> (special / there / anything / them / about / is / ?)

➡ _____

05 다음 대화의 빈칸에 들어갈 말로 알맞은 것은?

G: There's no monkey like this in the world. Its nose is too big. I think it's fake.
B: _____ I saw that kind of monkey on TV. It's real.

① I think so, too.
② I don't agree.
③ I agree with you.
④ You can say that again.
⑤ I couldn't agree with you more.

[06~07] 다음 대화를 읽고 물음에 답하시오.

G: How do you feel about this kid here?
B: (A) I think she is very pretty. ___(a)___ , why did she cut her hair? (B)
G: Can you guess?
B: Well, girls these days prefer short hair. (C)
G: I don't agree with that. (D) And this kid here is not a girl. ___(b)___ , he is a boy. (E)
B: Really?
G: Yes. He grew his hair to help sick children.

06 위 대화의 (A)~(E) 중 주어진 문장이 들어갈 위치로 알맞은 것은?

> Most girls like long hair better than short hair.

① (A)   ② (B)   ③ (C)   ④ (D)   ⑤ (E)

07 위 대화의 빈칸 (a)와 (b)에 들어갈 말로 알맞은 것은?

① By the way – Moreover
② In addition – On the other hand
③ By the way – In fact
④ However – Actually
⑤ Therefore – For example

08 다음 빈칸에 들어갈 말로 적절한 것을 <u>모두</u> 고르시오.

> Team A and Team B will debate _____ teenagers should work part-time job.

① that   ② if   ③ what
④ though   ⑤ whether

09 다음 화법 전환 문장들에서 빈칸에 알맞은 말을 쓰시오.

(1) She said to me, "How do you know the answer of this question?"
➡ She asked me how I knew _____ _____.

(2) He said, "I was in trouble."
➡ He said that he _____.

(3) Eric told me that he was happy with his new house then.
➡ Eric said to me, "I'm happy with _____."

(4) He told me he liked the job.
➡ He _____ me, "I like the job."

(5) He asked me if I was hungry then.
➡ He said to me, "_____?"

10 다음 우리말을 참고하여 괄호 안에 주어진 단어로 빈칸에 알맞은 말을 써 넣으시오.

> 선생님은 학생들에게 수업 중에 밖에 나가지 말라고 말씀하셨다. (go out, during)
> (1) The teacher said to students, "_____ _____."
> (2) The teacher _____ _____.

11 주어진 어휘를 이용하여 다음 우리말을 영어로 쓰시오.

> 나는 그들이 우리에게 부채춤을 보여 줄 것인지 궁금해. (wonder, the fan dance)

➡ _____

12 다음 대화의 빈칸에 밑줄 친 문장을 알맞은 형태로 바꾸어 써 넣으시오.

> (1) A: She said, "_____."
>   B: She said what?
>   A: She said that she was so tired then.
> (2) A: He said to me, "You are right."
>   B: What did he say?
>   A: He told me that _____.

[13~15] 다음 글을 읽고 물음에 답하시오.

> In October 2016, stories about scary clowns shook schools across the Washington area, but Danina Garcia-Fuller's students didn't believe them a bit.

"Some people were getting scared because they saw things on social media," said Patricia Visoso, one of Garcia-Fuller's students. "But they never checked up on who was saying this." The stories were actually made by teenagers, not by major newspapers or TV stations. They offered no ⓐhard evidence that clowns really were trying to attack students. The story ⓑturned out to be a complete lie.

📝출제율 95%

13 위 글의 밑줄 친 ⓐhard와 같은 의미로 쓰인 것을 고르시오.

① Wait for the concrete to go hard.
② You must try hard.
③ It is hard to believe that she's only nine.
④ The newspaper story is based on hard facts.
⑤ She's a very hard worker.

📝출제율 90%

14 위 글의 밑줄 친 ⓑturned out과 바꿔 쓸 수 있는 한 단어를 쓰시오.

➡ _____

📝출제율 95%

15 By whom were the stories about scary clowns made? Answer in English in a full sentence. (5 words)

➡ _____

[16~17] 다음 글을 읽고 물음에 답하시오.

"I think a lot of people just look at one thing and believe it's true," Patricia's classmate Ivy-Brooks said. "It's really important to look at the right sources and ⓐto pay attention to what is real and what is fake."

Like Garcia-Fuller's students, many teenagers in America are learning to think critically about information ⓑthey're seeing in the news and on the Internet. This skill is getting more important these days as stories can spread very fast, and anyone can make a website full of false information.

📝출제율 100%

16 아래 〈보기〉에서 위 글의 밑줄 친 ⓐto pay와 to부정사의 용법이 같은 것의 개수를 고르시오.

┌─ 보기 ─┐
① I turned on the computer to surf the Internet.
② I don't know where to go.
③ Do you have something interesting to read?
④ Everybody was surprised to see him.
⑤ His wish is to have good eyesight.
└─────┘

① 1개　② 2개　③ 3개　④ 4개　⑤ 5개

📝출제율 90%

17 위 글의 밑줄 친 ⓑthey가 가리키는 것을 본문에서 찾아 쓰시오.

➡ _____

[18~20] 다음 글을 읽고 물음에 답하시오.

Garcia-Fuller said she was teaching her students how to tell fake news from real news.
"(①) If a story or a photo seems too good to be true, stop and think: Is there any evidence that supports what the writer says? (②) And where is this coming from? (③)"
Garcia-Fuller's students also learn how to tell fact from opinion in the news. (④) "Opinions are good ⓐto read," said 15-year-old McKenzie Campbell, "but you also have to check if they are based on facts." (⑤)

18 위 글의 흐름으로 보아, 주어진 문장이 들어가기에 가장 적절한 곳은?

> One of the first steps is to slow down.

①   ②   ③   ④   ⑤

19 위 글의 밑줄 친 ⓐto read와 to부정사의 용법이 다른 것을 모두 고르시오.

① I'm sorry to hear the bad news.
② It's about time to go for a walk.
③ I think it wrong to tell a lie.
④ Jenny grew up to be a pianist.
⑤ Mom told me to stop watching TV.

20 According to the passage, which is NOT true?

① Garcia-Fuller was teaching her students how to tell fake news from real news.
② One of the first steps to tell fake news from real news is to slow down.
③ Garcia-Fuller's students also learn how to distinguish fact from opinion in the news.
④ 15-year-old McKenzie Campbell said that opinions are good to speak.
⑤ 15-year-old McKenzie Campbell said that we also had to check if the opinions were based on facts.

[21~23] 다음 글을 읽고 물음에 답하시오.

ⓐTeam NW danced on the stage while the school festival. They wondered ⓑif the students and teachers would like their dancing. ⓒBut they performed much better than any other team. A lot of students stood up and cheered loudly when the team danced. Ms. Yu, the P.E. teacher, said it was the performance of the year.

21 위 글의 밑줄 친 ⓐ에서 어법상 틀린 부분을 찾아 고치시오.

_____ ➡ _____

22 위 글의 밑줄 친 ⓑif와 문법적 쓰임이 같은 것을 모두 고르시오.

① I asked her if she knew Mr. White.
② If you see him, give him this note.
③ I'll work here if you offer me more money.
④ He couldn't tell if she was laughing or crying.
⑤ If necessary, I can come at once.

23 위 글의 밑줄 친 ⓒ를 다음과 같이 바꿔 쓸 때 빈칸에 들어갈 알맞은 한 단어를 쓰시오.

> But they performed _____ of all the teams.

01 다음 대화를 읽고 질문에 영어로 답하시오.

> Alex: Big Mouth's show is really cool. How do you feel about it?
>
> Somi: Well, I don't think it's that great.
>
> Alex: Come on. I love Mr. Big Mouth. He always makes me laugh out loud.
>
> Somi: He's funny, but don't believe everything he says.
>
> Alex: All right. Oh, look at his photo of an octopus. He said it lives in a tree.
>
> Somi: It doesn't make sense
>
> Alex: He took the photo when it was climbing the tree. I don't think he's lying. It's a great photo.
>
> Somi: I don't agree with you. It's a fake photo. An octopus can't live out of the sea.

Q: Why did Somi say it was a fake photo?

➡ _____

02 접속사 'if', 'that', 'whether' 중 적절한 것을 한 번씩만 골라 주어진 단어와 함께 알맞게 배열하시오.

(1) I am wondering (fit, these, feet, shoes, his).

➡ _____

(2) I am sure (is, the, crying, baby, now).

➡ _____

(3) (a boy, kid, this, is, a girl, or) doesn't matter to me at all.

➡ _____

03 다음 주어진 문장들을 간접화법으로 바꿔 쓰시오.

(1) She said, "I like Tony."

➡ She said that _____.

(2) The old man said, "I want some water."

➡ The old man said that _____

_____.

(3) Bob said, "My sister looks happy."

➡ Bob said that _____.

04 대화의 흐름에 맞게 빈칸에 들어갈 말을 영어로 쓰시오.

(1) A: She said to me, "Where are you living now?"

B: Pardon me? Can you repeat that again?

A: She asked me where _____.

(2) A: He said to me, "Do you like to study in this library?"

B: I can't hear what you are saying.

A: He asked me _____

_____.

05 다음 그림 속 내용을 다른 사람에게 전달하는 문장으로 완성하시오.

> The boy said _____
>
> _____ and he wondered
>
> _____.

"I think a lot of people just look at one thing and believe it's true," Patricia's classmate Ivy-Brooks said. "It's really important to look at the right sources and to pay attention to what is real and what is fake."

Like Garcia-Fuller's students, many teenagers in America are learning to think critically ⓐ뉴스에서 그리고 인터넷상에서 보고 있는 정보에 관해. This skill is getting more important these days as stories can spread very fast, and anyone can make a website full of false information.

06 위 글의 밑줄 친 ⓐ의 우리말에 맞게 주어진 어휘를 이용하여 11 단어로 영작하시오.

> about, seeing

➡ _____

_____

07 주어진 영영풀이에 해당하는 단어를 본문에서 찾아 쓰시오.

> not genuine or real; being an imitation of the genuine article

➡ _____

08 본문의 내용과 일치하도록 다음 빈칸 (A)와 (B)에 알맞은 단어를 쓰시오.

> According to Patricia's classmate Ivy-Brooks, looking at (A)_____ _____ _____ and paying attention to (B)_____ _____ _____ and what is fake are really important.

Garcia-Fuller said she was teaching her students how to tell fake news from real news.

"One of the first steps is to slow down. ⓐIf a story or a photo seems too good to be true, stop and think: Is there any evidence that supports what the writer says? And where is this coming from?"

Garcia-Fuller's students also learn how to tell fact from opinion in the news. "Opinions are good to read," said 15-year-old McKenzie Campbell, "ⓑbut you also have to check that they are based on facts."

09 위 글의 밑줄 친 ⓐ를 다음과 같이 바꿔 쓸 때 빈칸에 들어갈 알맞은 단어를 쓰시오.

> If a story or a photo seems _____ good _____ it _____ be true

10 위 글의 밑줄 친 ⓑ에서 어법상 틀린 부분을 찾아 고치시오.

_____ ➡ _____

11 According to McKenzie Campbell, when we read opinions in the news, what do we have to check? Answer in English in a full sentence.

➡ _____

창의사고력 서술형 문제

01 아래 표의 (A)의 과일이나 야채에 대해 (B)는 좋아하거나 싫어하는 것을 나타낸 것이다. 〈보기〉처럼 상대방의 의견을 묻는 말과 그 대답을 쓰시오.

보기

A: How do you feel about apples?
B: I really love them.

(A)	(B)
• apples • persimmons • cucumbers • pears	• I really love them. • I like them. • I hate them. • I don't like them.

02 다음은 야구선수 Kelly와의 인터뷰를 정리한 내용이다. 인터뷰를 읽고, 조건에 맞게 정리한 내용의 빈칸에 알맞은 말을 쓰시오. (The reporter is a woman and Kelly is a man. Complete the sentence using pronouns.)

보기

Reporter: Kelly, our readers want to know all about you. (1)Can you tell me about your day?
Kelly: (2)I always get up at 6 and go to the stadium at 7.
Reporter: You get up so early. (3)How long were your training hours today?
Kelly: (4)It took 5 hours and was really hard.
Reporter: (5)What will you do in your spare time today?
Kelly: (6)After this interview, I will go swimming or watch a movie.
Reporter: It's been really nice talking to you. Thank you for letting us take time for the interview.

(1) The reporter asked Kelly _____.
(2) Kelly said that _____.
(3) The reporter asked Kelly _____.
(4) Kelly said that _____.
(5) The reporter asked Kelly _____.
(6) Kelly said that _____.

단원별 모의고사

01 다음 단어에 대한 영어 설명이 <u>어색한</u> 것은?

① false: incorrect, untrue, or mistaken

② fact: what you think or believe about something

③ lie: an untrue statement

④ totally: completely, absolutely

⑤ octopus: a soft sea creature with eight long arms

02 다음 짝지어진 단어의 관계가 같도록 빈칸에 알맞은 말을 주어진 글자로 시작하여 쓰시오.

search – investigate : supply – p_____

03 다음 영영풀이에 해당하는 단어를 고르시오.

a particular part of a town, a country, or the world

① clown   ② social media

③ evidence   ④ source

⑤ area

04 다음 중 짝지어진 대화가 <u>어색한</u> 것은?

① A: What did the woman say to her brother?
   B: She told him that she was very happy to meet him.

② A: How do you feel about the girl?
   B: I think she's pretty.

③ A: How do you feel about the dog?
   B: I think it's cute.

④ A: How do you feel about the ducks?
   B: I don't agree with you.

⑤ A: How do you feel about this ad?
   B: I think it's great. It shows the phone is strong.

[05~06] 다음 대화를 읽고 물음에 답하시오.

G: How do you feel about this drama?

B: _____(A)_____ The boy gave up his life to save his sister. It's the best drama of this year.

G: I don't agree. It's not a good drama.

B: Come on. Why do you think so?

G: It doesn't seem real. And it's a little boring.

05 위 대화의 빈칸 (A)에 들어갈 말로 알맞은 것은?

① I think it's very boring.

② That's a good idea.

③ I think it's very touching.

④ I don't believe it.

⑤ It's not a good drama.

06 위 대화를 읽고 다음 물음에 대한 대답을 완성하시오.

> G: Why doesn't the girl think it's a good drama?

> Because _____ and _____.

07 다음 대화의 흐름상 밑줄 친 (1)~(5) 중 <u>어색한</u> 것은?

> G: How do you feel about this kid here?
> B: (1)I think she is very pretty. By the way, why did she cut her hair?
> G: (2)Can you guess?
> B: Well, girls these days prefer short hair.
> G: (3)I agree with that. Most girls like long hair better than short hair. And this kid here is not a girl. (4)In fact, he is a boy.
> B: Really?
> G: Yes. (5)He grew his hair to help sick children.

① (1)　② (2)　③ (3)　④ (4)　⑤ (5)

08 다음 대화의 밑줄 친 우리말에 맞게 주어진 단어를 알맞은 순서로 배열하시오.

> G: <u>저 여자애가 신고 있는 신발 좀 봐.</u> (the girl / those / is / look / wearing / at / shoes) I think they're great. How do you feel about them?
> B: I think they look light and comfortable.
> G: Right. I want to buy them for the school field trip.

➡ _____

09 다음 대화를 읽고, 아래의 〈Criticism〉에 해당하는 문장의 빈칸을 완성하시오.

> G: How do you feel about the teddy bears?
> B: They are cute. Is there anything special about them?
> G: They were made out of a police officer's uniform.
> B: Oh, I see.
> G: This police officer made them for the kids. Their dad was a police officer, and he passed away recently.
> B: That's very touching.

> The reporter says the police officer bought teddy bears for the kids. However, it's not a (1)_____. The police officer made them out of the kids' dad's (2)_____ for the kids. I wonder (3)_____ the reporter met them himself.

[10~11] 다음 대화를 읽고 물음에 답하시오.

> Alex: Big Mouth's show is really cool. How do you feel about it?
> Somi: Well, I don't think it's (A)that great.
> Alex: Come on. I love Mr. Big Mouth. He always makes me laugh out loud.
> Somi: He's funny, but don't believe everything he says.
> Alex: All right. Oh, look at his photo of an octopus. He said it lives in a tree.
> Somi: It doesn't make sense.
> Alex: He took the photo when it was climbing the tree. I don't think he's lying. It's a great photo.
> Somi: I don't agree with you. It's a fake photo. An octopus can't live out of the sea.

10 위 대화를 읽고 다음 질문에 영어로 답하시오.

> G: What is the octopus in the photo doing?

➡ _____

11 위 대화의 밑줄 친 (A)that과 같은 의미로 사용된 것은?

① This book is much thicker than that one.
② My arm doesn't reach that far.
③ The point is that you are still responsible.
④ It was yesterday that the accident happened.
⑤ That was the best time.

12 다음 중 밑줄 친 if의 의미가 다른 하나를 고르시오.

① We will discuss if this has a positive impact on our society.
② I will help you if you are busy now.
③ Any student will fail if he or she cheats on the test.
④ You can't come on board if you don't have your passport.
⑤ I will be angry if you tell a lie.

13 다음 문장을 간접화법으로 바꿔 쓰시오.

> Mr. Kim said to his daughter, "Can I ask you a few questions?"

➡ _____
_____

14 다음 각 문장에서 어법상 틀린 부분을 찾아 바르게 고쳐 쓰시오.

(1) He says her, "Where do you work now?"
➡ _____

(2) She told me that she hasn't been at school the day before.
➡ _____
_____

15 다음 두 문장을 한 문장으로 바르게 옮긴 것은?

> • Was this song composed by him?
> • That is unknown.

① Whether was this song composed by him is unknown.
② If was this song composed by him is unknown.
③ Whether this song was composed by him is unknown.
④ If this song was composed by him is unknown.
⑤ It is unknown that this song was composed by him

16 다음 우리말을 주어진 단어를 사용하여 영어로 옮기시오.

> (1) 나는 그녀가 내 선물을 좋아할지 궁금해. (if, present)
> (2) 너는 그녀가 결혼했는지 알고 있니? (if, is)

(1) _____
(2) _____

[17~18] 다음 글을 읽고 물음에 답하시오.

In October 2016, stories about (A)[scared / scary] clowns shook schools across the Washington area, but Danina Garcia-Fuller's students didn't believe ⓐthem a bit.

"Some people were getting (B)[scared / scary] because they saw things on social media," said Patricia Visoso, one of Garcia-Fuller's students. "But they never checked up on who was saying this." The stories were actually made by teenagers, not by major newspapers or TV stations. They (C)[offered / were offered] no hard evidence that clowns really were trying to attack students. The story turned out to be a complete lie.

17 위 글의 괄호 (A)~(C)에서 문맥이나 어법상 알맞은 낱말을 골라 쓰시오.

➡ (A) _____ (B) _____ (C) _____

18 위 글의 밑줄 친 ⓐthem이 가리키는 것을 본문에서 찾아 쓰시오.

➡ _____

[19~20] 다음 글을 읽고 물음에 답하시오.

"I think a lot of people just look at one thing and believe it's true," Patricia's classmate Ivy-Brooks said. "It's really important to look at the right sources and to pay attention ___ⓐ___ what is real and what is fake."

(A)Like Garcia-Fuller's students, many teenagers in America are learning to think critically about information they're seeing in the news and ___ⓑ___ the Internet. This skill is getting more important these days as stories can spread very fast, and anyone can make a website full of false information.

19 위 글의 빈칸 ⓐ와 ⓑ에 들어갈 전치사가 바르게 짝지어진 것은?

	ⓐ	ⓑ		ⓐ	ⓑ
①	for	to	②	to	by
③	to	on	④	for	on
⑤	on	to			

20 위 글의 밑줄 친 (A)Like와 같은 의미로 쓰인 것을 고르시오.

① I had a chance to meet people of like mind.

② There are many hobbies like photography or painting.

③ At weekends I like to sleep late.

④ He likes jazz, rock and the like.

⑤ Students were angry at being treated like children.

[21~22] 다음 글을 읽고 물음에 답하시오.

Garcia-Fuller said she was teaching her students how to tell fake news from real news.

"One of the first steps is to slow down. If a story or a photo seems too good to be true, stop and think: Is there any evidence that supports what the writer says? And where is this coming from?"

Garcia-Fuller's students also learn how to tell fact from opinion in the news. "Opinions are good to read," said 15-year-old McKenzie Campbell, "but you also have to check if they are based on facts."

21 다음 문장에서 위 글의 내용과 <u>다른</u> 부분을 찾아서 고치시오.

Garcia-Fuller was teaching her students how to tell fake news from opinion in the news.

➡ _____

22 만약 어떤 이야기나 어떤 사진이 진짜라고 하기엔 너무 좋아 보일 때 생각해 보아야 할 두 가지를 우리말로 쓰시오.

① _____
_____
② _____

[23~24] 다음 글을 읽고 물음에 답하시오.

(①) Garcia-Fuller also said sometimes it can be very hard to be a smart news reader. (②) She tests her students with a website that appears to provide information on an animal called a tree octopus. (③) But like the story of scary clowns, it's totally made up. (④)

The lesson, Garcia-Fuller tells her students, is to "check the information you're seeing once more carefully" and to "question everything, even things that I say." (⑤)

23 위 글의 흐름으로 보아, 주어진 문장이 들어가기에 가장 적절한 곳은?

The site is full of information on this animal, along with a few unclear photos of octopuses in trees.

①　　②　　③　　④　　⑤

24 According to the passage, which is NOT true?

① According to Garcia-Fuller, sometimes it can be very hard to be a smart news reader.
② Garcia-Fuller tests her students with a website that appears to provide information on a tree octopus.
③ The website is full of information on a tree octopus, together with a few unclear photos of octopuses in trees.
④ Unlike the story of scary clowns, the information on a tree octopus is true.
⑤ Garcia-Fuller tells her students to check the information carefully and to question everything.

MEMO

Lesson 8

Make Peace with Others

 의사소통 기능

- 화냄 표현하기
  I can't stand it.
- 화냄에 응대하기
  Calm down!

 언어 형식

- 부정대명사
  Some gave him angry looks, and **others** shouted at him.
- 5형식(동사 + 목적어 + to부정사)
  The king **ordered** him **to go** to a famous military school.

Words & Expressions

Key Words

- **above** [əbʌ́v] 전 ~보다 위에
- **anymore** [ènimɔ́ːr] 부 더 이상
- **approach** [əpróutʃ] 동 다가가다
- **army** [áːrmi] 명 군대, 육군
- **bark** [bɑːrk] 동 (개가) 짖다
- **during** [djúəriŋ] 전 ~ 동안
- **fast** [fæst] 동 단식하다
- **finally** [fáinəli] 부 마침내
- **fix** [fiks] 동 수리하다
- **follow** [fálou] 동 따르다, 따라가다
- **forget** [fərgét] 동 잊다
- **gate** [geit] 명 정문, 대문
- **general** [dʒénərəl] 명 장군
- **grass** [græs] 명 풀, 잔디
- **happen** [hǽpən] 동 일어나다, 발생하다
- **heater** [híːtər] 명 난방기, 히터
- **injured** [índʒərd] 형 부상당한
- **instead** [instéd] 부 대신에
- **knowing** [nóuiŋ] 형 다 안다는 듯한
- **look** [luk] 명 표정
- **might** [mait] 조 ~일지도 모른다

- **military** [mílitéri] 명 군대 형 군대의
- **movement** [múːvmənt] 명 (사람들이 조직적으로 벌이는) 운동
- **noise** [nɔiz] 명 소음
- **order** [ɔ́ːrdər] 동 명령하다
- **palace** [pǽlis] 명 궁, 궁전
- **patience** [péiʃəns] 명 인내심, 참을성
- **pole** [poul] 명 기둥, 막대, 장대
- **powerful** [páuərfəl] 형 강력한
- **push** [puʃ] 동 밀다
- **reason** [ríːzn] 명 이유
- **situation** [sitʃuéiʃən] 명 상황
- **stand** [stænd] 동 참다, 견디다
- **suddenly** [sʌ́dnli] 부 갑자기
- **sword** [sɔːrd] 명 검, 칼
- **tie** [tai] 동 묶다
- **war** [wɔːr] 명 전쟁
- **warrior** [wɔ́ːriər] 명 전사
- **weapon** [wépən] 명 무기
- **winner** [wínər] 명 승리자, 우승자
- **wise** [waiz] 형 현명한
- **yell** [jel] 동 소리 지르다

Key Expressions

- **at that moment** 그 순간에
- **be in trouble** 곤경에 처하다
- **calm down** 진정하다
- **focus on** ~에 집중하다
- **give up** 포기하다
- **harder and harder** 점점 더 심하게
- **I can't stand** ~을 참을 수가 없다
- **in all possible ways** 모든 가능한 방법으로
- **in the middle** 중간에서
- **keep -ing** 계속해서 ~하다
- **let ~ go** ~을 풀어주다, 석방하다
- **on the side of** ~을 편들어, ~의 면에

- **pass by** 옆을 지나가다
- **return to** ~로 돌아가다
- **set free** 자유의 몸이 되게 하다, 석방하다
- **should have been** ~이었어야 했다
- **sooner or later** 조만간, 머지않아
- **stand against** ~에 기대다
- **stand in line** 줄을 서다
- **step on** ~을 밟다
- **take care of** ~을 돌보다
- **wait for** ~을 기다리다
- **wait in line** 줄 서서 기다리다
- **win a war** 전쟁에서 이기다

Word Power

※ 서로 비슷한 뜻을 가진 어휘

- ☐ **above** ~보다 위에 – **over** ~을 넘어
- ☐ **injured** 부상당한 – **wounded** 부상당한
- ☐ **powerful** 강력한 – **mighty** 강력한, 강대한
- ☐ **sword** 검, 칼 – **knife** (짧은) 칼
- ☐ **let ~ go** ~를 풀어주다, 석방하다 – **set free** 자유의 몸이 되게 하다, 석방하다

- ☐ **gate** 정문, 대문 – **gateway** 출입구, 통로
- ☐ **pass by** 옆을 지나가다 – **go by** 지나가다
- ☐ **suddenly** 갑자기 – **unexpectedly** 갑자기, 예상 외로
- ☐ **warrior** 전사 – **fighter** 전사, 투사

※ 서로 반대의 뜻을 가진 어휘

- ☐ **above** ~보다 위에 ↔ **under** ~의 아래에
- ☐ **follow** 따르다, 따라가다 ↔ **avoid** 피하다, 비키다
- ☐ **knowing** 다 안다는 듯한 ↔ **unknowing** 자신도 모르는
- ☐ **patience** 인내심, 참을성 ↔ **impatience** 성급함, 조급함
- ☐ **push** 밀다 ↔ **pull** 당기다
- ☐ **winner** 승리자, 우승자 ↔ **loser** 실패자

- ☐ **approach** 다가가다 ↔ **withdraw** 물러나다
- ☐ **injured** 부상당한 ↔ **uninjured** 부상당하지 않은
- ☐ **tie** 묶다 ↔ **untie** 풀다
- ☐ **powerful** 강력한 ↔ **powerless** 무능한, 무력한
- ☐ **war** 전쟁 ↔ **peace** 평화
- ☐ **wise** 현명한 ↔ **unwise** 현명하지 못한

※ 접미사 -er/-or

- ☐ **win** + **-er** → **winner** 승리자
- ☐ **lead** + **-er** → **leader** 지도자, 대표
- ☐ **work** + **-er** → **worker** 노동자
- ☐ **war** + **-or** → **warrior** 전사
- ☐ **protect** + **-or** → **protector** 보호자, 보호기관
- ☐ **sculpt** + **-or** → **sculptor** 조각가

- ☐ **care** + **-er** → **carer** 간병인
- ☐ **drive** + **-er** → **driver** 운전기사
- ☐ **sing** + **-er** → **singer** 가수
- ☐ **project** + **-or** → **projector** 영사기
- ☐ **direct** + **-or** → **director** 감독, 책임자

English Dictionary

☐ **finally** 결국, 마침내
→ after a long period of time
기나긴 시간 후에

☐ **injured** 부상당한
→ having physical damage to a part of the body
신체의 일부분에 물리적인 상처를 입은

☐ **military** 군대
→ the armed forces of a country
한 국가의 무장한 세력

☐ **order** 명령하다
→ to tell someone to do something
어떤 일을 하라고 누군가에게 말하다

☐ **patience** 인내심
→ being able to stay calm and not get annoyed
화내지 않고 침착하게 있을 수 있는 것

☐ **powerful** 강력한
→ having a lot of power to control people and events
사람과 사건을 통제할 수 있는 많은 힘을 갖고 있는

☐ **reason** 이유
→ a fact or situation which explains why something happens
어떤 일이 왜 일어나는지 설명하는 사실이나 상황

☐ **realize** 깨닫다
→ to become aware of a fact or to understand it
어떤 사실을 알게 되거나 이해하다

☐ **warrior** 전사
→ a fighter or soldier, especially one in old times who was very brave and experienced in fighting
특히 옛날에 존재하던 매우 용감하고 싸움에 숙련된 군인 또는 투사

☐ **yell** 소리 지르다
→ to shout loudly 큰 소리로 고함지르다

서답형

01 다음 문장의 빈칸에 〈영어 설명〉에 맞게 한 단어로 쓰시오.

> Even if someone is _____ing at you,
> do not respond in the same way.
> 〈영어 설명〉 to shout loudly

➡ _____

중요

02 다음 빈칸에 공통으로 들어갈 말로 가장 적절한 것은?

> • The cello is still considered an unfamiliar
>   instrument to the _____ public.
> • Kim Yu-sin was a great _____ in
>   Korean history.

① common   ② traditional
③ general   ④ powerful
⑤ soldier

[03~04] 다음 설명에 해당하는 단어를 고르시오.

03
> a fighter or soldier, especially one in
> old times who was very brave and
> experienced in fighting

① attack   ② weapon   ③ army
④ sword   ⑤ warrior

중요

04
> to become aware of a fact or to understand
> it

① follow   ② realize   ③ pass
④ happen   ⑤ remember

서답형

05 다음 우리말에 맞게 두 단어로 쓰시오.

> 나는 길 위의 마른 낙엽을 밟을 때 나는 소리를 좋아해.
> ➡ I like the sound when I _____
>   _____ the dry fallen leaves on the
>   street.

중요

06 다음 빈칸에 들어갈 말로 알맞은 것은?

> (1) These voters _____ for hours
>   because they are passionate about
>   trying to change the society they live
>   in.
> (2) It wasn't easy for him, but he didn't
>   _____.

① stand against – set free
② take care of – give up
③ pass by – focus on
④ stand in line – give up
⑤ wait in line – wait for

서답형

07 다음 짝지어진 단어의 관계가 같도록 빈칸에 알맞은 말을 쓰시오.

> war – peace : patience – _____

08 다음 중 주어진 단어의 관계가 나머지와 다른 것은?

① cook – cooker
② sing – singer
③ lead – leader
④ drive – driver
⑤ win – winner

01 다음 〈보기〉에서 알맞은 단어를 선택하여 문장의 빈칸을 완성하시오. (필요하면 변형하거나 단어를 추가하시오.)

> ── 보기 ──
> army   reason   above   set

(1) His picture was placed on the shelf _____ the desk.

(2) My brother joined the _____ last year.

(3) The king ordered his men to _____ the prisoner _____.

(4) There are two _____ why I want to be a doctor.

02 다음 문장의 빈칸에 알맞은 단어를 쓰시오. (2)번은 주어진 영영 풀이에 어울리는 단어를 쓰시오.

> <영영 풀이> a long thin piece of wood or metal

(1) People must not bring any _____s, such as knives or guns, on an airplane.

(2) We saw the country's flag at the top of the _____.

03 다음 우리말과 같은 표현이 되도록 문장의 빈칸을 채우시오.

(1) 우리가 크게 웃자 한 선생님은 화난 표정을 지었다.
➡ Ms. Han gave us an angry _____ when we laughed out loud.

(2) 위험한 상황에 처해 있다면, 경찰에 전화해야 한다.
➡ If you are in a dangerous _____, you should call the police.

(3) 올해, 사람들은 경복궁에서 한복 패션쇼를 즐겼습니다.
➡ This year, people enjoyed a hanbok fashion show at Gyeongbokgung _____.

04 영영풀이에 해당하는 단어를 〈보기〉에서 찾아 첫 번째 빈칸에 쓰고, 두 번째 빈칸에는 우리말 뜻을 쓰시오.

> ── 보기 ──
> injured   wise   push   powerful

(1) _____ : having a lot of power to control people and events: _____

(2) _____ : having the power to judge properly what is true or right: _____

(3) _____ : having physical damage to a part of the body : _____

(4) _____ : to make someone or something move by pressing them with your hands: _____

05 다음 문장의 빈칸에 들어갈 말을 〈보기〉의 단어를 이용하여 완성하시오.

> ── 보기 ──
> pass   decrease   soon

(1) The number of elementary school students keeps _____.

(2) The vacation will begin and _____ _____, whether you do something or not.

(3) _____ _____ _____, he will realize she really loved him.

Conversation
교과서

① 화냄 표현하기

A Smoke is coming from the lower floor. I can't stand it.
아래층에서 담배 연기가 올라와. 참을 수 없어.

B Me, too. Let's go downstairs and ask them to close the window.
나도 그래. 아래층에 가서 창문 닫아달라고 말하자.

■ 화난 감정을 표현하는 문장으로 'I can't stand it.(참을 수 없어.)'을 사용할 수 있다. 이외에도 'I'm very angry.', 'I'm very upset.', 'I'm very annoyed.', 'How irritating!', 'I'm tired of it.', 'I'm fed up with it.', 'I'm disgusted with it.' 등을 대신 사용할 수 있다.

화난 상태 표현 정리 1

- angry (보편적 의미에서) 화가 난
- annoyed 짜증난
- irritated 짜증난
- upset 속상한. 섭섭한
- mad 성난

화난 상태 표현 정리 2

- I'm tired of it. 난 그게 지긋지긋해.
- I'm fed up with it. 난 그게 넌더리가 나.
- I'm disgusted with it. 난 그게 정말 역겨워.

핵심 Check

1. 다음 대화에서 밑줄 친 부분을 대체할 수 <u>없는</u> 표현은?

A: Children upstairs are running around all day. <u>I can't stand it.</u>

B: Calm down. They're having a birthday party.

① How annoying!
② How irritating!
③ I'm irritated.
④ I can't be tired of it.
⑤ I'm fed up with it.

② 화냄에 응대하기

> **A** I can't stand this place. It's too crowded. 이 장소를 견딜 수가 없어. 너무 사람이 많아.
>
> **B** Calm down! We're at the festival. Let's enjoy it. 진정해! 우리 축제에 와 있잖아. 축제를 즐기자.

■ 화낸 상대방에 응대할 때, 'Calm down!(진정해!)'이라는 표현을 쓸 수 있다. 이와 같은 표현으로는 'Relax.', 'Take it easy.', 'It's going to be okay. Take a deep breath and try to relax.', 'Chill out!', 'Don't stress yourself.', 'Control yourself.' 등이 있다.

화냄에 응대하는 표현 정리

- Relax. 진정해.
- Take it easy. 진정해
- It's going to be okay. Take a deep breath and try to relax. 괜찮아질 거야. 심호흡하고 진정해 봐.
- Chill out! 진정해!
- Don't stress yourself. 스트레스 받지 마.
- Control yourself. (화를) 자제해.

핵심 Check

2. 다음 대화의 빈칸에 들어갈 수 없는 표현은?

A: Ouch! He stepped on my foot again.

B: Are you okay?

A: No. This is the third time he did that today. I can't stand it. I'll go and talk to him.

B: _____ He's not wearing glasses today, so he can't see well.

① Calm down!   ② Cool down!

③ Don't stress yourself.   ④ Don't control yourself.

⑤ It's going to be okay. Take a deep breath and try to relax.

Step Up - Real-life Scene

Minji: Minsu, there is no cup ❶I can use. Why didn't you do the dishes?

Minsu: Sorry, but ❷I forgot to do them.

Minji: What? You always forget ❸what you have to do. ❹I can't stand it. I cleaned the living room all morning.

Minsu: Calm down! ❺I'm busy doing my homework.

Minji: Do the dishes first, and then do your homework.

Minsu: I can't. I don't think I can finish my homework today. Science is too difficult for me.

Minji: Science? ❻You know I'm good at science. ❼Let me help you.

Minsu: Great. Thanks. I'll wash your cup right now and I'll do ❽the rest of the dishes after finishing this.

민지: 민수야, 내가 사용할 컵이 없어. 왜 설거지를 안 했니?
민수: 미안하지만, 설거지하는 걸 잊었어.
민지: 뭐라고? 너는 항상 해야 할 일을 잊어버리는구나. 참을 수가 없어. 나는 아침 내내 거실 청소를 했어.
민수: 진정해! 나는 숙제하느라 바빠.
민지: 설거지를 먼저 하고 난 뒤에 숙제해.
민수: 안 돼! 오늘 숙제를 끝낼 수가 없을 것 같아. 과학은 나에게 너무 어려워.
민지: 과학이라고? 너도 알겠지만 내가 과학을 잘하잖아. 내가 도와줄게.
민수: 잘됐다. 고마워. 당장 누나 컵부터 씻을게. 그리고 나머지 설거지는 숙제 끝낸 후에 할게.

❶ 'I can use'는 선행사 'cup'을 수식하는 목적격 관계대명사절로 목적격 관계대명사 'that/which'가 생략되어 있다.
❷ 'forget to+동사원형'은 '~할 것을 잊다'라는 의미이다. 'them'은 'the dishes'를 가리키는 대명사다.
❸ 동사 'forget'의 목적어 역할을 하는 명사절로 'what'은 관계대명사로 '~하는 것'의 뜻이다. 'what'은 'the thing that[which]'으로 바꾸어 사용할 수 있다.
❹ 'I can't stand it.(참을 수 없어.)'은 화난 감정을 표현하는 문장이다.
❺ 'be busy -ing'는 '~하느라 바쁘다'라는 의미이다.
❻ 동사 'know' 뒤에는 목적어를 이끄는 접속사 'that'이 생략되어 있다.
❼ '사역동사(let)+목적어(me)+동사원형(help)' 형태로 '…가 ~하게 하다'라는 의미이다.
❽ 'the rest'는 '나머지'라는 뜻이다. 'rest'는 '휴식'의 의미이다.

Check(√) True or False

(1) Minsu hates doing the dishes.   T ☐ F ☐

(2) Minji will help Minsu do his homework.   T ☐ F ☐

Start Off - Listen & Talk A 1

B: What's ❶that noise outside?

G: They're fixing the heaters.

B: ❷I can't focus on my studies at all. I can't stand it.

G: ❸Calm down! They will finish it soon.

B: 밖에서 나는 저 소음은 뭐지?
G: 히터를 고치고 있어.
B: 공부에 전혀 집중할 수가 없잖아. 참을 수가 없어.
G: 진정해! 곧 끝날 거야.

❶ 'that'은 명사 'noise'를 수식하는 '지시형용사'로 '저'로 해석한다.
❷ 'not ~ at all'은 '전혀 ~ 않다'라는 뜻으로 부정문을 강조할 때 사용한다.
❸ 화낸 상대방에 응대할 때, 'Calm down!(진정해!)'이라는 표현을 쓸 수 있다. 같은 의미의 표현인 'Relax.', 'Take it easy.' 등으로 바꾸어 쓸 수 있다.

Check(√) True or False

(3) The boy can't concentrate on his studies because of noise outside.   T ☐ F ☐

(4) The girl is going to finish fixing the heaters.   T ☐ F ☐

Get Ready 2

(1) M: We've waited ❶for more than one hour, and we're still waiting.

W: Calm down! We're almost there.

(2) G: Brrr…. ❷What a cold day! I hate standing in line in cold weather.

B: Calm down! Drink this hot milk.

G: Oh, thank you so much.

(3) G: Look! That man didn't wait in line! I'm very angry.

B: Calm down! He works here.

(4) B: The boy behind me ❸keeps pushing me. I can't stand it.

G: Calm down. He's just a child.

❶ 'for+숫자 기간'은 '~ 동안'의 의미이다.
❷ 'What+a+형용사+명사!' 어순의 감탄문이다.
❸ 'keep+-ing'는 '계속해서 ~하다'라는 의미이다.

 Start Off - Listen & Talk A 2

G: I can't find my pencil case. Have you seen it?

B: No, I haven't. Where did you put it?

G: I put it on my desk, but now ❶it's gone. I'm really upset.

B: Calm down! I'll ❷help you find it.

❶ 'it's gone'은 '사라지다'라는 의미이다.
❷ 'help+목적어+목적보어(동사원형/to부정사)'로 '…가 ~하는 것을 돕다'라는 의미이다.

 Start Off - Listen & Talk B

B: Ouch! He stepped on my foot again.

G: Are you okay?

B: No. This is the third time ❶he did that today. I can't stand it. I'll go and talk to him.

G: Calm down! He's not wearing his glasses today, so he can't see well.

B: What happened to his glasses?

G: He broke his glasses ❷during a soccer game this morning.

B: I see, but he ❸should have been more careful.

❶ 'he did that today'는 'time'을 수식하는 관계부사절로 'time'과 'he' 사이에는 관계부사 'when'이 생략되어 있다. 'that'은 'stepping on my foot'을 가리키는 지시대명사다.
❷ 'during'은 전치사로 '~ 동안'의 의미이고, 뒤에는 특정 기간을 나타내는 명사가 온다.
❸ 'should have+과거분사'는 '~했어야 했는데'의 의미로 과거의 유감이나 후회를 나타내는 표현이다.

 Start Off - Speak Up

A: I can't ❶stand this place. It's too crowded.

B: Calm down! We're at the festival. Let's enjoy it.

❶ 'stand'는 '참다, 견디다'의 의미로 사용되었다. 'bear'의 의미와 같다.

 Express Yourself A

1. M1: The king sent me here. Open the door.

M2: Wait there. The door will open ❶in a hundred days.

M1: What? A hundred days? I can't ❷spend a hundred days doing nothing. I can't stand it.

M2: Calm down! It is an important rule ❸to get in this school.

2. M1: Why did you ❹tie me up here? Please ❺ set me free.

M2: How can you ❻get free? Think.

M1: I can't stand this sign. I'm not dangerous or bad.

M2: Calm down. I'm sure you'll find a way.

❶ 전치사 'in'은 '~ 후에'라는 의미이다.
❷ 'spend+시간+-ing' 구문으로 '~하면서 시간을 보내다'라는 의미이다.
❸ 'to get'은 명사 'rule'을 꾸며주는 형용사 용법이다.
❹ '동사+인칭대명사+부사' 어순의 이어 동사로 인칭대명사는 반드시 동사와 부사 사이에 위치해야 한다. 즉, 'tie up me'로 쓸 수 없다.
❺ 'set+목적어+free'는 '~를 자유롭게 하다, 풀어주다'라는 뜻이다.
❻ 'get free'는 '풀려나다, 자유의 몸이 되다'라는 뜻이다.

 Check yourself

G: What's that noise outside?

B: A dog is barking.

G: I ❶can't focus on my studies at all. I can't stand it.

B: Calm down! He will be quiet soon.

❶ 'not ~ at all'은 '전혀 ~ 않다'라는 의미로 부정문을 강조하는 말이다. 'never' 와 같은 의미이다.

● 다음 우리말과 일치하도록 빈칸에 알맞은 말을 쓰시오.

Get Ready 2

(1) **M:** We'_____ _____ for more than one hour, and we're still waiting.

W: _____ down! We're _____ there.

(2) **G:** Brrr.... _____ a cold day! I _____ standing _____ _____ in cold weather.

B: _____ _____! Drink this hot milk.

G: Oh, thank you so much.

(3) **G:** Look! That man didn't _____ _____ _____! I'm very angry.

B: _____ _____! He works here.

(4) **B:** The boy _____ me _____ _____ me. I _____ _____ it.

G: _____ _____. He's _____ a child.

Start Off - Listen & Talk A

1. **B:** What's that _____ outside?

G: They're _____ the _____.

B: I can't _____ _____ my studies _____ _____. I _____ _____ _____.

G: Calm down! They will finish it soon.

2. **G:** I _____ _____ my pencil case. Have you _____ it?

B: No, I haven't. Where did you _____ it?

G: I put it on my desk, but now it's _____. I'm really _____.

B: _____ down! I'll help you _____ it.

Start Off - Listen & Talk B

B: Ouch! He stepped _____ my _____ again.

G: Are you _____?

B: No. This is the _____ time he _____ _____ today. I _____ _____ it. I'll go and talk to him.

G: _____ _____! He's not _____ his _____ today, so he can't see well.

B: What _____ to his glasses?

G: He _____ his glasses _____ a soccer game this morning.

B: I see, but he _____ _____ _____ more careful.

해석

(1) **M:** 우리 한 시간 이상 기다렸는데 아직도 기다리고 있네.
W: 진정해! 거의 다 되어 가.

(2) **G:** 부르르…. 정말 추운 날이네! 나는 추운 날씨에 줄 서는 게 싫어.
B: 진정해! 이 뜨거운 우유를 마셔 봐.
G: 와, 정말 고마워.

(3) **G:** 저것 봐! 저 남자가 줄을 서지 않았어! 정말 화가 나.
B: 진정해! 저 사람은 여기서 일하는 사람이야.

(4) **B:** 내 뒤에 있는 남자아이가 자꾸 밀어. 참을 수가 없어.
G: 진정해. 아직 어린아이야.

1. **B:** 밖에서 나는 저 소음은 뭐지?
G: 히터를 고치고 있어.
B: 공부에 전혀 집중할 수가 없잖아. 참을 수가 없어.
G: 진정해! 곧 끝날 거야.

2. **G:** 내 필통을 찾을 수가 없어. 내 필통 봤니?
B: 아니, 못 봤어. 어디에 뒀어?
G: 내 책상 위에 뒀는데 사라졌어. 정말 화가 나.
B: 진정해! 내가 그걸 찾는 걸 도와줄게.

B: 아! 그 애가 또 내 발을 밟았어.
G: 괜찮니?
B: 아니. 이번이 오늘 그 애가 내 발을 세 번째로 밟은 거야. 참을 수가 없어. 가서 말해야겠어.
G: 진정해! 그 애는 오늘 안경을 안 쓰고 있어서 잘 볼 수가 없어.
B: 안경이 어떻게 됐는데?
G: 오늘 아침에 축구 경기를 하다가 안경을 깨뜨렸어.
B: 그렇구나. 하지만 그 애는 더 조심했어야 했어.

Start Off - Speak Up

A: I _____ _____ this place. It's too _____.

B: _____ _____! We're at the _____. Let's _____ it.

Step Up - Real-life Scene

Minji: Minsu, there is no cup _____ _____ _____. _____ _____ _____ do the _____?

Minho: Sorry, but I _____ _____ _____ them.

Minji: What? You always forget _____ you _____ _____ _____. _____ _____ _____ it. I _____ the living room all morning.

Minho: Calm down! I'm _____ _____ my homework.

Minji: _____ the dishes first, and then do your homework.

Minho: I can't. I don't think I can _____ my homework today. Science is _____ _____ for me.

Minji: Science? You know I'_____ _____ _____ science. _____ _____ _____ you.

Minho: Great. Thanks. I'll wash your cup _____ _____ and I'll do _____ _____ of the dishes after _____ this.

A: 나는 이 장소를 참을 수가 없어. 너무 사람이 많아.
B: 진정해! 우리는 축제에 와 있잖아. 축제를 즐기자.

민지: 민수야, 내가 사용할 컵이 없어. 왜 설거지를 안 했니?
민수: 미안하지만, 설거지하는 걸 잊었어.
민지: 뭐라고? 너는 항상 해야 할 일을 잊어버리는구나. 참을 수가 없어. 나는 아침 내내 거실 청소를 했어.
민수: 진정해! 나는 숙제하느라 바빠.
민지: 설거지를 먼저 하고 난 뒤에 숙제해.
민수: 안 돼! 오늘 숙제를 끝낼 수가 없을 것 같아. 과학은 나에게 너무 어려워.
민지: 과학이라고? 너도 알겠지만 내가 과학을 잘하잖아. 내가 도와줄게.
민수: 잘됐다. 고마워. 당장 누나 컵부터 씻을게. 그리고 나머지 설거지는 숙제 끝낸 후에 할게.

Express Yourself A

1. M1: The king _____ me here. Open the door.

   M2: Wait there. The door will open _____ a _____ days.

   M1: What? A hundred days? I can't _____ a hundred days _____ _____. I _____ _____ _____ _____.

   M2: _____ _____! It is an important _____ in this school.

2. M1: Why did you _____ _____ _____ here? Please _____ _____ _____.

   M2: How can you _____ _____? Think.

   M1: I _____ _____ this _____. I'm not _____ or bad.

   M2: Calm down. _____ _____ you'll find a _____.

1. M1: 왕이 나를 여기에 보냈소. 문을 여시오.
   M2: 거기서 기다리시오. 100일 후 문이 열릴 것이오.
   M1: 뭐라고요? 100일이라고요? 아무것도 하지 않고 100일을 보낼 수는 없소. 참을 수가 없소.
   M2: 진정하시오! 그것이 이 학교에 들어오기 위한 중요한 규칙이오.

2. M1: 저를 왜 여기에 묶어 두셨습니까? 저를 풀어 주십시오.
   M2: 어떻게 풀려날 수 있겠느냐? 생각해 보아라.
   M1: 저는 이 푯말을 참을 수가 없습니다. 저는 위험하지도 나쁘지도 않습니다.
   M2: 진정하거라. 나는 네가 방법을 찾을 것이라고 확신한다.

Check yourself

G: What's that noise _____?

B: A dog is _____.

G: I _____ _____ _____ my studies at all. I can't _____ _____.

B: _____ _____! He will be _____ soon.

01 다음 우리말에 맞도록 주어진 단어를 활용하여 빈칸을 채우시오.

나는 이 장소를 참을 수가 없어. 너무 사람이 많아. (stand / crowd)
➡ I _____ _____ this place. It's too _____.

02 다음 대화의 빈칸에 들어갈 말로 <u>어색한</u> 것은?

G: Look! That man didn't wait in line! I'm very angry.
B: _____ He works here.

① Calm down!   ② Relax.
③ Take it easy.   ④ Take care of yourself.
⑤ Take a deep breath and try to relax.

03 다음 대화의 빈칸에 들어갈 말로 알맞지 <u>않은</u> 것은?

G: I can't find my pencil case. Have you seen it?
B: No, I haven't. Where did you put it?
G: I put it on my desk, but now it's gone. _____
B: Calm down! I'll help you find it.

① I'm really upset.   ② I can't stand it.
③ I'm very annoying.   ④ I'm very angry.
⑤ How irritating!

04 다음 대화의 밑줄 친 말의 의도로 알맞은 것은?

M: We've waited for more than one hour, and we're still waiting.
W: <u>Calm down!</u> We're almost there.

① 감사하기   ② 이의 제기하기
③ 기원하기   ④ 화냄에 응대하기
⑤ 화냄 표현하기

[01~02] 다음 대화를 읽고 물음에 답하시오.

Ben: Ouch! He stepped on my foot again.

Gary: Are you okay?

Ben: No. This is the third time he did that today. I can't stand it. I'll go and talk to him.

Gary: Calm down! He's not wearing his glasses today, so he can't see well.

Ben: What happened to his glasses?

Gary: He broke his glasses during a soccer game this morning.

Ben: I see, but _____(A)_____ .

01 위 대화의 빈칸 (A)에 들어갈 말로 적절한 것은?

① he must have been more careful

② he may have been more careful

③ he should have been more careful

④ he needn't have been more careful

⑤ he shouldn't have been more careful

서답형

02 Write the reason why Ben is angry.

> Because a boy _____ _____ foot _____ times.

[03~04] 다음 대화의 빈칸에 들어갈 말로 알맞은 것은?

03

> **B:** What's that noise outside?
> **G:** They're fixing the heaters.
> **B:** I can't focus on my studies at all. I can't stand it.
> **G:** _____ They will finish it soon.

① I'll help you.

② Is it okay if they are fixing the heaters?

③ Calm down!

④ I'm fed up with it.

⑤ I'm disgusted with it.

04

> **G:** Brrr.... What a cold day! _____
> **B:** Calm down! Drink this hot milk.
> **G:** Oh, thank you so much.

① I like winter.

② I hate standing in line in cold weather.

③ Take a deep breath and try to relax.

④ Don't stress yourself.

⑤ I didn't wait in line.

서답형

05 위 대화의 빈칸에 들어갈 단어를 주어진 영영풀이를 보고 쓰시오.

> **M1:** Why did you tie me up here? Please _____ me _____ .
> **M2:** How can you get free? Think.
> **M1:** I can't stand this sign. I'm not dangerous or bad.
> **M2:** Calm down. I'm sure you'll find a way.

> <영영풀이> to allow someone to leave prison

➡ _____

[06~07] 다음 대화를 읽고 물음에 답하시오.

M1: The king sent me here. Open the door.

M2: Wait there. The door will open in a hundred days.

M1: What? A hundred days? (A)아무것도 하지 않고 100일을 보낼 수는 없소. I can't stand it.

M2: Calm down! (B)It is an important rule to get in this school.

서답형

06 위 대화의 밑줄 친 (A)의 우리말에 맞게 주어진 어구를 알맞은 순서로 배열하시오.

(I / a hundred / can't / spend / doing nothing / days)

➡ _____

07 위 대화의 밑줄 친 (B)It에 대한 설명으로 올바른 것은?

① 가주어로 사용된 'It'이다.
② 앞 문장의 'I can't stand it'을 가리키는 대명사이다.
③ 비인칭 주어로 사용된 'It'이다.
④ 'Waiting there for 100 days'를 가리키는 대명사이다.
⑤ 'the door'를 가리키는 대명사이다.

[08~09] 다음 대화를 읽고 물음에 답하시오.

Minji: Minsu, there is no cup I can use. Why didn't you do the dishes?
Minsu: Sorry, but I forgot (a)doing them.
Minji: What? You always forget (b)what you have to do. I can't stand it. I cleaned the living room all morning.
Minsu: Calm down! I'm busy (c)doing my homework.
Minji: Do the dishes first, and then do your homework.
Minsu: I can't. I don't think I can finish my homework today. Science is too difficult for me.
Minji: Science? You know I'm good at science. (d)Let me help you.
Minsu: Great. Thanks. I'll wash your cup right now and I'll do the rest of the dishes (e)after finishing this.

중요

08 위 대화를 읽고 답할 수 없는 질문은?

① Does Minsu feel sorry to his sister?
② Why is Minsu's sister angry at Minsu?
③ Why didn't Minsu do the dishes?
④ Does Minsu find science homework easy?
⑤ What is Minsu's sister's favorite subject?

09 위 대화의 (a)~(e) 중 문법적으로 잘못된 것은?

① (a)   ② (b)   ③ (c)   ④ (d)   ⑤ (e)

[10~11] 다음 대화를 읽고 물음에 답하시오.

(1) G: Look! That man didn't wait in line!
        _____(A)_____
    B: Calm down! He works here.
(2) B: 내 뒤에 있는 남자아이가 자꾸 밀어.
        _____(A)_____
    G: Calm down. He's just a child.

10 위 대화의 빈칸 (A)에 공통으로 들어갈 말로 적절하지 않은 것은?

① I'm very angry.   ② I can't stand it.
③ I'm really upset.   ④ Chill out!
⑤ I'm very annoyed.

서답형

11 위 대화 (2)의 밑줄 친 우리말에 맞게 주어진 단어를 활용하여 영어로 문장을 완성하시오.

(behind / keep / push)

➡ _____

[01~02] 다음 대화를 읽고 물음에 답하시오.

Minji: Minsu, there is no cup I can use. Why didn't you do the dishes?

Minsu: Sorry, but I forgot to do them.

Minji: What? You always forget what you have to do. I can't stand it. I cleaned the living room all morning.

Minsu: Calm down! I'm busy doing my homework.

Minji: Do the dishes first, and then do your homework.

Minsu: I can't. I don't think I can finish my homework today. Science is too difficult for me.

Minji: Science? You know I'm good at science. Let me help you.

Minsu: Great. Thanks. I'll wash your cup right now and I'll do the rest of the dishes after finishing this.

01 위 대화를 읽고 다음 물음에 영어로 답하시오.

Q: When will Minsu do the dishes?

➡ _____

02 다음은 위 대화의 요약문이다. 빈칸에 알맞은 말을 쓰시오.

Minsu and his sister are talking about Minsu's forgetting _____ _____ _____ _____. Minsu's sister is angry because he always forgets _____ _____ _____ _____. Minsu's excuse is his _____ science homework. His sister will _____ him _____ his homework, and he will do the dishes _____ finishing his homework.

03 Look at the picture and make a dialogue about getting angry and calming an angry woman.

Woman: Smoke is coming from the lower floor. _____ _____ _____ _____.

Man: _____ _____! They're having a birthday party.

04 다음 그림을 보고 대화의 빈칸을 완성하시오. (주어진 철자로 단어를 쓰시오.)

M1: Why did you t_____ _____ _____ here? Please s_____ _____ _____.

M2: How can you get free? Think.

M1: I _____ s_____ this sign. I'm not dangerous or bad.

M2: C_____ _____. I'm sure you'll find a way.

Grammar

교과서

① 부정대명사

> • **Some** gave him angry looks, and **others** shouted at him.
> 몇몇은 그를 화난 표정으로 쳐다봤고, 다른 몇몇은 그에게 소리를 질렀다.

- 부정대명사란 불특정한 사람, 사물 또는 일정하지 않은 수량을 나타내는 대명사이다.

- one, the other 둘 중 하나, 나머지 하나

  - We have two computers in the office. **One** is new and **the other** is 3 years old.
    사무실에 컴퓨터 두 대가 있습니다. 하나는 새 것이고, 나머지 하나는 (구매한지) 3년이 되었습니다.

- some, others 몇몇, 다른 몇몇

  - **Some** scientists think we should focus on renewable energy to prevent global warming but **others** disagree. 몇몇 과학자들은 지구 온난화를 예방하기 위해 재생 가능 에너지에 집중해야 한다고 생각하지만, 다른 몇몇은 동의하지 않는다.

- some, the others 몇몇, 나머지 전부

  - Here are many boxes. **Some** are for clothes and **the others** are for books.
    여기 많은 상자가 있어. 몇몇은 옷을 담기 위한 것이고, 나머지는 모두 책을 담기 위한 것이야.

핵심 Check

1. 다음 괄호 안에서 알맞은 것을 고르시오.

   (1) Here are two books. One is yours, and (another / the other) is mine.

   (2) There are many candies in the dish. Some are for Ann, and (the others / the other) are for me.

   (3) Among various kinds of movies, (one / some) like to see comedies. Others like to see horror movies.

② 5형식(동사 + 목적어 + to부정사)

> • The king **ordered** him **to go** to a famous military school.
> 왕은 그에게 유명한 군사학교에 갈 것을 명령했다.

■ 'order'는 목적격보어 자리에 to부정사가 오는 동사이다. 이와 같은 종류의 동사로는 'want, ask, tell, allow, teach, advise, expect' 등이 있다.

• The king **ordered** his servants **to bring** the wizard to his court.
왕은 그의 신하들에게 그 마법사를 그의 궁정으로 데려오라고 명령했다.

■ 목적격보어에 원형부정사를 쓰는 동사들도 있다. 이와 같은 종류의 동사로는 'let, make, have, see, watch, hear, feel' 등이 있다.

• The king was surprised to **see** the wizard **destroy** his palace.
왕은 그 마법사가 그의 궁전을 파괴하는 것을 보고 놀랐습니다.

■ 'see, watch, hear, feel' 등은 목적격보어로 현재분사를 쓸 수 있다.

• I **watched** the dog **waiting** for her owner under the bridge.
나는 그 개가 다리 밑에서 주인을 기다리는 것을 지켜보았습니다.

■ 목적어와 목적격보어의 관계가 수동이면 목적격보어로 과거분사를 쓴다.

• Maybe we could go to an amusement park and **have** our faces **painted**.
어쩌면 우리는 놀이동산에 가서 얼굴에 그림을 그릴 수 있을 거야.

핵심 Check

2. 다음 괄호 안에서 알맞은 것을 고르시오.

(1) My mother wants me (being / to be) a doctor.

(2) My father allowed me (go / to go) camping with friends.

(3) My teacher (told / made) her to be quiet.

01 다음 우리말에 맞게 괄호 안에 주어진 단어를 이용하여 문장을 완성하시오.

(1) 몇몇은 눈사람을 만들고 있고, 다른 몇몇은 눈싸움을 하고 있다.

(other, play, snowballs)

➡ Some are making snowmen, and _____.

(2) 새 두 마리가 있어. 한 마리는 날고 있고 나머지 한 마리는 나무 위에 앉아 있어.

(other, sit, tree)

➡ There are two birds. One is flying, and _____.

(3) 남자는 그 개에게 공을 가져오라고 명령했다. (dog, get)

➡ The man ordered _____.

(4) 여자는 그 소년에게 조심하라고 말했다. (boy, careful)

➡ The woman told _____.

02 다음 문장에서 어법상 어색한 부분을 바르게 고치시오.

(1) Here are two shapes. One is a star and another is a circle.

_____ ➡ _____

(2) Some went on foot, and the others went by bike, and the others went by bus.

_____ ➡ _____

(3) I don't want you tell anybody this secret.

_____ ➡ _____

(4) My uncle advised me studying hard.

_____ ➡ _____

03 다음 〈보기〉와 같이 주어진 어구를 이용하여 빈칸을 완성하시오.

┌─ 보기 ─┐

(jump up and down)

A: What are the two dogs doing?

B: One is eating snow, and the other is jumping up and down

(1) (dance)

A: What are the five singers doing?

B: One is singing, and _____.

(2) (wave their hands, the singer)

A: What are the seven people doing?

B: Some are taking pictures, and _____

_____.

01 다음 빈칸에 'help'를 적절한 형태로 넣을 때 다른 하나를 고르시오.

① The girl asked the boy _____ her.

② The girl told the boy _____ her.

③ The girl ordered the boy _____ her.

④ The girl wanted the boy _____ her.

⑤ The girl made the boy _____ her.

02 다음 주어진 우리말을 영어로 바르게 쓴 것을 고르시오.

> 선생님은 나에게 사전을 사라고 조언하셨다.

① My teacher advises me to buy a dictionary.

② My teacher advises me buy a dictionary.

③ My teacher advised me buying a dictionary.

④ My teacher advised me to buy a dictionary.

⑤ My teacher advised me buy a dictionary.

03 다음 빈칸에 들어갈 말로 적절한 것을 고르시오.

> Some went on foot, and _____ went by bike, and the others went by bus.

① one   ② the other   ③ other

④ others   ⑤ the others

04 다음 중 어법상 어색한 문장을 고르시오.

① Here are two hats. One is yours, and the other is mine.

② Here are two dogs. One is black, and the other is white.

③ He ordered the girl to wait there.

④ What did the woman tell the boy to do?

⑤ The woman asked the boy to feeding the ducks.

05 다음 빈칸에 'go'를 적절한 형태로 넣을 때 다른 하나를 고르시오.

① My father allowed me _____ to the concert with my girlfriend.

② My teacher told us _____ outside.

③ You should keep the hula hoop _____ around your waist.

④ Don't order the dog _____ out of the house.

⑤ The doctor advised Tom _____ hiking at least once a week.

06 다음 밑줄 친 우리말을 영어로 바르게 옮긴 것은?

> 아버지는 내가 용돈을 아끼기를 원하신다.

① Dad wants me saved my allowance.

② Dad wants me save my allowance.

③ Dad wants me to save my allowance.

④ Dad wants me saving my allowance.

⑤ Dad wants me to saving my allowance.

서답형

07 다음 괄호 안에 주어진 단어들을 바르게 배열하여 문장을 완성하시오.

> help / to / us / peace / each / other / tells

➡ _____

08 다음 빈칸에 들어갈 말을 순서대로 바르게 연결한 것은?

> • My friend Eunah has two strong points. One is that she sings well. _____ is that she is fun.
> • Many teenagers like idol groups. Some love TTS and _____ like Wanna Love.

① The others – others
② The other – other
③ The other – others
④ Another – the other
⑤ Another – the others

서답형

09 다음 문장에서 어법상 어색한 것을 바르게 고쳐 다시 쓰시오.

(1) He ordered his robot done his homework.

➡ _____

_____

(2) She told him locking the door.

➡ _____

_____

서답형

10 다음 빈칸에 주어진 단어 중 필요한 것만 골라 문장을 완성하시오.

> get, getting, got, gotten, to, up

> My mom told me _____ early in the morning. (엄마는 나에게 아침에 일찍 일어나라고 말씀하셨다.)

11 다음 중 어법상 어색한 문장을 고르시오.

① Ms. Green told him to wait in her office.
② I saw some children to play chess.
③ My boss asked me to send this book by parcel post.
④ The members want Jane to be their leader.
⑤ His word encouraged me to restart my life.

서답형

12 다음 괄호 안에서 알맞은 말을 고르시오.

(1) Two boys are singing. One is singing well and (another / the other) is not.

(2) Students in the classroom are taking a test. Some finished it, but (others / the others) do not yet.

(3) Mom has five brothers. One lives in Japan, and (the other / the others) live in Korea.

(4) Two people are talking. One is holding pizza, and (the other / the others) is holding balloons.

(5) In the park, there are many people. (One / Some) are taking picturers, and others are lying on the grass.

서답형

13 다음 그림을 보고 문장을 완성하시오.

> ★★★★○○ : Here are 6 shapes. _____ _____ _____ and the others are circles.

➡ _____

14 다음 주어진 단어들을 바르게 배열하여 문장을 완성하시오.

> to / him / the / I / truth / want / know

➡ _____

15 다음 우리말을 바르게 영작한 것은?

> 나는 내 아들이 내 휴대전화를 사용하는 것을 허락하지 않는다.

① I don't allow my son use my cell phone.
② I don't let my son to use my cell phone.
③ I don't allow my son to use my cell phone.
④ I don't let my son using my cell phone.
⑤ I don't allow my son using my cell phone.

16 다음 문장의 밑줄 친 부분을 괄호 안의 단어로 바꾸어 문장을 다시 쓰시오.

(1) Can you <u>make</u> your brothers stop fighting? (force)

➡ _____
_____

(2) My parents <u>allowed</u> me to buy a new tablet PC. (let)

➡ _____
_____

17 다음 빈칸에 들어갈 말을 순서대로 바르게 연결한 것은?

> • My friend Minsu has two good points. _____ is that he plays soccer well. The other is that he is handsome.
> • I like summer because I can swim. _____ reason I like summer is that I can enjoy a lot of fruits.

① One – Another
② One – Other
③ Some – The other
④ Some – Another
⑤ Another – Other

18 주어진 어휘를 이용하여 다음 우리말을 영어로 쓰시오.

> 엄마는 내가 캠핑을 가도록 허락하셨다.
> (allow, camping)

➡ _____

19 다음 우리말을 바르게 영작한 것은?

> 엄마는 나에게 설거지를 하라고 시키셨다.

① My mom had me wash the dishes.
② My mom got me wash the dishes.
③ My mom had mc to wash the dishes.
④ My mom got me washed the dishes.
⑤ My mom had me washed the dishes.

20 다음 중 어법상 <u>어색한</u> 문장을 고르시오.

① Mom wants me to become a golfer.
② I asked the students to answer the survey.
③ Let me know your address and phone number.
④ The English teacher got us write an essay.
⑤ We saw the sun rise over the sea.

01 다음 문장의 <u>틀린</u> 곳을 바르게 고쳐 다시 쓰시오.

(1) Here are two birds. One is flying, and other is sitting on the tree.

➡ _____

_____

(2) The woman told the boy be careful.

➡ _____

(3) She has a lot of pens. Some are yellow, and other are red.

➡ _____

_____

(4) Jane asks me teach math.

➡ _____

(5) The farmer wanted me feeding the pigs.

➡ _____

02 다음 우리말을 주어진 어휘를 이용하여 영어로 옮기시오.

(1) 어머니는 나에게 일찍 일어나라고 말씀하셨다. (my, tell, get up)

➡ _____

(2) 나는 네가 어느 누구에게도 이 비밀을 말하는 것을 원하지 않는다. (tell, anybody, secret)

➡ _____

(3) 아버지는 삼촌이 차를 사용하는 것을 허락하셨다. (my, allow, uncle, use)

➡ _____

03 주어진 문장의 밑줄 친 부분을 괄호 안의 단어로 바꾸어 문장을 다시 쓰시오.

(1) Mr. Kim <u>let</u> us bring what we wanted to eat. (allow)

➡ _____

_____

(2) Dr. Wang <u>advised</u> her patients to work out regularly during the day. (see)

➡ _____

_____

04 다음 그림을 보고 괄호 안의 단어를 사용하여 빈칸에 알맞은 말을 써 넣으시오.

(1) (other, curly)

There are two children. One has short hair and _____ .

(2) (other, boy)

There are five children. Some are girls and _____ .

(3) (roll, the snow)

There are three children. One is holding branches, _____ into a ball, the other is carrying a large snowball.

05 다음 우리말을 괄호 안의 단어를 사용하여 영어로 바르게 옮기시오.

(1) 그 남자는 소년이 잔디에 들어가는 것을 허락했다. (allow, enter)

➡ _____

_____

(2) 그녀는 세 명의 아들이 있다. 한 명은 가수이고 나머지는 댄서이다. (singer, dancer)

➡ _____

_____

06 주어진 어휘를 바르게 배열하여 영작하시오.

(1) (his / peacefully / He / people / fight / asked / to)

➡ _____

(2) (ordered / man / The police officer / come / out / the / to)

➡ _____

(3) (help / to / her / the boy / asked / The girl)

➡ _____

(4) (the boy / The teacher / hard / told / study / to)

➡ _____

07 다음 잘못된 부분을 바르게 고쳐 문장을 다시 쓰시오.

(1) I want everyone came here.

➡ _____

(2) I'd like you listen carefully.

➡ _____

(3) They allow people fishing here.

➡ _____

(4) I advise you to not walk home alone.

➡ _____

(5) The dentist told Daniel given up eating sweets.

➡ _____

08 〈보기〉에 주어진 부정대명사를 빈칸에 적절하게 찾아 넣으시오.

┤ 보기 ├

some, one, another, others, the other, the others

• There are five people in the room. (1)_____ is a man. The others are women.

• Four people are walking on the street. (2)_____ have long hair. The others have short hair.

• There are three desks in the classroom. One is big, and (3)_____ _____ are small.

Reading

Corky, the Best Warrior

Corky was a brave young man. He wanted to be a general, but the king said, "You're the <u>strongest</u> man in my army, but you have much
'strong'의 최상급, '가장 힘이 센'

to learn." He ordered Corky <u>to go</u> to a famous military school.
형용사적 용법의 to부정사   order+목적어+to부정사(목적격 보어): …에게 ～하라고 명령하다

"Wait there. <u>In</u> a hundred days, your training will start," a voice said
in: (시간상으로) ～ 후에

from inside the school gate. Corky got angry. But then he thought there

<u>might</u> be a reason, so he waited. On the hundred and first day, the gate
추측의 의미를 나타내는 조동사   아마 ～일 것이다

opened. An old man said, "You have learned <u>to use</u> your first weapon:
명사적 용법의 to부정사   콜론(:)은 동격을 의미(첫 번째 무기는 '인내심')

patience. Patience is the most important thing to win a war."

Then, the teacher <u>told Corky to stand</u> against a pole. Suddenly, he <u>tied</u>
tell+목적어+to부정사: …에게 ～하라고 말하다

Corky to the pole. Above his head, he put a sign <u>that</u> <u>read</u> "Dangerous
tie A to B': A를 B에 묶다   that: 주격 관계대명사 read: ～라고 적혀 있다(쓰여 있다)(자동사)

and Bad." Many people passed by. <u>Some</u> gave Corky angry looks, and
불특정 다수의 여러 사람 중 '몇몇 사람들'

others shouted at him. Corky shouted back. He yelled, "Set me free, <u>or</u>
'(그 밖의) 다른 사람들'   명령문+접속사 'or': …해라. 그렇지 않으면 ～할 것이다.

you all will be in big trouble!" That made the situation worse.

---

warrior 전사

patience 인내심, 참을성

war 전쟁

military 군대; 군대의

general 장군

army 군대

order 명령하다

gate 정문, 대문

might ～일지도 모른다

reason 이유

weapon 무기

pole 기둥, 막대, 장대

tie 묶다

above ～보다 위에

look 표정

yell 소리 지르다

 **확인문제**

● 다음 문장이 본문의 내용과 일치하면 T, 일치하지 <u>않으면</u> F를 쓰시오.

1 Corky wanted to be a general. ☐

2 The teacher ordered Corky to go to a famous military school. ☐

3 Corky has learned to use his first weapon: patience. ☐

4 The general told Corky to stand against a pole. ☐

5 Corky yelled, "Set me free, or you all will be in big trouble!" ☐

6 Corky made the situation better. ☐

"I need to try another way," he thought. Then, Corky began to speak softly. He said he was <u>not</u> dangerous or bad <u>but</u> was a good man. He
not A but B: A가 아니라 B
kept saying this in all possible ways. Finally, the people <u>let him go</u>.
let(사역동사)+목적어+동사원형(목적격 보어): …가 ~하도록 허락하다
"Now you control the most powerful weapon: words. Soft words are stronger than sharp swords," said the teacher.

Next, the teacher <u>took Corky to a large hall</u> with a chair in the
take A to B: A를 B로 데려가다
middle. There were 19 <u>other</u> warriors <u>who</u> <u>had passed</u> their tests. "The
other: (그 밖의) 다른   who: 주격 관계대명사   과거완료: 과거보다 앞선 시제를 나타냄.
first one to sit in the chair will be the winner," the teacher said.

Corky and <u>the others</u> began fighting. They pushed, pulled, ran, and
나머지 사람들 모두
jumped. They fought <u>harder and harder</u>, so Corky became tired.
비교급 and 비교급: 점점 더 ~핸[하게]
Finally, he said, "I will not fight anymore. Instead, I will take care of
the <u>injured</u>." The other warriors saw this and fought even harder. <u>As</u>
부상자들(the+과거분사 = 복수 보통명사)   ~함에 따라(접속사)
they fought, more warriors became tired and hurt. Corky took good care of them, so they followed him. Soon, all the warriors except Thunder were following Corky.

set free 석방하다, 풀어 주다
situation 상황
powerful 강력한
sword 검, 칼
in the middle ~의 가운데에
winner 승리자, 우승자
push 밀다
finally 결국, 마침내
take care of ~을 돌보다
injured 부상당한

📎 **확인문제**

● 다음 문장이 본문의 내용과 일치하면 T, 일치하지 <u>않으면</u> F를 쓰시오.

1 Corky said he was not dangerous or bad but was a good man. ☐

2 "Sharp swords are stronger than soft words," said the teacher. ☐

3 The teacher took Corky to a large hall with a chair in the middle. ☐

4 The first one to lift the chair will be the winner. ☐

5 As Corky and the others fought harder and harder, Corky became tired. ☐

6 Soon, all the warriors including Thunder were following Corky. ☐

Thunder walked toward the chair to sit in it. Then, he <u>saw Corky</u>

<u>지각동사+목적어+현재분사/동사원형(목적격 보어): …가 ~하는 것을 보다</u>

<u>standing</u> with his 18 followers. Thunder realized he was all alone. "I

give up. You're the real winner," Thunder said to Corky.

At that moment, the teacher appeared and said. "Of all the great

weapons, peace is my favorite. Sooner or later, everyone wants to

stand on the side of peace."

Corky returned to the palace after his training ended. When the king

saw him approach, he <u>gave Corky a wise and knowing smile</u> and said,

<u>수여동사+간접목적어+직접목적어(4형식)</u>

"What's up, General?"

realize 깨닫다

give up 포기하다

favorite 특히 좋아하는 것(사람)

sooner or later 조만간, 머잖아

on the side of ~ 편에

palace 궁, 궁전

approach 다가가다

wise 현명한

📎 **확인문제**

● 다음 문장이 본문의 내용과 일치하면 T, 일치하지 <u>않으면</u> F를 쓰시오.

1 Thunder walked toward the chair in order to sit in it. ☐

2 Corky saw Thunder standing with his 18 followers. ☐

3 Thunder realized he was all by himself. ☐

4 Corky said that of all the great weapons, peace was his favorite. ☐

5 Sooner or later, everyone wants to stand on the side of peace. ☐

6 Corky returned to the palace before his training ended. ☐

● 우리말을 참고하여 빈칸에 알맞은 말을 쓰시오.

1 Corky, _____ _____ _____

2 Corky was a _____ _____ man.

3 He wanted to be a general, but the king said, "You're the _____ man in my army, but you _____ _____ _____ _____."

4 He ordered Corky _____ _____ to a famous military school.

5 "Wait there. _____ _____ _____ _____, your training will start," a voice said from inside the school gate.

6 Corky _____ _____.

7 But then he thought there _____ _____ _____ _____, so he waited.

8 _____ _____ _____ _____ _____ _____, the gate opened.

9 An old man said, "You have learned to use your _____ _____ : _____.

10 Patience is the most important thing _____ _____ _____ _____."

11 Then, the teacher told Corky to _____ _____ a pole.

12 Suddenly, he _____ Corky _____ the pole.

13 Above his head, he put a sign _____ _____ "Dangerous and Bad."

14 Many people _____ _____.

1 최고의 전사, Corky

2 Corky는 용감한 청년이었다.

3 그는 장군이 되기를 원했지만 왕은 이렇게 말했다. "자네는 우리 군대에서 가장 강한 전사이네. 하지만 자네는 아직도 배울 게 많아."

4 왕은 Corky에게 유명한 군사 학교에 갈 것을 명령했다.

5 "거기서 기다려라. 훈련은 100일 후에 시작할 것이다." 군사 학교 안에서 이렇게 외치는 목소리가 들렸다.

6 Corky는 화가 났다.

7 하지만 이유가 있을 것으로 생각하고 기다렸다.

8 101일째 되던 날, 문이 열렸다.

9 한 노인이 이렇게 말했다. "너는 첫 번째 무기인 '인내'를 사용하는 법을 배운 것이다.

10 인내는 전쟁에서 이기기 위해 가장 중요한 것이다."

11 그리고 난 뒤, 스승은 Corky에게 기둥 앞에 서라고 말했다.

12 갑자기 그는 Corky를 기둥에 묶었다.

13 그의 머리 위에는 '위험하고 나쁨'이라는 푯말을 붙였다.

14 많은 사람이 지나갔다.

15 _____ gave Corky angry looks, and _____ shouted at him.

16 Corky _____ _____.

17 He yelled, "_____ _____ _____, _____ you all will be in big trouble!"

18 That _____ the situation _____.

19 "I need to try _____ way," he thought.

20 Then, Corky began to speak _____.

21 He said he was _____ dangerous or bad _____ was a good man.

22 He _____ _____ this in all possible ways.

23 Finally, the people _____ _____ _____.

24 "Now you control _____ _____ _____ _____ : words.

25 Soft words are _____ _____ sharp swords," said the teacher.

26 Next, the teacher _____ Corky _____ a large hall with a chair in the middle.

27 There were 19 other warriors who _____ _____ their tests.

28 "_____ _____ _____ _____ sit in the chair will be the winner," the teacher said.

29 Corky and _____ _____ began fighting.

30 They _____, _____, ran, and jumped.

---

15 몇몇은 Corky를 화난 표정으로 쳐다봤고, 다른 몇몇은 그에게 소리를 질렀다.

16 Corky도 그들에게 소리를 질렀다.

17 그는 "나를 풀어 줘. 그러지 않으면 모두 혼쭐날 줄 알아!"라고 외쳤다.

18 그것은 상황을 더 악화시켰다.

19 그는 '다른 방법을 써야겠어.'라고 생각했다.

20 그리고 나서 Corky는 부드럽게 말하기 시작했다.

21 그는 자신이 위험하거나 나쁘지 않고 좋은 사람이라고 말했다.

22 그는 모든 방법을 동원해 계속해서 이렇게 말했다.

23 마침내 사람들은 그를 풀어 주었다.

24 "이제 너는 가장 강력한 무기인 '말'을 통제하게 되었다.

25 부드러운 말은 날카로운 칼보다 강하니라."라고 스승은 말했다.

26 다음 단계로 스승은 Corky를 중앙에 의자가 놓여 있는 커다란 홀로 데리고 갔다.

27 그곳에는 시험에 통과한 19명의 다른 전사들이 있었다.

28 "저 의자에 가장 먼저 앉는 사람이 승자가 될 것이다."라고 스승이 말했다.

29 Corky와 나머지 전사들은 싸우기 시작했다.

30 그들은 밀고 당기고 달리고 뛰어올랐다.

31 They fought _____ _____ _____, so Corky became tired.

32 Finally, he said, "I will not fight _____.

33 Instead, I will take care of _____ _____."

34 The other warriors saw this and fought _____ _____.

35 _____ they fought, more warriors became tired and hurt.

36 Corky _____ _____ _____ _____ them, so they followed him.

37 Soon, all the warriors _____ Thunder were _____ Corky.

38 Thunder walked toward the chair _____ _____ _____ _____.

39 Then, he saw Corky _____ _____ his 18 followers.

40 Thunder realized he was _____ _____.

41 "I give up. You're _____ _____ _____," Thunder said to Corky.

42 _____ _____ _____, the teacher appeared and said. "Of all the great weapons, peace is _____ _____.

43 _____ _____ _____, everyone wants to stand on the side of peace."

44 Corky _____ _____ the palace after his training ended.

45 When the king saw him _____, he gave Corky a wise and _____ smile and said, "_____ _____, General?"

---

31 그들은 점점 더 격렬히 싸웠고, Corky는 지쳤다.

32 마침내 그가 말했다. "나는 더는 싸움을 하지 않겠다.

33 대신에 부상당한 자들을 돌볼 것이다."

34 나머지 전사들은 이것을 보고 더 심하게 싸움을 했다.

35 그들이 싸움을 할수록 더 많은 전사들이 지치고 다쳤다.

36 Corky는 그들을 잘 돌봐 주었고, 그들은 Corky를 따르게 되었다.

37 곧 Thunder를 제외한 모든 전사들이 Corky를 따르고 있었다.

38 Thunder는 의자로 걸어가 그곳에 앉으려 했다.

39 그러다 그는 Corky가 18명의 추종자들과 함께 서 있는 것을 봤다.

40 Thunder는 자신이 혼자라는 사실을 깨달았다.

41 "나는 포기하겠다. 네가 진정한 승자다."라고 Thunder가 Corky에게 말했다.

42 그때 스승이 나타나 말했다. "모든 훌륭한 무기 중에서 평화는 내가 가장 좋아하는 것이다.

43 조만간 모든 사람은 평화의 편에 서기를 원한다."

44 Corky는 훈련을 마친 후 성으로 돌아갔다.

45 Corky가 다가오는 것을 본 왕은 그에게 이미 모든 것을 알고 있다는 듯한 현명한 미소를 띠며 말했다. "안녕하시오, 장군?"

● 우리말을 참고하여 본문을 영작하시오.

1 최고의 전사, Corky

➡ _____

2 Corky는 용감한 청년이었다.

➡ _____

3 그는 장군이 되기를 원했지만 왕은 이렇게 말했다. "자네는 우리 군대에서 가장 강한 전사이네. 하지만 자네는 아직도 배울 게 많아."

➡ _____

4 왕은 Corky에게 유명한 군사 학교에 갈 것을 명령했다.

➡ _____

5 "거기서 기다려라. 훈련은 100일 후에 시작할 것이다." 군사 학교 안에서 이렇게 외치는 목소리가 들렸다.

➡ _____

6 Corky는 화가 났다.

➡ _____

7 하지만 이유가 있을 것으로 생각하고 기다렸다.

➡ _____

8 101일째 되던 날, 문이 열렸다.

➡ _____

9 한 노인이 이렇게 말했다. "너는 첫 번째 무기인 '인내'를 사용하는 법을 배운 것이다.

➡ _____

10 인내는 전쟁에서 이기기 위해 가장 중요한 것이다."

➡ _____

11 그리고 난 뒤, 스승은 Corky에게 기둥 앞에 서라고 말했다.

➡ _____

12 갑자기 그는 Corky를 기둥에 묶었다.

➡ _____

13 그의 머리 위에는 '위험하고 나쁨'이라는 푯말을 붙였다.

➡ _____

14 많은 사람이 지나갔다.

➡ _____

15 몇몇은 Corky를 화난 표정으로 쳐다봤고, 다른 몇몇은 그에게 소리를 질렀다.

➡ _____

16 Corky도 그들에게 소리를 질렀다.

➡ _____

17 그는 "나를 풀어 줘. 그러지 않으면 모두 혼쭐날 줄 알아!"라고 외쳤다.

➡ _____

18 그것은 상황을 더 악화시켰다.

➡ _____

19 그는 '다른 방법을 써야겠어.'라고 생각했다.

➡ _____

20 그러고 나서 Corky는 부드럽게 말하기 시작했다.

➡ _____

21 그는 자신이 위험하거나 나쁘지 않고 좋은 사람이라고 말했다.

➡ _____

22 그는 모든 방법을 동원해 계속해서 이렇게 말했다.

➡ _____

23 마침내 사람들은 그를 풀어 주었다.

➡ _____

24 "이제 너는 가장 강력한 무기인 '말'을 통제하게 되었다.

➡ _____

25 부드러운 말은 날카로운 칼보다 강하니라."라고 스승은 말했다.

➡ _____

26 다음 단계로 스승은 Corky를 중앙에 의자가 놓여 있는 커다란 홀로 데리고 갔다.

➡ _____

27 그곳에는 시험에 통과한 19명의 다른 전사들이 있었다.

➡ _____

28 "저 의자에 가장 먼저 앉는 사람이 승자가 될 것이다."라고 스승이 말했다.

➡ _____

29 Corky와 나머지 전사들은 싸우기 시작했다.

➡ _____

30 그들은 밀고 당기고 달리고 뛰어올랐다.

➡ _____

31 그들은 점점 더 격렬히 싸웠고, Corky는 지쳤다.

➡ _____

32 마침내 그가 말했다. "나는 더는 싸움을 하지 않겠다.

➡ _____

33 대신에 부상당한 자들을 돌볼 것이다."

➡ _____

34 나머지 전사들은 이것을 보고 더 심하게 싸움을 했다.

➡ _____

35 그들이 싸움을 할수록 더 많은 전사들이 지치고 다쳤다.

➡ _____

36 Corky는 그들을 잘 돌봐 주었고, 그들은 Corky를 따르게 되었다.

➡ _____

37 곧 Thunder를 제외한 모든 전사들이 Corky를 따르고 있었다.

➡ _____

38 Thunder는 의자로 걸어가 그곳에 앉으려 했다.

➡ _____

39 그러다 그는 Corky가 18명의 추종자들과 함께 서 있는 것을 봤다.

➡ _____

40 Thunder는 자신이 혼자라는 사실을 깨달았다.

➡ _____

41 "나는 포기하겠다. 네가 진정한 승자다."라고 Thunder가 Corky에게 말했다.

➡ _____

42 그때 스승이 나타나 말했다. "모든 훌륭한 무기 중에서 평화는 내가 가장 좋아하는 것이다.

➡ _____

43 조만간 모든 사람은 평화의 편에 서기를 원한다."

➡ _____

44 Corky는 훈련을 마친 후 성으로 돌아갔다.

➡ _____

45 Corky가 다가오는 것을 본 왕은 그에게 이미 모든 것을 알고 있다는 듯한 현명한 미소를 띠며 말했다. "안녕하시오, 장군?"

➡ _____

_____

[01~03] 다음 글을 읽고 물음에 답하시오.

Corky was a brave young man. ①He wanted to be a general, but the king said, "You're the strongest man in my army, but you have much ⓐto learn." ②He ordered Corky to go to a famous military school.

"Wait there. In a hundred days, your training will start," a voice said from inside the school gate. Corky got angry. But then ③he thought there might be a reason, so ④he waited. On the hundred and first day, the gate opened. An old man said, "⑤You have learned to use your first weapon: patience. Patience is the most important thing to win a war."

01 밑줄 친 ①~⑤ 중에서 가리키는 대상이 나머지 넷과 다른 것은?

①   ②   ③   ④   ⑤

02 위 글의 밑줄 친 ⓐto learn과 to부정사의 용법이 같은 것을 모두 고르시오.

① There is no one to do it.
② She must be a fool to say like that.
③ I want a chair to sit on.
④ I think it wrong to tell a lie.
⑤ He is the last man to tell a lie.

03 According to the passage, which is NOT true?

① The king said that Corky was the strongest man in his army.
② The king ordered Corky to go to a famous military school.
③ Corky got angry when he heard a voice from inside the school gate.

④ On the hundredth day, the gate opened.
⑤ An old man said, "You have learned to use your first weapon: patience. Patience is the most important thing to win a war."

[04~06] 다음 글을 읽고 물음에 답하시오.

Then, the teacher told Corky to stand against a pole. Suddenly, he tied Corky to the pole. Above his head, he put a sign that read "Dangerous and Bad." Many people passed by. Some gave Corky angry looks, and others shouted at him. Corky shouted back. He yelled, "Set me free, or you all will be in big trouble!" That made the situation worse.

"I need to try another way," he thought. Then, Corky began to speak softly. He said he was not dangerous or bad but was a good man. He kept saying this in all possible ways. Finally, the people ⓐ him go.

"Now you control the most powerful weapon: words. ⓑ부드러운 말은 날카로운 칼보다 강하니라," said the teacher.

04 위 글의 빈칸 ⓐ에 들어갈 알맞은 말을 고르시오.

① wanted   ② let
③ ordered   ④ told
⑤ allowed

서답형

05 위 글의 밑줄 친 ⓑ의 우리말에 맞게 주어진 어휘를 이용하여 7 단어로 영작하시오.

sharp swords

➡ _____

⭐ **중요**

06 Which question CANNOT be answered after reading the passage?

① What did the teacher tell Corky to do?

② What did people do when they passed by the pole?

③ Why did Corky begin to speak softly though people shouted at him?

④ How long was Corky tied to the pole?

⑤ What weapon did Corky come to control?

08 위 글의 밑줄 친 ⓑeven과 바꿔 쓸 수 없는 말을 고르시오.

① much   ② still   ③ more

④ far   ⑤ a lot

서답형

09 위 글을 읽고 스승의 시험에 대한 Corky의 행동 변화를 우리말로 쓰시오.

➡ _____

_____

[07~09] 다음 글을 읽고 물음에 답하시오.

Next, the teacher took Corky to a large hall with a chair in the middle. There were 19 other warriors who had passed their tests. "The first one to sit in the chair will be the winner," the teacher said.

Corky and the others began fighting. They pushed, pulled, ran, and jumped. They fought harder and harder, so Corky became tired.

Finally, he said, "I will not fight anymore. ___ⓐ___, I will take care of the injured." The other warriors saw this and fought ⓑeven harder. As they fought, more warriors became tired and hurt. Corky took good care of them, so they followed him. Soon, all the warriors except Thunder were following Corky.

07 위 글의 빈칸 ⓐ에 들어갈 알맞은 말을 고르시오.

① Still   ② Instead

③ In fact   ④ For example

⑤ Therefore

[10~11] 다음 글을 읽고 물음에 답하시오.

Thunder walked toward the chair to sit in it. Then, ①he saw Corky standing with ②his 18 followers. Thunder realized he was all alone. "I give up. ③You're the real winner," Thunder said to Corky.

At that moment, the teacher appeared and said. "Of all the great weapons, peace is my favorite. Sooner or later, everyone wants to stand on the side of peace."

Corky returned to the palace after ④his training ended. When the king saw ⑤him approach, he gave Corky a wise and knowing smile and said, "What's up, General?"

10 밑줄 친 ①~⑤ 중에서 가리키는 대상이 나머지 넷과 다른 것은?

①   ②   ③   ④   ⑤

⭐ **중요**

11 위 글의 교훈으로 알맞은 것을 고르시오.

① It is difficult to fight with others without any help.

② Sometimes it is wise to give up.

③ There are various ways to be the real winner.

④ There are no winners in the battle of life.

⑤ Everyone wants to stand on the side of peace.

[12~14] 다음 글을 읽고 물음에 답하시오.

Then, the teacher told Corky to stand against a pole. Suddenly, he tied Corky to the pole. Above his head, he put a sign that (A)read "Dangerous and Bad." Many people passed by. Some gave Corky angry looks, and others shouted at him. Corky shouted back. He yelled, "Set me free, or you all will be in big trouble!" That made the situation worse.

"I need to try another way," he thought. Then, Corky began to speak softly. He said he was not dangerous or bad but was a good man. He kept _____ⓐ_____ this in all possible ways. Finally, the people let him go.

"Now you control the most powerful weapon: words. Soft words are stronger than sharp swords," said the teacher.

서답형

12 위 글의 빈칸 ⓐ에 say를 알맞은 형태로 쓰시오.

➡ _____

13 위 글의 밑줄 친 (A)read와 같은 의미로 쓰인 것을 고르시오.

① I read about the accident in the local paper.

② How do you read the present situation?

③ A man came to read the gas meter.

④ The sign read 'No admittance.'

⑤ My computer can't read the disk you sent.

서답형

14 위 글을 읽고 스승의 시험에 대한 Corky의 행동 변화를 우리말로 쓰시오.

첫 번째 반응: _____

_____

두 번째 반응: _____

_____

[15~17] 다음 글을 읽고 물음에 답하시오.

Next, the teacher took Corky to a large hall with a chair in the middle. There were 19 other warriors who had passed their tests. "The first one to sit in the chair will be the winner," the teacher said.

Corky and ⓐthe others began fighting. They pushed, pulled, ran, and jumped. They fought harder and harder, so Corky became tired.

Finally, he said, "I will not fight anymore. Instead, I will take care of ⓑthe injured." The other warriors saw this and fought even harder. As they fought, more warriors became tired and hurt. Corky took good care of them, so they followed him. Soon, all the warriors except Thunder were following Corky.

서답형

15 위 글의 밑줄 친 ⓐthe others가 가리키는 것을 본문에서 찾아 쓰시오.

➡ _____

서답형

16 위 글의 밑줄 친 ⓑthe injured와 바꿔 쓸 수 있는 말을 두 단어로 쓰시오.

➡ _____

Reading **93**

17 위 글의 주제로 알맞은 것을 고르시오.

① The teacher made the warriors fight with each other to sit first in the chair.
② The warriors fought harder and harder.
③ Corky became tired, so he gave up fighting.
④ All the warriors except Corky fought even harder.
⑤ Corky got many followers by taking care of the injured.

[18~20] 다음 글을 읽고 물음에 답하시오.

Thunder walked toward the chair to sit in it. ⓐThen, he saw Corky to stand with his 18 followers. Thunder realized he was all alone. "I give up. You're the real winner," Thunder said to Corky.

At that moment, the teacher appeared and said. "Of all the great weapons, peace is my favorite. ⓑ조만간 모든 사람은 평화의 편에 서기를 원한다."

Corky returned to the palace after his training ended. When the king saw him approach, he gave Corky a wise and knowing smile and said, "What's up, General?"

서답형

18 위 글의 밑줄 친 ⓐ에서 어법상 틀린 부분을 찾아 고치시오.

_____ ➡ _____

서답형

19 위 글의 밑줄 친 ⓑ의 우리말에 맞게 주어진 어휘를 이용하여 12 단어로 영작하시오.

sooner, on the side of

➡ _____

_____

20 위 글의 제목으로 가장 알맞은 것을 고르시오.

① Thunder Saw Corky Standing with His 18 Followers
② Corky, the Real Winner, Got the Last Weapon, Peace
③ Thunder Realized He Was All Alone
④ Peace Is My Favorite of All the Great Weapons
⑤ The King Gave Corky a Wise and Knowing Smile

[21~23] 다음 글을 읽고 물음에 답하시오.

Corky was a brave young man. He wanted to be a general, but the king said, "You're the strongest man in my army, but (A)you have much to learn." He ordered Corky to go to a famous military school.

(①) "Wait there. ___ⓐ___ a hundred days, your training will start," a voice said from inside the school gate. (②) But then he thought there might be a reason, so he waited. (③) ___ⓑ___ the hundred and first day, the gate opened. (④) An old man said, "You have learned to use your first weapon: patience. Patience is the most important thing to win a war." (⑤)

21 위 글의 빈칸 ⓐ와 ⓑ에 들어갈 전치사가 바르게 짝지어진 것은?

	ⓐ	ⓑ		ⓐ	ⓑ
①	For	In	②	In	By
③	In	On	④	On	In
⑤	For	On			

서답형

22 위 글의 밑줄 친 (A)를 다음과 같이 바꿔 쓸 때 빈칸에 들어갈 알맞은 말을 두 단어로 쓰시오.

you have much _____ _____ learn

23 위 글의 흐름으로 보아, 주어진 문장이 들어가기에 가장 적절한 곳은?

Corky got angry.

① ② ③ ④ ⑤

[24~26] 다음 글을 읽고 물음에 답하시오.

Then, the teacher told Corky to stand against a pole. Suddenly, he tied Corky to the pole. Above his head, he put a sign ⓐ_____ read "Dangerous and Bad." Many people passed by. Some gave Corky angry looks, and others shouted at him. Corky shouted back. He yelled, "Set me free, or you all will be in big trouble!" ⓑThat made the situation better.

"I need to try another way," he thought. Then, Corky began to speak softly. He said he was not dangerous or bad but was a good man. He kept saying this in all possible ways. ⓒFinally, the people let him go.

"Now you control the most powerful weapon: words. Soft words are stronger than sharp swords," said the teacher.

서답형

24 위 글의 빈칸 ⓐ에 들어갈 알맞은 말을 쓰시오.

➡ _____

서답형

25 위 글의 밑줄 친 ⓑ에서 흐름상 어색한 부분을 찾아 고치시오.

_____ ➡ _____

26 위 글의 밑줄 친 ⓒFinally와 바꿔 쓸 수 없는 단어를 고르시오.

① At last   ② In the end
③ After all   ④ Immediately
⑤ Eventually

[27~28] 다음 글을 읽고 물음에 답하시오.

Next, the teacher took Corky to a large hall with a chair in the middle. There were 19 other warriors who had passed their tests. "The first one to sit in the chair will be the winner," the teacher said.

Corky and the others began fighting. They pushed, pulled, ran, and jumped. They fought harder and harder, so Corky became tired. Finally, he said, "I will not fight anymore. Instead, I will ⓐtake care of the injured." The other warriors saw this and fought even harder. As they fought, more warriors became tired and hurt. Corky took good care of them, so they followed him. Soon, all the warriors except Thunder were following Corky.

27 위 글의 밑줄 친 ⓐtake care of와 바꿔 쓸 수 있는 말을 모두 고르시오.

① look after   ② take off
③ deal in   ④ care for
⑤ look for

28 위 글을 읽고 알 수 없는 것을 고르시오.

① Where did the teacher take Corky?
② How many warriors were there in the large hall except Corky?
③ Who will be the winner?
④ How long did the warriors fight?
⑤ Why did the warriors except Thunder follow Corky?

Reading **95**

[01~03] 다음 글을 읽고 물음에 답하시오.

Corky was a brave young man. He wanted to be a general, but the king said, "You're the strongest man in my army, but you have much to learn." He ordered Corky to go to a famous military school.

"Wait there. In a hundred days, your training will start," a voice said from inside the school gate. Corky got angry. ⓐBut then he thought there might be a reason, so he waited. On the hundred and first day, the gate opened. An old man said, "You have learned to use your first weapon: patience. Patience is the most important thing to win a war."

01 Why did the king order Corky to go to a famous military school? Fill in the blanks (A) and (B) with suitable words.

Because he thought that though Corky was (A)_____ _____ _____ in his army, he had much (B)_____ _____.

02 다음 빈칸 (A)와 (B)에 알맞은 단어를 넣어, 위 글의 밑줄 친 문장 ⓐ 뒤에 생략된 부분을 완성하시오.

But then he thought there might be a reason for making him (A)_____ _____ for (B)_____ _____ days.

03 본문의 내용과 일치하도록 다음 빈칸 (A)와 (B)에 알맞은 단어를 쓰시오.

Corky went to a famous military school but had to wait (A)_____ _____ _____ its gate for a hundred days. On the hundred and first day, an old man said that Corky had learned to use his first weapon, (B)_____, for the past one hundred days.

[04~05] 다음 글을 읽고 물음에 답하시오.

Then, the teacher told Corky to stand against a pole. Suddenly, he tied Corky to the pole. Above his head, he put a sign that read "Dangerous and Bad." Many people passed by. Some gave Corky angry looks, and others shouted at him. Corky shouted back. He yelled, "ⓐSet me free, or you all will be in big trouble!" That made the situation worse.

"I need to try ⓑanother way," he thought. Then, Corky began to speak softly. He said he was not dangerous or bad but was a good man. He kept saying this in all possible ways. Finally, the people let him go.

"Now you control the most powerful weapon: words. Soft words are stronger than sharp swords," said the teacher.

04 위 글의 밑줄 친 ⓐ를 다음과 같이 바꿔 쓸 때 빈칸에 들어갈 알맞은 말을 쓰시오.

(1) _____ _____ _____ set me free, you all will be in big trouble!

(2) _____ _____ set me free, you all will be in big trouble!

05 위 글의 밑줄 친 ⓑ가 가리키는 구체적인 방법 두 가지를 우리말로 쓰시오.

(1) _____

(2) _____

_____

[06~08] 다음 글을 읽고 물음에 답하시오.

Next, the teacher took Corky to a large hall with a chair in the middle. There were 19 other warriors who had passed their tests. "ⓐ 저 의자에 가장 먼저 앉는 사람이 승자가 될 것이다," the teacher said.

Corky and the others began fighting. They pushed, pulled, ran, and jumped. They fought harder and harder, so Corky became (A) [tiring / tired].

Finally, he said, "I will not fight anymore. Instead, I will take care of the (B)[injured / victims]." The other warriors saw this and fought even harder. As they fought, more warriors became tired and hurt. Corky took good care of them, so they followed him. Soon, all the warriors except Thunder were (C)[following / followed] Corky.

06 위 글의 밑줄 친 ⓐ의 우리말에 맞게 주어진 어휘를 이용하여 12 단어로 영작하시오.

| first one, in, will be |

➡ _____

07 위 글의 괄호 (A)~(C)에서 문맥이나 어법상 알맞은 낱말을 골라 쓰시오.

➡ (A) _____ (B) _____ (C) _____

08 본문의 내용과 일치하도록 다음 빈칸 (A)와 (B)에 알맞은 단어를 쓰시오.

| Corky got many followers by (A)_____ _____ _____ the injured instead of (B)_____ with other warriors. |

[09~11] 다음 글을 읽고 물음에 답하시오.

Thunder walked toward the chair to sit in it. Then, he saw Corky standing with his 18 followers. Thunder realized he was all alone. "I give up. You're the real winner," Thunder said to Corky.

At that moment, the teacher appeared and said. "Of all the great weapons, peace is my favorite. Sooner or later, everyone wants to stand on the side of peace."

Corky returned to the palace after his training ended. When the king saw him approach, ⓐ he gave Corky a wise and knowing smile and said, "What's up, General?"

09 위 글의 밑줄 친 ⓐ를 3형식 문장으로 고치시오.

➡ _____

10 What's the last weapon that Corky got? Answer in English beginning with "It". (3 words)

➡ _____

11 본문의 내용과 일치하도록 다음 빈칸 (A)와 (B)에 알맞은 단어를 쓰시오.

| Thunder said that Corky was the (A)_____ _____. Finally, Corky got the last (B)_____ which was also his teacher's favorite weapon. After all the training, Corky returned and became a general. |

After You Read A

1. Corky <u>wanted to be</u> a general in the army.
   want는 to부정사를 목적어로 취함.

2. Corky went to the military school and waited <u>for a hundred days</u>.
   for+숫자: ~ 동안

3. Corky <u>kept saying</u> he was not dangerous[bad], so people finally <u>set him</u>
   keep ~ing: 계속해서 ~하다   set free: 석방하다, 풀어 주다
   <u>free</u>.

4. Corky <u>stopped fighting</u> and took care of <u>the injured</u>.
   stop ~ing: ~을 그만두다   the injured: 부상자들(the+과거분사 = 복수 보통명사)

구문해설 • **general**: 장군 • **army**: 군대 • **military**: 군대; 군대의 • **set free**: 석방하다, 풀어 주다
• **take care of**: ~을 돌보다 • **injured**: 부상당한

1. Corky는 군대에서 장군이 되기를 원했다.
2. Corky는 군사 학교에 가서 100일 동안 기다렸다.
3. Corky는 계속해서 자신이 위험하지[나쁘지] 않다고 말해서, 사람들이 마침내 그를 풀어 주었다.
4. Corky는 싸움을 멈추고 부상당한 자들을 돌보아 주었다.

Inside the Story

Two people are talking in the hall. One is the king, and the other is Corky.

The king orders Corky <u>to go</u> to the military school. Many people are standing
                        orders의 목적격보어
around Corky. One is talking to Corky, <u>the others</u> are listening. The teacher
                                        나머지 모두
tells Corky <u>to be quiet</u> and <u>stay</u> there.
            tell의 목적격보어 ①   tell의 목적격보어 ②
Two men are standing inside the gate. <u>One</u> is holding a sword, and <u>the other</u>
                                        둘 중 하나   둘 중 나머지 하나
is holding a stick. The man holding a sword tells Corky <u>to wait</u> there for 100
                                                        tells의 목적격보어
days.

Many warriors are listening to the teacher. Some are standing, and <u>the others</u>
                                                                    나머지 모두
are kneeling. The teacher wants them <u>to keep</u> fighting to sit in the chair.
                                      want의 목적격보어

구문해설 • **military**: 군사의 • **sword**: 칼 • **kneel**: 무릎을 꿇다

두 사람이 홀에서 말하고 있다. 한 사람은 왕이고 나머지 한 사람은 Corky이다. 왕은 Corky에게 군사 학교로 가라고 명령한다. 많은 사람이 Corky 주변에 서 있다. 한 사람은 Corky에게 말하고 있고 나머지 사람들은 듣고 있다. 스승은 Corky에게 조용히 하고 거기 있으라고 말한다. 두 남자가 문 안에 서 있다. 한 명은 칼을 들고 있고 나머지 한 명은 곤봉을 들고 있다. 칼을 들고 있는 남자는 Corky에게 100일 동안 거기서 기다리라고 말한다. 많은 전사가 스승의 말을 듣고 있다. 몇몇은 서 있고 나머지는 무릎을 꿇고 있다. 스승은 그들이 의자에 앉기 위해 계속 싸우기를 원한다.

Link to the World

• Mahatma Gandhi led a peaceful movement <u>to free</u> India.
                                          'movement'를 수식하는 형용사적 용법
• He asked his people <u>to fight</u> <u>peacefully</u> against England.
   ask+목적어+to부정사: …가 ~하도록 요청하다   'fight'를 수식하는 부사
• He fasted for a long time instead <u>of fighting</u> with weapons.
                                      전치사 of 뒤에 동명사를 사용한다.
• "<u>An eye for an eye</u> will only <u>make the whole world blind</u>," he said.
   눈에는 눈이라는 식의 복수(같은 방법에 의한 보복)   make+목적어+목적보어(형용사)

구문해설 • **lead**(-led-led): 이끌다 • **movement**: 운동 • **free**: 해방시키다 • **against**: ~에 대항하여
• **fast**: 단식하다, 굶다 • **instead of**: ~ 대신에 • **weapon**: 무기 • **blind**: 눈 먼

• 마하트마 간디는 인도를 해방하기 위한 평화 운동을 이끌었다.
• 그는 그의 국민들에게 영국에 대항하여 평화롭게 싸울 것을 요청했다.
• 그는 무기를 들고 싸우는 대신 오랫동안 단식 투쟁을 했다.
• "눈에는 눈이라는 식의 복수는 오직 전 세계를 눈멀게 할 뿐이다."라고 그는 말했다.

01 다음 짝지어진 두 단어의 관계가 같도록 빈칸에 알맞은 단어를 쓰시오.

> fighter – warrior : wounded – _____

02 다음 문장의 빈칸 (a)와 (b)에 들어갈 어구가 바르게 짝지어진 것은?

> - (a)_____ you will have to make a decision.
> - She hoped to (b)_____ her native land.

① In all possible ways – step on
② In all possible ways – wait for
③ Sooner or later – should have been
④ Sooner or later – return to
⑤ Sooner or later – pass by

[03~04] 다음 영영풀이에 해당하는 것을 고르시오.

03

> to tell someone to do something

① order   ② insist
③ yell   ④ stand
⑤ forget

04

> the person that wins a competition

① grass   ② winner
③ general   ④ situation
⑤ patience

05 다음 대화의 빈칸에 들어갈 말을 〈영영풀이〉를 참고하여 두 단어로 쓰시오.

> G: I can't find my pencil case. Have you seen it?
> B: No, I haven't. Where did you put it?
> G: I put it on my desk, but now it's gone. I'm really upset.
> B: _____! I'll help you find it.

> 〈영영풀이〉 to stop feeling angry, upset, or excited

06 다음 밑줄 친 부분의 뜻이 잘못된 것은?

① He drank too much, and that <u>finally</u> made him sick. (마침내)
② The children learned how to <u>take care of</u> the hamster. (돌보다)
③ I didn't <u>realize</u> how late it was. (깨닫다)
④ Ms. Han gave us an angry <u>look</u> when we laughed out loud. (바라보다)
⑤ The couple <u>approached</u> the woman to ask her a question. (다가갔다)

07 다음 대화의 빈칸에 알맞은 것은?

> A: I can't stand this place. _____
> B: Calm down! We're at the festival. Let's enjoy it.

① It's very fantastic.
② It's exciting.
③ The music sounds great.
④ They are enjoying themselves.
⑤ It's too crowded.

08 다음 대화의 순서를 바르게 배열한 것은?

(A) I can't focus on my studies at all. I can't stand it.
(B) What's that noise outside?
(C) They're fixing the heaters.
(D) Calm down! They will finish it soon.

① (B) – (A) – (C) – (D)
② (B) – (C) – (A) – (D)
③ (C) – (A) – (D) – (B)
④ (C) – (B) – (D) – (A)
⑤ (D) – (B) – (A) – (C)

09 다음 짝지어진 대화 중 어색한 것은?

① A: Wait here for 100 days? I can't stand it.
   B: Calm down! If you get through this situation, you'll be a great general.
② A: Keep fighting to sit in the chair? I can't stand it.
   B: Take it easy!
③ A: Be quiet and stay here? I can't stand it.
   B: Don't stress yourself.
④ A: What are the singers doing?
   B: One is singing, and another are dancing.
⑤ A: The baby keeps crying. I can't stand it.
   B: Calm down! He must be sick.

[10~11] 다음 대화를 읽고 물음에 답하시오.

B: Ouch! He (a)stepped on my foot again.
G: Are you okay?
B: No. This is the third time he did that today. I (b)can't stand it. I'll go and talk to him.
G: (c)Calm down! He's not wearing his glasses today, so he (d)can see well.
B: What happened to his glasses?
G: He (e)broke his glasses during a soccer game this morning.
B: I see, but (A)he should be more careful.

10 위 대화의 밑줄 친 (a)~(e) 중 어휘의 쓰임이 어색한 것은?

① (a) ② (b) ③ (c) ④ (d) ⑤ (e)

11 위 대화의 밑줄 친 (A)를 어법이나 문맥상 알맞게 고쳐 쓰시오.

➡ _____

12 다음 대화의 빈칸에 들어갈 말로 알맞은 것은?

B: The boy behind me keeps pushing me. I can't stand it.
G: _____

① Calm down! I don't know him.
② Calm down! He's waiting for you.
③ Calm down. He's just a child.
④ Calm down! They're having a birthday party.
⑤ Calm down! I'll help you find him.

Grammar

13 다음 빈칸에 들어갈 말로 적절한 것을 모두 고르시오.

The color green _____ us feel relaxed and refreshed.

① makes ② helps ③ keeps
④ allows ⑤ leaves

14 다음 중 어법상 <u>어색한</u> 문장의 개수로 알맞은 것은?

> a. The woman advised the boy to be careful.
> b. Look at the two dogs. One is eating meat, and another is jumping up and down.
> c. Josh heard Olly to talk about his new car.
> d. I saw you getting on the bus this morning.
> e. The man ordered us to go out.
> f. Here are five singers on the stage. One is singing, and others are dancing.

① 1개   ② 2개   ③ 3개   ④ 4개   ⑤ 5개

15 다음 빈칸 (A)와 (B)에 들어갈 말로 적절한 것은?

> Two men are standing inside the gate. One is holding a sword, and (A)_____ is holding a stick. The man holding a sword tells Corky (B)_____ there for 100 days.

① the other–wait   ② another–to wait
③ the other–to wait   ④ another– wait
⑤ the other–waiting

16 다음 글에서 어법상 <u>어색한</u> 부분을 찾아 바르게 고치시오.

> Many people are ①standing around Corky. ②One is talking to Corky, ③the others are listening. The teacher tells Corky ④be quiet and ⑤stay there.

_____ ➡ _____

17 다음 우리말을 주어진 어휘를 이용하여 영어로 옮기시오.

(1) 우리는 평화를 위해 두 가지가 필요하다. 하나는 사랑, 나머지 하나는 희망이다.
(things, peace, love, and, hope)

➡ _____

_____

(2) 우리는 당신이 평화를 위해 우리와 함께하기를 요청한다. (ask, join, peace)

➡ _____

(3) 나는 네가 싸움을 그만두기를 원한다.
(want, stop, fight)

➡ _____

18 다음 빈칸에 들어갈 말로 알맞지 <u>않은</u> 것은?

> Dad _____ me to set the table.

① got   ② helped
③ ordered   ④ told
⑤ had

19 다음 중 어법상 <u>어색한</u> 문장의 개수로 알맞은 것은?

> a. This skirt is too small. Show me another, please.
> b. There are fifty patients in the hospital. Some are emergency patients and the others are non-emergency patients.
> c. I have many foreign friends. One is from France, and other are from China.
> d. He has quadruplet daughters. Some like Pengsoo, and others like Pororo.
> e. Jack has six cats. One is yellow, other is black, and the others are white.
>
> *quadruplet: 네쌍둥이

① 1개   ② 2개   ③ 3개   ④ 4개   ⑤ 5개

Reading

20 주어진 문장 다음에 이어질 글의 순서로 가장 적절한 것은?

> Then, the teacher told Corky to stand against a pole.

> (A) "I need to try another way," he thought. Then, Corky began to speak softly. He said he was not dangerous or bad but was a good man. He kept saying this in all possible ways. Finally, the people let him go.
> (B) Suddenly, he tied Corky to the pole. Above his head, he put a sign that read "Dangerous and Bad." Many people passed by. Some gave Corky angry looks, and others shouted at him. Corky shouted back. He yelled, "Set me free, or you all will be in big trouble!" That made the situation worse.
> (C) "Now you control the most powerful weapon: words. Soft words are stronger than sharp swords," said the teacher.

① (A) – (C) – (B) ② (B) – (A) – (C)
③ (B) – (C) – (A) ④ (C) – (A) – (B)
⑤ (C) – (B) – (A)

[21~23] 다음 글을 읽고 물음에 답하시오.

> Corky was a brave young man. He wanted to be a general, but the king said, "You're the strongest man in my army, but you have much to learn." ⓐHe ordered Corky to go to a famous military school.
> "Wait there. In a hundred days, your training will start," a voice said from inside the school gate. Corky got angry. But then he thought there might be a reason, so he waited. On the hundred and first day, the gate opened. An old man said, "You have learned to use your first weapon: patience. ⓑ인내는 전쟁에서 이기기 위해 가장 중요한 것이다."

21 위 글의 밑줄 친 ⓐ를 복문으로 고칠 때, 빈칸에 들어갈 알맞은 말을 두 단어로 쓰시오.

> He ordered Corky _____ _____ to a famous military school.

22 위 글의 밑줄 친 ⓑ의 우리말에 맞게 주어진 어휘를 알맞게 배열하시오.

> a war / the / thing / patience / to win / most important / is

➡ _____

23 위 글의 제목으로 가장 알맞은 것을 고르시오.

① Corky, a Brave Young Man
② Corky, You Have Much to Learn!
③ Finally, Corky Got the First Weapon, Patience!
④ Wait in Front of the Gate!
⑤ Corky's Training Will Start in a Hundred Days.

[24~25] 다음 글을 읽고 물음에 답하시오.

> Finally, he said, "I will not fight anymore. (①) Instead, I will take care of the injured." (②) The other warriors saw this and fought ⓐeven harder. (③) As they fought, more warriors became tired and hurt. (④) Soon, all the warriors except Thunder were following Corky. (⑤)

24 위 글의 흐름으로 보아, 주어진 문장이 들어가기에 가장 적절한 곳은?

> Corky took good care of them, so they followed him.

①   ②   ③   ④   ⑤

25 위 글의 밑줄 친 ⓐeven과 같은 의미로 쓰인 것을 고르시오.

① 4, 6, 8, 10 are all even numbers.
② She's even more intelligent than her sister.
③ You need an even surface to work on.
④ It was cold there even in summer.
⑤ Our scores are now even.

[26~28] 다음 글을 읽고 물음에 답하시오.

    Then, the teacher told Corky to stand against a pole. Suddenly, he tied Corky   ⓐ   the pole. Above his head, he put a sign that read "Dangerous and Bad." Many people passed by. Some gave Corky angry looks, and others shouted at him. Corky shouted back. He yelled, "Set me free, or you all will be   ⓑ   big trouble!" That made the situation worse.
    "I need to try another way," he thought. Then, Corky began to speak softly. He said he was not dangerous or bad but was a good man. He kept saying ⓒthis in all possible ways. Finally, the people let him go.
    "Now you control the most powerful weapon: words. Soft words are stronger than sharp swords," said the teacher.

26 위 글의 빈칸 ⓐ와 ⓑ에 들어갈 전치사가 바르게 짝지어진 것은?

① to – in   ② in – at   ③ to – at
④ for – in   ⑤ in – to

27 위 글의 밑줄 친 ⓒthis가 가리키는 것을 본문에서 찾아 쓰시오.

➡ _____

28 According to the passage, which is NOT true?

① The teacher put a sign that read "Dangerous and Bad" above Corky's head.
② Some gave angry looks to Corky, and others shouted at him.
③ Corky began to speak softly when the situation got worse.
④ The people allowed Corky to go.
⑤ According to the teacher, the most important weapon is courage.

[29~30] 다음 글을 읽고 물음에 답하시오.

    Two men are standing inside the gate. One is holding a sword, and _____ⓐ_____ is holding a stick. The man ⓑholding a sword tells Corky to wait there for 100 days.

29 위 글의 빈칸 ⓐ에 들어갈 알맞은 말을 쓰시오.

➡ _____

30 위 글의 밑줄 친 ⓑholding과 문법적 쓰임이 같은 것을 모두 고르시오.

① He's saving money to buy a bike.
② Taking a walk every day is very good for you.
③ Who is the girl playing the piano?
④ My hobby is reading books.
⑤ I enjoyed playing soccer.

01 출제율 90%

다음 짝지어진 단어의 관계가 같도록 빈칸에 알맞은 말을 쓰시오.

> push – pull : tie – _____

02 출제율 95%

다음 영영풀이에 해당하는 단어는?

> a fact or situation which explains why something happens

① thought   ② search

③ situation   ④ pole

⑤ reason

[03~04] 다음 대화를 읽고 물음에 답하시오.

B: Ouch! He stepped on my foot again.

G: Are you okay?

B: No. (a)이번이 오늘 그 애가 내 발을 세 번째로 밟은 거야. I can't stand it. I'll go and talk to him.

G: Calm down! He's not wearing his glasses today, so he can't see well.

B: _____(A)_____

G: He broke his glasses during a soccer game this morning.

B: I see, but he should have been more careful.

03 출제율 100%

위 대화의 빈칸 (A)에 들어갈 말로 알맞은 것은?

① How come he played soccer?

② When was he playing soccer?

③ What happened to his glasses?

④ Without his glasses, could he play soccer?

⑤ How long has he been wearing glasses?

04 출제율 95%

위 대화의 우리말 (a)에 맞게 주어진 단어를 알맞은 순서로 배열하시오.

> (he / did / this / the / is / time / that / today / third)

➡ _____

05 출제율 100%

다음 대화의 빈칸에 들어갈 말로 어색한 것은?

G: I can't find my pencil case. Have you seen it?

B: No, I haven't. Where did you put it?

G: I put it on my desk, but now it's gone.

_____

B: Calm down! I'll help you find it.

① I'm really upset.

② How irritating!

③ I'm very refreshed.

④ I'm very angry.

⑤ I'm fed up with it.

06 출제율 95%

다음 대화의 빈칸에 들어갈 말로 알맞은 것은?

G: Look! _____ I'm very angry.

B: Calm down! He works here.

① He can't stand it.

② The boy behind me keeps pushing me.

③ That man didn't wait in line!

④ I hate standing in line in cold weather.

⑤ They're playing music too loud.

07 다음 짝지어진 대화 중 <u>어색한</u> 것은?

① A: That baby keeps crying. I can't stand it.

　 B: Chill out! He must be sick.

② A: Children upstairs are running around. I can't stand it.

　 B: It's going to be okay. Take a deep breath and try to relax.

③ A: Look! That man didn't wait in line! I'm very angry.

　 B: Calm down! He works here.

④ A: His head keeps hitting me on my shoulder.

　 B: Calm down! He is very old. He can't hear well.

⑤ A: I can't stand this place. It's too crowded.

　 B: Calm down! We're at the festival.

[08~09] 다음 대화를 읽고 물음에 답하시오.

Minji: Minsu, there is no cup I can use. Why didn't you do the dishes?

Minsu: Sorry, but I forgot to do them.

Minji: What? (A)<u>너는 항상 해야 할 일을 잊어버리는 구나</u>. I can't stand it. I cleaned the living room all morning.

Minsu: Calm down! I'm busy doing my homework.

Minji: Do the dishes first, and then do your homework.

Minsu: I can't. I don't think I can finish my homework today. Science is too difficult for me.

Minji: Science? You know I'm good at science. Let me help you.

Minsu: Great. Thanks. I'll wash your cup right now and I'll do the rest of the dishes after finishing this.

08 위 대화의 밑줄 친 우리말 (A)에 맞게 주어진 단어를 활용하여 영작하시오.

> (always / what / have)

➡ _____

09 위 대화의 내용과 일치하지 <u>않는</u> 것은?

① Because Minsu didn't wash the dishes, he feels sorry to his sister.

② Minsu's sister thinks Minsu always forgets what he has to do.

③ Minsu says he was busy doing his homework.

④ Minsu thinks science is so easy for him.

⑤ Minsu's sister thinks she is good at science.

10 다음 빈칸에 들어갈 말로 적절한 것을 고르시오.

> He has five daughters. One is a teacher, and _____ are doctors.

① another　② the one　③ other

④ others　⑤ the others

11 다음 우리말에 맞게 주어진 단어를 활용하여 영어로 문장을 완성하시오. (중복 사용 가능)

> 홍 선생님은 그녀의 학생들에게 대화를 들으라고 말씀하셨다. (tell, listen, dialog)

➡ Ms. Hong _____

_____ .

12 다음 문장에서 <u>잘못된</u> 부분을 바르게 고쳐 문장을 다시 쓰시오.

(1) She told him locked the door.

➡ _____

(2) She wouldn't allow him used her phone.

➡ _____

(3) The grapes on the dish look very delicious. Some are green, and others are purple.

➡ _____

_____

(4) Many children are big fans of animals. Some like monkeys, and the others like lions.

➡ _____

(5) I bought two pens. Another is for me, and the other is for you.

➡ _____

_____

13 다음 우리말에 맞게 주어진 단어를 배열하시오.

> 그는 그의 국민들에게 영국에 대항하여 평화롭게 싸울 것을 요청했다.
> (people / asked / He / England / fight / to / his / against / peacefully)

➡ _____

_____

[14~16] 다음 글을 읽고 물음에 답하시오.

Corky was a brave young man. He wanted to be a general, but the king said, "You're the strongest man in my army, but you have much to learn." He ordered Corky to go to a famous military school.

"Wait there. In a hundred days, your training will start," a voice said from inside the school gate. Corky got angry. But then he thought there might be a reason, so he waited. ⓐ <u>101일째 되던 날, 문이 열렸다.</u> An old man said, "You have learned to use your first weapon: patience. Patience is the most important thing to win a war."

14 위 글의 밑줄 친 ⓐ의 우리말에 맞게 주어진 어휘를 이용하여 9 단어로 영작하시오.

> the hundred and first

➡ _____

15 위 글의 종류로 알맞은 것을 고르시오.

① essay   ② short story
③ article   ④ review
⑤ book report

16 What is the most important thing to win a war? Answer in English in a full sentence.

➡ _____

[17~19] 다음 글을 읽고 물음에 답하시오.

Then, the teacher told Corky to stand against a pole. Suddenly, he tied Corky to the pole. Above his head, he put a sign that read "Dangerous and Bad." (①) Many people passed by. (②) Some gave Corky angry looks, and others shouted at him. (③) Corky shouted back. (④) He yelled, "Set me free, or you all will be in big trouble!" (⑤)

"I need to try another way," he thought. Then, Corky began to speak softly. He said he was not dangerous or bad but was a good man. He kept saying this in all possible ways. Finally, the people let him go.

"Now you control the most powerful weapon: words. Soft words are stronger than sharp swords," said the teacher.

17 위 글의 흐름으로 보아, 주어진 문장이 들어가기에 가장 적절한 곳은?

That made the situation worse.

①   ②   ③   ④   ⑤

18 위 글의 주제로 알맞은 것을 고르시오.

① The teacher made Corky stand against a pole.
② Many people blamed Corky for being dangerous and bad.
③ Corky came to control the most powerful weapon: words.
④ Corky reacted to people's blame in two ways.
⑤ The people finally let Corky go.

19 본문의 내용과 일치하도록 다음 빈칸 (A)와 (B)에 알맞은 단어를 쓰시오.

The teacher tied Corky to the pole and put a sign that read "Dangerous and Bad" above Corky's head in order to teach Corky how to (A)_____ the most powerful weapon: (B)_____.

[20~21] 다음 글을 읽고 물음에 답하시오.

Next, the teacher took Corky to a large hall with a chair in the middle. There were 19 other warriors who had passed their tests. "The first one ⓐto sit in the chair will be the winner," the teacher said.

Corky and the others began fighting. They pushed, pulled, ran, and jumped. They fought harder and harder, so Corky became tired.

Finally, he said, "I will not fight anymore. Instead, I will take care of the injured." The other warriors saw ⓑthis and fought even harder. As they fought, more warriors became tired and hurt. Corky took good care of them, so they followed him. Soon, all the warriors except Thunder were following Corky.

20 위 글의 밑줄 친 ⓐto sit과 to부정사의 용법이 다른 것을 모두 고르시오.

① They came here to ask me a question.
② It is not difficult to read this book.
③ Do you have anything to eat?
④ It's time to go home.
⑤ I use a computer to draw a picture.

21 위 글의 밑줄 친 ⓑthis가 가리키는 내용을 우리말로 쓰시오.

➡ _____
_____

01 다음 대화의 빈칸 (A)와 (B)에 들어갈 말을 주어진 단어를 이용하여 완성하시오.

> **A:** You're late again. (A)_____
> (stand)
> **B:** (B)_____(take) I woke up late.
> **A:** You always wake up late when you meet me.
> **B:** I'm really sorry.

02 대화의 빈칸 (A)에 들어갈 말을 제시된 〈조건〉을 만족하는 문장으로 쓰시오.

> **B:** Ouch! He stepped on my foot again.
> **G:** Are you okay?
> **B:** No. This is the third time he did that today. I can't stand it. I'll go and talk to him.
> **G:** Calm down! He's not wearing his glasses today, so he can't see well.
> **B:** What happened to his glasses?
> **G:** He broke his glasses during a soccer game this morning.
> **B:** I see, but _____ (A) _____.

> (1) He ought to have been more careful.
> (2) I'm sorry that he wasn't more careful.

> ┤ 조건 ├
> 조동사를 사용하여 위 (1)~(2)의 의미와 같은 문장을 한 문장으로 영작하시오.

➡ _____

03 대화를 읽고 질문에 영어로 답하시오.

> **Minji:** Minsu, there is no cup I can use. Why didn't you do the dishes?
> **Minsu:** Sorry, but I forgot to do them.
> **Minji:** What? You always forget what you have to do. I can't stand it. I cleaned the living room all morning.
> **Minsu:** Calm down! I'm busy doing my homework.
> **Minji:** Do the dishes first, and then do your homework.
> **Minsu:** I can't. I don't think I can finish my homework today. Science is too difficult for me.
> **Minji:** Science? You know I'm good at science. Let me help you.
> **Minsu:** Great. Thanks. I'll wash your cup right now and I'll do the rest of the dishes after finishing this.

> **Q:** What's Minsu's excuse for forgetting to do the dishes?
> ➡ His excuse is that _____
> _____.

04 다음 문장에서 어법상 틀린 곳을 찾아 바르게 다시 쓰시오.

(1) Three of six people came to the party. The other didn't.

➡ _____

(2) Amy wants Brian tell her about his problem.

➡ _____

05 우리말과 같은 의미가 되도록 문장을 완성하시오.

(1) 그것들 중 어떤 것들은 빨간색이다; others are brown.

➡ _____

(2) 내가 남기를 원한다면, say you want me to stay.

➡ _____

06 괄호 안에 주어진 표현을 사용하여 우리말로 된 대화를 영어로 쓰시오.

(1) (order, get down, on the ground)

A: What did the man order his dog to do?

B: 그는 그의 개에게 바닥에 엎드리라고 명령했어.

➡ _____

(2) (tell, close the door)

A: What did the girl say to the boy?

B: 그녀는 그에게 문을 닫지 말라고 말했어.

➡ _____

(3) (allow, go there)

A: Will you go to Eighteen's concert next month?

B: I'm not sure. 나의 엄마는 내가 거기 가는 것을 허락해 주시지 않을 거야.

➡ _____

[07~09] 다음 글을 읽고 물음에 답하시오.

Then, the teacher told Corky to stand against a pole. Suddenly, he tied Corky to the pole. Above his head, he put a sign that read "Dangerous and Bad." Many people passed by. (A)[One / Some] gave Corky angry looks, and (B)[others / the other] shouted at him. Corky shouted back. He yelled, "Set me free, or you all will be in big trouble!" ⓐThat made the situation worse.

"I need to try (C)[another / the other] way," he thought. Then, Corky began to speak softly. He said he was not dangerous or bad but was a good man. He kept saying this in all possible ways. Finally, the people let him go.

"Now you control the most powerful weapon: words. Soft words are stronger than sharp swords," said the teacher.

07 위 글의 괄호 (A)~(C)에서 어법상 알맞은 낱말을 골라 쓰시오.

➡ (A) _____ (B) _____ (C) _____

08 위 글의 밑줄 친 ⓐThat이 가리키는 것을 본문에서 찾아 쓰시오.

➡ _____

_____

09 본문의 내용과 일치하도록 다음 빈칸 (A)와 (B)에 알맞은 단어를 쓰시오.

Corky was tied to a pole under a sign saying "Dangerous and Bad." He made the situation (A)_____ by yelling, "Set me free, or you all will be in big trouble!" But when he (B)_____ _____ that he was not dangerous or bad but was a good man, he was set (C)_____ and got the second (D)_____, words.

창의사고력 서술형 문제

01 지하철에서 화가 나는 상황들을 나타낸 다음 그림을 보고, 화를 진정시키는 대화를 〈보기〉처럼 완성하시오.

=보기=

A: That baby keeps crying. I can't stand it.
B: Calm down! He must be sick.

02 다음 내용을 바탕으로 그림 속의 장면을 설명하는 글을 쓰시오.

There is a chair in the middle. The teacher is talking to the warriors, and the warriors are listening.
The teacher: Keep fighting to sit in the chair.

Many (A)_____ are listening to (B)_____. Some are (C)_____, and the others are kneeling. The teacher wants them to keep fighting (D)_____.

단원별 모의고사

01 다음 단어에 대한 영어 설명이 <u>어색한</u> 것은?

① military: the armed forces of a country

② finally: after a long period of time

③ impatience: being able to stay calm and not get annoyed

④ war: fighting using soldiers and weapons between two or more countries

⑤ general: a high-ranking officer in the army

02 다음 짝지어진 단어의 관계가 같도록 빈칸에 알맞은 말을 쓰시오.

pass by – go by : mighty – _____

03 다음 영영풀이에 해당하는 단어를 고르시오.

a door in a fence or outside a wall

① gate   ② goat   ③ pole

④ gather   ⑤ sword

04 다음 중 짝지어진 대화가 <u>어색한</u> 것은?

① A: What are the birds doing?

B: One is flying, and the other is sitting on the tree.

② A: There are two dogs over there. What are the dogs doing?

B: One is playing with a ball, and the other is jumping up and down.

③ A: What are the people doing?

B: Some are playing soccer, and the others are playing badminton.

④ A: Go to the military school? I can't stand it.

B: Control yourself! If you get through this situation, you'll be a great general.

⑤ A: A dog is barking. I can't focus on my studies at all. I can't stand it.

B: That's great! He'll keep barking all the way.

05 다음 그림에 맞게 대화의 빈칸에 주어진 철자로 시작하는 단어를 써서 대화를 완성하시오.

B: What's that n_____ outside?

G: They're f_____ the heaters.

B: I can't f_____ _____ my studies at all. I can't s_____ _____.

G: C_____ _____! They will finish it soon.

06 대화의 밑줄 친 (a)~(e)에 관한 설명으로 <u>잘못된</u> 것은?

B: Ouch! He stepped on my foot again.

G: Are you okay?

B: No. This is the third time (a)<u>he did that today</u>. (b)<u>I can't stand it</u>. I'll go and talk to him.

G: (c)<u>Calm down</u>! He's not wearing his glasses today, so he can't see well.

B: What happened to his glasses?

G: He broke his glasses (d)<u>during</u> a soccer game this morning.

B: I see, but he (e)<u>should have been</u> more careful.

① (a) 'the third time'을 수식하는 역할을 하고, 관계부사 'when'이 생략되어 있다.

② (b) 화난 감정을 표현하는 문장으로 'I'm very annoyed.'로 바꾸어 말할 수 있다.

③ (c) 화낸 상대방에 응대하여 진정시키는 표현으로 'Relax.'로 바꾸어 말할 수 있다.

④ (d) 전치사로 '~ 동안'의 의미를 가지고 있고 'for'로 바꾸어 쓸 수 있다.

⑤ (e) 과거의 유감을 나타내는 표현으로 'ought to have been'으로 바꾸어 쓸 수 있다.

07 대화의 흐름상 밑줄 친 ①~⑤ 중 어색한 것은?

> M1: ①The king sent me here. Open the door.
>
> M2: Wait there. ②The door will open in a hundred days.
>
> M1: What? A hundred days? ③I can't spend a hundred days doing nothing. I can't stand it.
>
> M2: ④Calm down! It is an important rule to get in this school. ⑤However, how can you get free? Think.

①   ②   ③   ④   ⑤

08 다음 대화의 밑줄 친 우리말에 맞게 주어진 단어를 이용하여 영작하시오. (동명사 형태를 쓸 것.)

> G: Brrr.... What a cold day! 나는 추운 날씨에 줄 서는 게 싫어.
>
> B: Calm down! Drink this hot milk.

(hate / stand / line / in)

➡ _____

[09~11] 다음 대화를 읽고 물음에 답하시오.

> Minji: Minsu, there is no cup I can use. Why didn't you do the dishes?
>
> Minsu: Sorry, but I forgot (A)(do) them.
>
> Minji: What? You always forget what you have to do. I can't stand it. I cleaned the living room all morning.
>
> Minsu: Calm down! I'm busy (B)(do) my homework.
>
> Minji: Do the dishes first, and then do your homework.
>
> Minsu: I can't. I don't think I can finish my homework today. Science is too difficult for me.
>
> Minji: Science? You know I'm good at science. Let me help you.
>
> Minsu: Great. Thanks. I'll wash your cup right now and I'll do the (C)rest of the dishes after finishing this.

09 위 대화의 괄호 (A)와 (B)의 단어를 알맞은 형태로 고치시오.

(A) _____   (B) _____

10 Why is Minsu's sister angry at Minsu?

> Because she thinks _____
> _____ .

11 위 대화의 밑줄 친 (C)rest와 같은 의미로 사용된 것은?

① Now I see why taking a rest is so important!

② I will devote the rest of my life to making people happy.

③ When we're adults, we won't have much time to rest and relax.

④ Can you feel your brain taking a rest when you blink?

⑤ I just wanted to take a rest while watching my favorite TV show.

12 다음 빈칸 (A)~(C)에 들어갈 말이 바르게 짝지어진 것은?

> The guys keep five dogs. (A)_____ is white, (B)_____ is brown, and (C)_____ are spotted.

① One – another – the other
② One – another – the others
③ Some – other – the other
④ Some – other – the others
⑤ Another – other – the other

13 다음 대화를 읽고 빈칸에 적절한 것은?

> Minsu: Will you help me?
> Kelly: Sure.
> ➡ Minsu asked _____.

① Kelly help him
② Kelly to help him
③ Kelly helped him
④ Kelly helps him
⑤ Kelly helping him

14 다음 대화의 내용을 영어로 바르게 옮긴 것은?

> Mom: Go to bed.
> Son: OK.

① She told her son to go to bed.
② She made her son to go to bed.
③ She told her son go to bed.
④ She made her son going to bed.
⑤ She ordered her son going to bed.

15 다음 대화를 읽고 빈칸을 완성하시오.

> (1) Mina: Can I use your pen?
>   Aaron: Sure.
>   ➡ Aaron allowed _____.
> (2) The lawyer: Don't say anything to the police.
>   The man: OK. I won't.
>   ➡ The lawyer advised _____
>   _____.

16 다음 밑줄 친 우리말을 영어로 옮기시오.

> (1) I have a lot of friends. 몇몇은 친절하고, and others aren't.
>   ➡ _____
> (2) I have two bags. One is black, and 나머지 하나는 갈색이다.
>   ➡ _____

[17~18] 다음 글을 읽고 물음에 답하시오.

> Corky was a brave young man. He wanted to be a general, but the king said, "You're the strongest man in my army, but you have much to learn." He ordered Corky to go to a famous military school.
>
> "Wait ⓐthere. In a hundred days, your training will start," a voice said from inside the school gate. Corky got angry. But then he thought there might be a reason, so he waited. On the hundred and first day, the gate opened. An old man said, "You have learned ⓑto use your first weapon: patience. Patience is the most important thing to win a war."

17 위 글의 밑줄 친 ⓐthere가 가리키는 것을 우리말로 쓰시오.

➡ _____

18 아래 〈보기〉에서 위 글의 밑줄 친 ⓑ와 to부정사의 용법이 다른 것의 개수를 고르시오.

┌─── 보기 ───┐
① It is important to use your time well.
② He went to the store to buy some fruit.
③ I don't have any friends to talk with.
④ He promised me to work hard.
⑤ He can't be rich to ask me for some money.
└───────────┘

① 1개　② 2개　③ 3개　④ 4개　⑤ 5개

[19~20] 다음 글을 읽고 물음에 답하시오.

Then, the teacher told Corky to stand against a pole. Suddenly, he tied Corky to the pole. Above his head, he put a sign that read "Dangerous and Bad." Many people passed by. Some gave Corky angry looks, and others shouted at him. Corky shouted back. He yelled, "ⓐ나를 풀어 줘. 그러지 않으면 모두 혼쭐날 줄 알아!" That made the situation worse.

"I need to try another way," he thought. Then, Corky began to speak softly. He said he was not dangerous or bad but was a good man. He kept saying this in all possible ways. Finally, the people let him go.

"Now you control the most powerful weapon: words. ⓑSoft words are stronger than sharp swords," said the teacher.

19 위 글의 밑줄 친 ⓐ의 우리말에 맞게 한 단어를 보충하여, 주어진 어휘를 알맞게 배열하시오.

┌─────────────────────────┐
you / big / free / will / trouble / be / all / set / in / me / , /
└─────────────────────────┘

➡ _____

20 위 글의 밑줄 친 ⓑ를 다음과 같이 바꿔 쓸 때 빈칸에 들어갈 알맞은 말을 4 단어로 쓰시오.

┌─────────────────────────┐
Sharps words are _____ _____
_____ _____ soft words
└─────────────────────────┘

[21~22] 다음 글을 읽고 물음에 답하시오.

Next, the teacher took Corky to a large hall with a chair in the middle. There were 19 other warriors who ___ⓐ___ their tests. "The first one to sit in the chair will be the winner," the teacher said.

Corky and the others began fighting. They pushed, pulled, ran, and jumped. They fought harder and harder, so Corky became tired.

Finally, he said, "I will not fight anymore. Instead, I will take care of the injured." The other warriors saw this and fought even harder. ⓑAs they fought, more warriors became tired and hurt. Corky took good care of them, so they followed him. Soon, all the warriors except Thunder were following Corky.

21 위 글의 빈칸 ⓐ에 pass를 알맞은 형태로 쓰시오.

➡ _____

22 위 글의 밑줄 친 ⓑAs와 같은 의미로 쓰인 것을 고르시오.

① I respect him as a lawyer.
② Leave the papers as they are.
③ As you were out, I left a message.
④ As we go up, the air grows colder.
⑤ As you know, Julia is leaving soon.

Lesson

Special

Teen's Magazine

Words & Expressions

Key Words

- **about** [əbáut] ⊕ 대략
- **average** [ǽvəridʒ] ⑲ 평균 ⑱ 평균의
- **backward** [bǽkwərd] ⊕ 뒤에서부터, 역방향으로
- **bookmark** [búkmàːrk] ⑲ 책갈피
- **case** [keis] ⑲ 사건
- **control** [kəntróul] ⑧ 통제하다, 조종하다
- **cook** [kuk] ⑲ 요리사 ⑧ 요리하다
- **create** [kriéit] ⑧ 창조하다, 만들어 내다
- **critic** [krítik] ⑲ 비평가
- **dog ear, dog-ear** ⑧ 책장의 모서리를 접어 표시하다 ⑲ 책장의 모서리가 접힌 부분
- **effort** [éfərt] ⑲ 노력
- **fake** [feik] ⑱ 가짜의
- **fold** [fould] ⑧ 접다
- **forest** [fɔ́ːrist] ⑲ 숲, 삼림
- **hate** [heit] ⑧ 싫어하다
- **hold** [hould] ⑧ 잡다
- **imagine** [imǽdʒin] ⑧ 상상하다
- **instead** [instéd] ⊕ 대신에
- **invite** [inváit] ⑧ 초대하다
- **joke** [dʒouk] ⑲ 농담
- **mean** [miːn] ⑧ 의미하다

- **million** [míljən] ⑲ 백만
- **neighbor** [néibər] ⑲ 이웃, 옆집 사람
- **officer** [ɔ́ːfisər] ⑲ 관리, 관료
- **once** [wʌns] ⑳ 일단 ~하기만 하면
- **own** [oun] ⑱ (주로 소유격 뒤에서) ~ 자신의
- **peace** [piːs] ⑲ 평화
- **piece** [piːs] ⑲ 조각
- **public** [pʌ́blik] ⑱ 공공의
- **public officer** 공무원
- **quickly** [kwíkli] ⊕ 빨리
- **race car** 경주용 차
- **realize** [ríːəlàiz] ⑧ 깨닫다
- **save** [seiv] ⑧ 구하다, 절약하다
- **shape** [ʃeip] ⑲ 모양, 형태
- **share** [ʃɛər] ⑧ 공유하다, 나누다
- **shout** [ʃaut] ⑧ 소리치다
- **solve** [salv] ⑧ 해결하다
- **square feet** 평방 피트
- **stone** [stoun] ⑲ 돌멩이
- **tiny** [táini] ⑱ 작은
- **tip** [tip] ⑲ 조언, 도움말

Key Expressions

- **cut ~ into small pieces** ~를 잘게 썰다
- **don't forget to** 잊지 않고 ~하다
- **dream of** ~에 관해 꿈꾸다
- **end up -ing** 결국 ~가 되다
- **every second letter** 두 번째 글자마다
- **get closer to** ~와 가까워지다
- **had better+동사원형** ~하는 게 좋다
- **keep ~ away** ~를 멀리하게 하다

- **laugh out loud** 큰 소리로 웃디
- **make sure** 틀림없이 ~하다
- **need to+동사원형** ~할 필요가 있다
- **rain cats and dogs** 비가 억수같이 오다
- **say hello to** ~에게 인사하다
- **stop+-ing** ~하는 것을 멈추다
- **would rather A than B** B하느니 A하겠다

Word Power

※ 서로 반대의 뜻을 가진 어휘

☐ **hate** (싫어하다) ↔ **like** (좋아하다)

☐ **quickly** (빨리) ↔ **slowly** (느리게)

☐ **backward** (뒤에서부터) ↔ **forward** (앞으로)

☐ **fake** (가짜의) ↔ **genuine** (진짜의)

☐ **public** (공공의) ↔ **private** (사적인)

☐ **fold** (접다) ↔ **unfold** (펼치다)

☐ **tiny** (작은) ↔ **huge** (거대한)

※ 서로 비슷한 뜻을 가진 어휘

☐ **save** : **rescue** (구하다)

☐ **secret** : **confidential** (비밀의)

☐ **imagine** : **visualize** (상상하다)

☐ **solve** : **resolve** (해결하다)

☐ **piece** : **bit** (조각)

☐ **shout** : **yell** (외치다)

English Dictionary

☐ **backward** 뒤에서부터
→ in the direction behind you
당신 뒤에 있는 방향에서

☐ **critic** 비평가
→ someone whose job is to give their opinion of a book, play, movie, etc.
책, 연극, 영화 등에 대한 의견을 말하는 것이 직업인 사람

☐ **delicious** 맛있는
→ very good to eat or drink   먹거나 마시기에 매우 좋은

☐ **effort** 노력
→ an attempt to do something
무언가를 하려는 시도

☐ **fold** 접다
→ to bend something so that one part of it lies flat on top of another part
어떤 것의 일부분이 다른 부분 위에 평평하게 놓이도록 어떤 것을 구부리다

☐ **forest** 숲
→ a large area of trees growing close together
가까이 함께 자라는 나무들의 넓은 지역

☐ **imagine** 상상하다
→ to make an idea or picture of something in your mind
당신의 마음속에 어떤 생각이나 그림을 만들다

☐ **instead** 대신에
→ in the place of someone or something else
다른 사람 또는 다른 어떤 것을 대신하여

☐ **invite** 초대하다
→ to ask someone to come to your house, to a party, etc.
누군가에게 당신의 집이나 파티에 오라고 부탁하다

☐ **make sure** 틀림없이 ~하다
→ to take action so that you are certain that something happens, is true, etc.
어떤 일이 일어나거나, 사실이거나, 기타 등등일 거라고 확신하도록 조치를 취하다

☐ **neighbor** 이웃 사람
→ someone who lives near you
당신 근처에 사는 사람

☐ **peace** 평화
→ a situation in which there is no war, violence, or arguing
전쟁, 폭력 또는 논쟁이 없는 상황

☐ **rain cats and dogs** 비가 억수같이 오다
→ to rain very heavily   비가 심하게 내리다

☐ **realize** 깨닫다
→ to notice or understand something that you did not notice or understand before
이전에는 알아차리지 못하거나 이해하지 못했던 것을 알아차리거나 이해하다

☐ **share** 공유하다
→ to have or use something at the same time as someone else
다른 사람과 동시에 무언가를 가지거나 사용하다

Reading

Teens' Magazine

Ways to Make Your Town Better
형용사적 용법의 to부정사

Doing something nice for your neighbors can change your town.
동명사 주어   'something'을 형용사가 수식할 때는 뒤에서 수식
Start small. Here are some tips.

1. Say hello to your neighbors and smile.

2. Don't forget to say, "Thank you."
   forget+to부정사: (미래에) ~해야 할 것을 잊다

3. Share your umbrella on a rainy day.

4. Laugh out loud when your neighbor tells a joke.

5. Make something for your neighbors.

6. Hold the door for the person behind you.
   형용사구

7. Invite your neighbors to your party.

If you just do one thing each day, you can make your town better.

Messages for Peace

On World Peace Day, we put our peace messages on the board.

Peace means having friends around the world. - Kim Jimin
동명사

I'd rather have peace on Earth than pieces of Earth. - Seo Eunji

I want peace every place I go because there is always someone

fighting or shouting. - Park Hansol
'someone'을 꾸며 주는 현재분사

Peace makes everyone smile. - Yang Miran

Peace is inside all of us. We just need to share it. - Jang Jaehee

LET'S LAUGH

An apple a day

Jake came in to see his dad. "Dad!" he said, "Is it true that an apple a
'it'은 가주어, 'that' 이하의 명사절이 진주어
day keeps the doctor away?"

"That's what they say," said his dad.
관계대명사(~하는 것)
"Well, give me an apple quickly! I just broke the doctor's window!"
과거형이 'just'와 함께 쓰여 '바로 전에 ~했다'

neighbor 이웃, 옆집 사람

say hello to ~에게 인사하다

don't forget to 잊지 않고 ~하다

share 공유하다, 나누다

hold 잡다

invite 초대하다

peace 평화

would rather … than ~하느니 …하겠다

piece 조각

need to+동사원형 ~할 필요가 있다

keep … away …를 멀리하게 하다

quickly 빨리

Be Kind to Books!

Do you know <u>what books hate</u>? They hate water, the sun, and dog
ears. Why dog ears?

Water is bad for WITCHES and BOOKS! / The SUN also TURNs
Books YELLOW / Don't DOG-EAR! Use a bookmark! / Be Kind to
Books!

Stop folding dog ears in books. Use a bookmark instead. <u>It is a
bookmark that can save your books.</u> Be kind to your books. <u>The more
you love your books, the happier your books will be.</u> How about
making your own?

Facts That Sound Fake

1. <u>About</u> 7% of all people who have ever lived are living on the Earth
   today. About 108,200 <u>million</u> people have ever been born in the
   history of the world. And about 7,442 million are living on the
   Earth today.

2. Bangladesh has more people than Russia. Russia is the world's
   <u>largest</u> country, but tiny Bangladesh has 166.3 million people in
   2018. Russia has 143.9 million people.

3. A banyan tree near Kolkata, India, is <u>bigger</u> than the average
   Walmart. The average Walmart store covers <u>about</u> 104,000 <u>square
   feet</u>. The Great Banyan Tree in Kolkata, India, is about the size of a
   forest, covering 155,000 square feet.

4. Baby carrots <u>were invented</u> in 1986. Baby carrots are not actually
   baby carrots. Big ugly carrots are cut into small pieces <u>that have</u>
   the shape of a baby carrot. Farmer Mike Yurosek invented them in
   1986 as a way to use ugly carrots <u>that</u> weren't sold.

hate 싫어하다
dog ear. dog-ear 귀 모양으로 책장의 모서리를 접어 표시하다. 귀 모양으로 책장 모서리가 접힌 부분
fold 접다
instead 대신에
save 구하다
about 대략
million 백만
average 평균; 평균의
square feet 평방피트
forest 숲
cut … into small pieces …를 잘게 썰다
shape 모양, 형태

Jobs in the Movies

Zootopia (2016) It's the greatest movie ever!
지금까지

Flash is a public officer. He is very slow but works hard. You will be surprised to see <u>what he does in his free time</u>. It's driving a race car!
간접의문문(의문사+주어+동사)

Nick is a fox with a big mouth. <u>Helping Judy,</u> he gets closer to her. He
동시동작을 나타내는 분사구문. 'Judy를 도우면서'
later becomes a police officer like Judy. Judy is a small rabbit, but she's smart and strong. After a lot of effort, she becomes a police officer and solves many cases.

Ratatouille (2007) Everyone will love this movie.

Anton Ego is a food critic. After he eats the food Remy cooked, he realizes <u>that</u> anyone can cook.
접속사

Remy, a little mouse, dreams of becoming a cook. He goes into a restaurant and meets a boy named Linguini. <u>Controlling Linguini,</u> he
동시동작을 나타내는 분사구문. Linguini를 통제하면서
makes delicious food and <u>ends up becoming</u> a great cook.
end up ~ing: 결국 ~하다

Say It with Emojis

Do you know what these emojis mean? <u>Killing</u> two birds with one
동명사(주어)
stone. / The apple of your eyes. / Don't play games with fire. / Once in a blue moon. / Let's call it a day. / Money does not grow on trees. / It's raining cats and dogs. / A piece of cake.

Emoji Song

Now, let's sing a Christmas song together! The louder, the happier!
The+비교급, the+비교급: …하면 할수록 더 ~하다!

public 공공의
officer 관리, 관료
public officer 공무원
race car 경주용 차
get closer to ~와 가까워지다
effort 노력
critic 비평가
realize 깨닫다
control 통제하다, 조종하다
stone 돌멩이
rain cats and dogs 비가 억수같이 오다
You better = You'd better 너는 ~하는 게 좋다

Secret Messages

Imagine you can send messages to your friend that no one else can
read! It's not so difficult for you to learn how to read and write your
own secret messages.

1. Read Backward

This is easy to solve. Just read the words backward! It seems simple
once you know the secret, but it can be a hard one when you don't.

2. Read Every Second Letter

Read every second letter starting with the first letter, and when you
finish, start again on the letters you missed.

3. Pig-pen

The Pig-pen is easier than it looks. The lines around each letter mean
the letter inside the lines.

Now create your own set of secret letters and write secret messages to
send to your friends. Make sure you send along a key so your friends
can understand your messages!

imagine 상상하다

backward 뒤에서부터, 역방향으로

once 일단 ~하기만 하면

every second letter 두 번째 글자마다

create 창조하다, 만들어 내다

make sure 틀림없이 ~하다

● 우리말을 참고하여 빈칸에 알맞은 말을 쓰시오.

1 _____ Magazine

2 Ways to _____ Your Town _____

3 Doing _____ _____ for your neighbors can change your town. Start small. Here are some tips.

4 1. _____ _____ _____ your neighbors and smile.

5 2. Don't forget _____ _____, "Thank you."

6 3. Share your umbrella _____ _____ _____ _____.

7 4. _____ _____ _____ when your neighbor tells a joke.

8 5. Make something _____ your neighbors.

9 6. Hold the door for the person _____ _____.

10 7. _____ your neighbors _____ your party.

11 If you just do one thing each day, you can _____ your town _____.

12 Messages for _____

13 On World Peace Day, we _____ our peace messages _____ the board.

14 Peace means _____ _____ around the world. - Kim Jimin

15 _____ _____ have peace on Earth than pieces of Earth. - Seo Eunji

16 I want peace every place I go because there is always someone _____ or _____. - Park Hansol

17 Peace makes everyone _____.- Yang Miran

18 Peace is _____ all of us. We just need to share it. - Jang Jaehee

19 LET'S _____

20 An apple _____ _____

1	십대들의 잡지
2	마을을 더 좋게 만드는 방법들
3	이웃들을 위해 뭔가 좋은 일을 하면 여러분의 마을을 변화시킬 수 있다. 작은 것부터 시작하라. 여기 몇 가지 도움말이 있다.
4	1. 이웃들에게 인사를 하고 미소를 지어라.
5	2. 잊지 말고 "고맙습니다."라고 말해라.
6	3. 비 오는 날에 당신의 우산을 함께 써라.
7	4. 이웃이 농담하면 크게 소리 내어 웃어라.
8	5. 이웃들을 위해 뭔가를 만들어라.
9	6. 뒤에 오는 사람을 위해 문을 잡아 줘라.
10	7. 이웃을 당신의 파티에 초대해라.
11	만약 당신이 매일 한 가지씩 하기만 하면, 당신의 마을을 더 좋게 만들 수 있다.
12	평화 메시지
13	우리는 세계 평화의 날에 게시판에 평화 메시지를 붙였다.
14	평화는 세상 어디에서나 친구가 있다는 것을 의미한다. – 김지민
15	나는 지구의 조각들을 갖느니 지구 위의 평화를 갖겠다. – 서은지
16	항상 싸우거나 소리치는 누군가가 있으므로 나는 내가 가는 모든 곳에서 평화를 원한다. – 박한솔
17	평화는 모든 사람을 미소 짓게 만든다. – 양미란
18	평화는 우리 모두의 내면에 있다. 우리는 단지 그것을 공유할 필요가 있을 뿐이다. – 장재희
19	웃읍시다
20	하루에 사과 한 개

21 Jake came in to see his dad. "Dad!" he said, "Is it true that an apple a day _____ the doctor _____?"

22 "That's _____ _____ _____," said his dad.

23 "Well, give me an apple quickly! I _____ _____ the doctor's window!"

24 _____ _____ to Books!

25 Do you know _____ _____ _____? They hate water, the sun, and dog ears. _____ dog ears?

26 Water is bad for WITCHES and BOOKS! / The SUN also TURNs Books YELLOW / Don't DOG-EAR! Use a _____! / Be Kind to Books!

27 Stop _____ dog ears in books. Use a bookmark instead.

28 _____ _____ a bookmark _____ can save your books. Be kind to your books.

29 _____ _____ you love your books, _____ _____ your books will be. _____ _____ making your own?

30 _____ That Sound _____

31 1. About 7% of all people who _____ _____ _____ are living on the Earth today.

32 About 108,200 million people _____ _____ _____ _____ in the history of the world. And about 7,442 million are living on the Earth today.

33 2. Bangladesh has _____ people _____ Russia.

34 Russia is the world's _____ country, but tiny Bangladesh has 166.3 million people in 2018. Russia has 143.9 million people.

35 3. A banyan tree near Kolkata, India, is _____ _____ the average Walmart.

36 The average Walmart store _____ about 104,000 square feet. The Great Banyan Tree in Kolkata, India, is about _____ _____ _____ a forest, _____ 155,000 square feet.

37 4. Baby carrots _____ _____ in 1986.

38 Baby carrots are not actually baby carrots. Big ugly carrots _____ _____ _____ small _____ that have the shape of a baby carrot. Farmer Mike Yurosek invented them in 1986 as a way to use ugly carrots that weren't sold.

39 _____ in the Movies

40 Zootopia (2016) It's _____ _____ _____ ever!

21 Jake가 아빠를 보러 들어왔다. "아빠!" 그는 "하루에 사과 한 개가 의사를 멀리하게 만든다는 것이 사실이에요?"라고 말했다.

22 "사람들이 그렇게 말하지," 아빠가 말했다.

23 "자, 저에게 빨리 사과 한 개를 주세요! 제가 방금 의사 선생님의 유리창을 깨뜨렸어요!"

24 책들을 친절하게 대해 주세요!

25 여러분은 책들이 무엇을 싫어하는지 아나요? 그들은 물, 햇빛, 그리고 강아지 귀를 싫어합니다. 왜 강아지 귀일까요?

26 물은 마녀와 책에 해롭다! / 햇빛도 책을 누렇게 뜨게 한다. / 강아지 귀처럼 책을 접지 마라! 책갈피를 사용해라! / 책들을 친절하게 대해 주세요!

27 강아지 귀 모양으로 책을 접는 것을 멈춰 주세요. 대신에 책갈피를 이용하세요.

28 여러분의 책을 구해 주는 것은 바로 책갈피입니다. 여러분의 책들을 친절하게 대해 주세요.

29 여러분이 책을 더 많이 사랑하면 할수록 여러분의 책들은 더 행복해질 겁니다. 여러분 자신의 책갈피를 만들어 보는 게 어떨까요?

30 가짜 같은 사실

31 1 지금까지 살아온 모든 사람의 약 7%가 오늘날 지구상에 살고 있다.

32 세계 역사에서 약 1천8십2억 명의 사람들이 지금까지 태어났다. 그리고 약 7십4억 4천2백만 명이 오늘날 지구상에 살고 있다.

33 2 방글라데시는 러시아보다 인구가 더 많다.

34 러시아는 세계에서 가장 큰 나라이지만, 아주 작은 방글라데시에는 2018년 기준으로 1억 6천6백3십만 명의 인구가 있다. 러시아는 1억 4천3백9십만 명의 인구가 있다.

35 3 인도 Kolkata 부근의 한 바니안(banyan) 나무는 평균적인 월마트보다 크다.

36 평균적인 월마트 상점은 약 10만4천 평방피트의 넓이이다. 인도 Kolkata에 있는 그레이트 바니안 나무는 대략 숲 하나의 크기로 15만5천 평방피트를 차지한다.

37 4 베이비 당근은 1986년 발명되었다.

38 베이비 당근은 실제로 아기처럼 작은 당근이 아니다. 크고 못생긴 당근들이 베이비 당근 모양을 가진 작은 조각으로 잘린다. 농부 Mike Yurosek이 팔리지 않는 못생긴 당근을 사용할 하나의 방편으로 1986년에 그것을 발명하였다.

39 영화 속 직업들

40 주토피아(2016) 그것은 이제까지 가장 대단한 영화이다!

41 Flash is a public officer. He is very slow but works hard. You will be surprised to see _____ _____ _____ in his free time. It's driving a race car!

42 Nick is a fox _____ a big mouth. _____ _____, he gets closer to her. He later becomes a police officer like Judy.

43 Judy is a small rabbit, but she's smart and strong. After a lot of effort, she becomes a police officer and _____ _____ _____.

44 Ratatouille (2007) _____ will love this movie.

45 Anton Ego is a food critic. After he eats the food Remy cooked, he realizes that _____ can cook.

46 Remy, a little mouse, dreams of becoming a cook. He goes into a restaurant and meets a boy _____ Linguini. _____ Linguini, he makes delicious food and _____ _____ _____ a great cook.

47 Say It _____ Emojis

48 Do you know _____ _____ _____ _____ _____?

49 Killing two birds with one stone. / The apple of your eyes. / Don't play games with fire. / _____ _____ _____ blue moon. / Let's call it a day. / Money does not grow on trees. / It's raining cats and dogs. / _____ _____ _____ cake.

50 Emoji Song

51 Now, let's sing a Christmas song together! _____ _____, _____ _____!

52 _____ Messages

53 Imagine you can send messages to your friend that _____ _____ _____ _____ _____! It's not so difficult for you to learn how to read and write your own secret messages.

54 1. Read _____

55 This is _____ _____ _____. Just read the words _____! It seems simple once you know the secret, but it can be a hard one when you don't.

56 2. Read _____ Second Letter

57 Read every second letter _____ _____ the first letter, and when you finish, start again on the letters you missed.

58 3. Pig-pen

59 The Pig-pen is _____ _____ _____ _____. The lines around each letter mean the letter inside the lines.

60 Now create your own set of secret letters and write secret messages _____ _____ _____ your friends. _____ _____ you _____ _____ a key so your friends can understand your messages!

41 Flash는 공무원이다. 그는 아주 느리지만 열심히 일한다. 여러분은 그가 여가 시간에 무엇을 하는지 알게 되면 놀랄 것이다. 그것은 경주용 자동차를 운전하는 것이다!

42 Nick은 커다란 입을 가진 여우이다. Judy를 도우면서 그녀와 가까워진다. 나중에 Judy처럼 경찰관이 된다.

43 Judy는 작은 토끼지만, 영리하고 강하다. 많은 노력을 한 후에, 그녀는 경찰관이 되었고 많은 사건을 해결한다.

44 라따뚜이(2007) 누구라도 이 영화를 사랑할 것이다.

45 Anton Ego는 음식 비평가이다. Remy가 요리한 음식을 먹은 후에, 그는 "누구라도 요리할 수 있다."라는 것을 깨닫는다.

46 작은 쥐 Remy는 요리사가 되기를 꿈꾼다. 그는 식당에 들어가서 Linguini라는 이름의 소년을 만난다. Linguini를 통제하면서 그는 맛있는 음식을 만들고 결국에는 훌륭한 요리사가 된다.

47 이모지로 말하자

48 이 이모지들이 무엇을 의미하는지 아니?

49 돌 하나로 새 두 마리 잡기. (일석이조.) / 당신이 가장 사랑하는 사람. (눈에 넣어도 안 아플 사람.) / 불을 가지고 장난치지 마라. / 극히 드물게. / 오늘은 이만하자. / 돈이 나무에서 자라는 것은 아니다. (돈이 그냥 생기는 건 아니다.) / 비가 억수같이 온다. / 케이크 한 조각. (누워서 떡 먹기.)

50 이모지 노래

51 자, 함께 크리스마스 노래를 불러 봅시다! 더 크게 부를수록, 더 행복해집니다!

52 비밀 메시지

53 다른 어떤 사람도 읽을 수 없는 메시지를 친구에게 보낼 수 있다고 상상해 봐! 여러분 자신의 비밀 메시지를 읽고 쓰는 법을 배우는 것이 그렇게 어렵지는 않다.

54 1. 거꾸로 읽어라

55 이것은 풀기 쉽다 – 그냥 단어들을 거꾸로 읽어라! 일단 여러분이 비밀을 알면 간단하지만, 그렇지 못하면 어려울 수 있다.

56 2. 두 번째 글자마다 읽어라

57 첫 번째 글지에서 시작해서 두 번째 글자마다 읽어라. 그리고 끝나면 여러분이 빠뜨린 글자로 다시 시작하라.

58 3. 피그펜

59 피그펜(돼지우리)은 보기보다 쉽다. 각 글자 주변의 선들은 그 선들 안에 있는 글자를 의미한다.

60 이제 여러분은 자신만의 비밀 문자 세트를 만들어서 친구들에게 보낼 비밀 메시지를 써 보아라. 친구들이 메시지를 이해할 수 있도록 해결의 열쇠도 함께 보내도록 해라.

● 우리말을 참고하여 본문을 영작하시오.

1 십대들의 잡지
➡ _____

2 마을을 더 좋게 만드는 방법들
➡ _____

3 이웃들을 위해 뭔가 좋은 일을 하면 여러분의 마을을 변화시킬 수 있다. 작은 것부터 시작하라. 여기 몇 가지 도움말이 있다.
➡ _____

4 1. 이웃들에게 인사를 하고 미소를 지어라.
➡ _____

5 2. 잊지 말고 "고맙습니다."라고 말해라.
➡ _____

6 3. 비 오는 날에 당신의 우산을 함께 써라.
➡ _____

7 4. 이웃이 농담하면 크게 소리 내어 웃어라.
➡ _____

8 5. 이웃들을 위해 뭔가를 만들어라.
➡ _____

9 6. 뒤에 오는 사람을 위해 문을 잡아 줘라.
➡ _____

10 7. 이웃을 당신의 파티에 초대해라.
➡ _____

11 만약 당신이 매일 한 가지씩 하기만 하면, 당신의 마을을 더 좋게 만들 수 있다.
➡ _____

12 평화 메시지
➡ _____

13 우리는 세계 평화의 날에 게시판에 평화 메시지를 붙였다.
➡ _____

14 평화는 세상 어디에서나 친구가 있다는 것을 의미한다. – 김지민
➡ _____

15 나는 지구의 조각들을 갖느니 지구 위의 평화를 갖겠다. – 서은지
➡ _____

16 항상 싸우거나 소리치는 누군가가 있으므로 나는 내가 가는 모든 곳에서 평화를 원한다. – 박한솔
➡ _____

17 평화는 모든 사람을 미소 짓게 만든다. – 양미란
➡ _____

18 평화는 우리 모두의 내면에 있다. 우리는 단지 그것을 공유할 필요가 있을 뿐이다. – 장재희
➡ _____

19 웃읍시다
➡ _____

20 하루에 사과 한 개
➡ _____

21 Jake가 아빠를 보러 들어왔다. "아빠!" 그는 "하루에 사과 한 개가 의사를 멀리하게 만든다는 것이 사실이에요?"라고 말했다.

➡ _____

22 "사람들이 그렇게 말하지," 아빠가 말했다.

➡ _____

23 "자, 저에게 빨리 사과 한 개를 주세요! 제가 방금 의사 선생님의 유리창을 깨뜨렸어요!"

➡ _____

24 책들을 친절하게 대해 주세요!

➡ _____

25 여러분은 책들이 무엇을 싫어하는지 아나요? 그들은 물, 햇빛, 그리고 강아지 귀를 싫어합니다. 왜 강아지 귀일까요?

➡ _____

26 물은 마녀와 책에 해롭다! / 햇빛도 책을 누렇게 뜨게 한다. / 강아지 귀처럼 책을 접지 마라! 책갈피를 사용해라! / 책들을 친절하게 대해 주세요!

➡ _____

27 강아지 귀 모양으로 책을 접는 것을 멈춰 주세요. 대신에 책갈피를 이용하세요.

➡ _____

28 여러분의 책을 구해 주는 것은 바로 책갈피입니다. 여러분의 책들을 친절하게 대해 주세요.

➡ _____

29 여러분이 책을 더 많이 사랑하면 할수록 여러분의 책들은 더 행복해질 겁니다. 여러분 자신의 책갈피를 만들어 보는 게 어떨까요?

➡ _____

30 가짜 같은 사실

➡ _____

31 1. 지금까지 살아온 모든 사람의 약 7%가 오늘날 지구상에 살고 있다.

➡ _____

32 세계 역사에서 약 1천8십2억 명의 사람들이 지금까지 태어났다. 그리고 약 7십4억 4천2백만 명이 오늘날 지구상에 살고 있다.

➡ _____

33 2. 방글라데시는 러시아보다 인구가 더 많다.

➡ _____

34 러시아는 세계에서 가장 큰 나라이지만, 아주 작은 방글라데시에는 2018년 기준으로 1억 6천6백3십만 명의 인구가 있다. 러시아는 1억 4천3백9십만 명의 인구가 있다.

➡ _____

35 3. 인도 Kolkata 부근의 한 바니안(banyan) 나무는 평균적인 월마트보다 크다.

➡ _____

36 평균적인 월마트 상점은 약 10만4천 평방피트의 넓이이다. 인도 Kolkata에 있는 그레이트 바니안 나무는 대략 숲 하나의 크기로 15만5천 평방피트를 차지한다.

➡ _____

37 4. 베이비 당근은 1986년 발명되었다.

➡ _____

38 베이비 당근은 실제로 아기처럼 작은 당근이 아니다. 크고 못생긴 당근들이 베이비 당근 모양을 가진 작은 조각으로 잘린다. 농부 Mike Yurosek이 팔리지 않는 못생긴 당근을 사용할 하나의 방편으로 1986년에 그것을 발명하였다.

➡ _____

39 영화 속 직업들

➡ _____

40 주토피아(2016) 그것은 이제까지 가장 대단한 영화이다!

➡ _____

41 Flash는 공무원이다. 그는 아주 느리지만 열심히 일한다. 여러분은 그가 여가 시간에 무엇을 하는지 알게 되면 놀랄 것이다. 그것은 경주용 자동차를 운전하는 것이다!
➡ _____

42 Nick은 커다란 입을 가진 여우이다. Judy를 도우면서 그녀와 가까워진다. 나중에 Judy처럼 경찰관이 된다.
➡ _____

43 Judy는 작은 토끼지만, 영리하고 강하다. 많은 노력을 한 후에, 그녀는 경찰관이 되었고 많은 사건을 해결한다.
➡ _____

44 라따뚜이(2007) 누구라도 이 영화를 사랑할 것이다.
➡ _____

45 Anton Ego는 음식 비평가이다. Remy가 요리한 음식을 먹은 후에, 그는 "누구라도 요리할 수 있다."라는 것을 깨닫는다.
➡ _____

46 작은 쥐 Remy는 요리사가 되기를 꿈꾼다. 그는 식당에 들어가서 Linguini라는 이름의 소년을 만난다. Linguini를 통제하면서 그는 맛있는 음식을 만들고 결국에는 훌륭한 요리사가 된다.
➡ _____

47 이모지로 말하자
➡ _____

48 이 이모지들이 무엇을 의미하는지 아니?
➡ _____

49 돌 하나로 새 두 마리 잡기. (일석이조.) / 당신이 가장 사랑하는 사람. (눈에 넣어도 안 아플 사람.) / 불을 가지고 장난치지 마라. / 극히 드물게. / 오늘은 이만하자. / 돈이 나무에서 자라는 것은 아니다. (돈이 그냥 생기는 건 아니다.) / 비가 억수같이 온다. / 케이크 한 조각. (누워서 떡 먹기.)
➡ _____
_____

50 이모지 노래
➡ _____

51 자, 함께 크리스마스 노래를 불러 봅시다! 더 크게 부를수록, 더 행복해집니다!
_____

52 비밀 메시지
➡ _____

53 다른 어떤 사람도 읽을 수 없는 메시지를 친구에게 보낼 수 있다고 상상해 봐라! 여러분 자신의 비밀 메시지를 읽고 쓰는 법을 배우는 것이 그렇게 어렵지는 않다.
➡ _____

54 1. 거꾸로 읽어라
➡ _____

55 이것은 풀기 쉽다 – 그냥 단어들을 거꾸로 읽어라! 일단 여러분이 비밀을 알면 간단하지만, 그렇지 못하면 어려울 수 있다.
➡ _____
_____

56 2. 두 번째 글자마다 읽어라
➡ _____

57 첫 번째 글자에서 시작해서 두 번째 글자마다 읽어라. 그리고 끝나면 여러분이 빠뜨린 글자로 다시 시작하라.
➡ _____

58 3. 피그펜
➡ _____

59 피그펜(돼지우리)은 보기보다 쉽다. 각 글자 주변의 선들은 그 선들 안에 있는 글자를 의미한다.

60 이제 여러분은 자신만의 비밀 문자 세트를 만들어서 친구들에게 보낼 비밀 메시지를 써 보아라. 친구들이 메시지를 이해할 수 있도록 해결의 열쇠도 함께 보내도록 해라.
➡ _____
_____

01 다음 문장에 공통으로 들어갈 말을 쓰시오.

> (1) In some _____s people had to wait several weeks for an appointment.
> (2) The police have decided to reopen the _____.

02 다음 빈칸에 들어갈 말을 〈보기〉에서 찾아 쓰시오. (필요하면 변형하거나 단어를 추가하여 쓰시오.)

> ┤ 보기 ├
> end   better   keep   sure

(1) You _____ _____ do the dishes before you go out.

(2) An apple a day _____ the doctor _____.

(3) Schools should focus on _____ _____ that students are learning.

03 우리말과 같은 뜻이 되도록 주어진 단어를 활용하여 빈칸을 채우시오.

(1) 당신은 결국 주변 사람들과 논쟁하거나 싸우게 된다.
➡ You _____ _____ _____ or fighting with people around you. (argue)

(2) 딸꾹질을 할 때 설탕을 한 숟가락 먹으면 멈추게 할 수 있습니다.
➡ You can usually _____ _____ by eating a spoonful of sugar. (hiccup)

(3) 여기엔 비가 억수같이 쏟아졌어.
➡ It _____ _____ _____ _____ here. (cat, dog)

04 다음 문장을 간접화법으로 바꾸어 쓰시오.

(1) Jake said, "I just broke the doctor's window!"
➡ Jake _____
_____.

(2) Jake said to his dad, "Give me an apple quickly"
➡ Jake _____
_____.

05 다음 첫 번째 문장의 it 대신 두 번째 문장의 의문문을 넣어 문장을 다시 쓰시오.

> • You will be surprised to see it.
> • What does he do in his free time?

➡ _____
_____

06 주어진 문장에서 어법상 틀린 곳을 찾아 고치고 이유를 쓰시오.

> Big ugly carrots cut into small pieces that has the shape of a baby carrot.

(1) _____ ➡ _____
➡ 이유: _____
_____

(2) _____ ➡ _____
➡ 이유: _____
_____

[07~09] 다음 글을 읽고 물음에 답하시오.

Be Kind to Books!

Do you know what books hate? They hate water, the sun, and dog ears. ⓐWhy dog ears?

Water is bad for WITCHES and BOOKS! / The SUN also TURNs Books YELLOW / Don't DOG-EAR! Use a bookmark! / Be Kind to Books!

ⓑStop to fold dog ears in books. Use a bookmark instead. It is a bookmark that can save your books. Be kind to your books. ⓒ The more you love your books, the happier your books will be. How about making your own?

07 위 글의 밑줄 친 문장 ⓐ에 생략된 말을 넣어 문장을 다시 쓰시오.

➡ _____

08 위 글의 밑줄 친 ⓑ에서 어법상 틀린 부분을 찾아 고치시오.

_____ ➡ _____

09 위 글의 밑줄 친 ⓒ를 접속사 As를 사용하여 고칠 때, 빈칸에 들어갈 알맞은 말을 쓰시오.

As you love your books _____, your books will be _____.

[10~12] 다음 글을 읽고 물음에 답하시오.

Secret Messages

• ⓐ**YEOAUTLTOOODKAGYR**

Read ⓑ매 두 번째 글자 starting with the first letter, and when you finish, start again on the letters you missed.

• Pig-pen

ⓒ
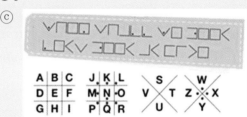

The Pig-pen is easier than it looks. The lines around each letter mean the letter inside the lines.

10 위 글의 밑줄 친 비밀 메시지 ⓐ의 내용을 영어로 쓰시오.

➡ _____

11 위 글의 밑줄 친 ⓑ의 우리말에 맞게 3 단어로 영작하시오.

➡ _____

12 위 글의 비밀 메시지 ⓒ의 내용을 영어로 쓰시오.

➡ _____

01 다음 단어에 대한 영어 설명이 <u>어색한</u> 것은?

① effort: an attempt to do something

② forest: a large area of trees growing close together

③ playwriter: someone whose job is to give their opinion of a book, play, movie, etc.

④ delicious: very good to eat or drink

⑤ wave: to put your hand up and move it from side to side in order to attract someone's attention or to say goodbye

02 다음 짝지어진 단어의 관계가 같도록 빈칸에 알맞은 말을 쓰시오.

> save : rescue – yell : _____

03 다음 영영풀이에 해당하는 단어를 고르시오.

> to ask someone to come to your house, to a party, etc.

① invite
② stop by
③ cook
④ visit
⑤ worry

04 다음 문장의 빈칸에 공통으로 들어갈 단어를 쓰시오.

> • Today I _____d the importance of energy for the first time.
> • He recently _____d his dream.

➡ _____

05 다음 주어진 문장과 같은 의미를 가진 문장을 쓰시오. (would를 사용할 것.)

> • I prefer staying home to going there.
> • I prefer to stay home rather than to go there.

➡ _____

06 다음 빈칸에 들어갈 말이 알맞게 짝지어진 것은?

> • Many actors dream _____ performing at Broadway theaters in New York.
> • I can chat more with my friends and get closer _____ them.
> • So, who knows? You may end _____ becoming a wonderful chef!

① on – with – down
② into – of – up
③ by – of – up
④ of – to – up
⑤ by – of – down

07 다음 중 짝지어진 단어의 관계가 <u>다른</u> 것은?

① quickly : slowly
② hate : like
③ backward : forward
④ tiny : huge
⑤ imagine : visualize

출제율 100%

08 다음 영영풀이에 해당하는 단어를 〈보기〉에서 찾아 첫 번째 빈칸에 쓰고, 두 번째 빈칸에는 우리말 뜻을 쓰시오.

┌─── 보기 ───┐
share   fold   instead   realize
└─────────────────────────────┘

(1) _____ : in the place of someone or something else: _____

(2) _____ : to have or use something at the same time as someone else: _____

(3) _____ : to bend something so that one part of it lies flat on top of another part: _____

(4) _____ : to notice or understand something that you did not notice or understand before: _____

출제율 90%

09 다음 밑줄 친 that의 쓰임이 다른 하나를 고르시오.

① It is a bookmark that can save your books.
② It was last Sunday that I visited my uncle's house.
③ It is my dog that makes me happy.
④ It was in front of the Eiffel Tower that I took this selfie.
⑤ It was so hot and humid that we couldn't walk anymore.

출제율 90%

10 다음 우리말에 맞게 주어진 어휘를 배열하시오.

(1) 너의 책을 네가 더 많이 사랑할수록, 너의 책은 더 행복해질 것이다.
(your / the / books / be / love / you / books / happier / more / the / your / will)

➡ _____

_____

(2) 너는 더 많이 운동할수록, 더 열심히 공부할 수 있다.
(out / you / can / the / you / study / harder / work / the / more)

➡ _____

_____

(3) 날씨가 더워질수록, 우리의 바지가 더 짧아진다.
(shorter / the / it / our / the / gets / hotter / pants / get)

➡ _____

_____

출제율 95%

11 다음 두 문장을 한 문장으로 바르게 옮긴 것은?

• Do you know?
• What do books hate?

① Do you know what do books hate?
② Do you know what books hate?
③ Do you know what books do hate?
④ What do you know books hate?
⑤ What books do you know hate?

출제율 95%

12 다음 문장의 틀린 곳을 바르게 고치지 않은 것은?

It's not so ①difficultly ②of you to ③ learning how ④read and write ⑤yours own secret messages.

① difficultly → difficult
② of → for
③ learning → learn
④ read → reading
⑤ yours → your

13 다음 우리말을 영어로 바르게 옮긴 것을 <u>모두</u> 고르시오.

> 우리가 더 크게 노래할수록, 우리는 더 행복해 진다.

① The loud we sing, the happy we become.
② The more loud we sing, the more happy we become.
③ The louder we sing, the happier we become.
④ As we sing more loudly, we become more happily.
⑤ As we sing louder, we become happier.

14 다음 밑줄 친 <u>it</u>의 쓰임이 나머지 넷과 <u>다른</u> 하나를 고르시오.

① Is <u>it</u> okay to go out without anything to eat?
② <u>It</u> is a bad idea to go there alone.
③ <u>It</u> must be dark in the cave.
④ Is <u>it</u> true that an apple a day keeps the doctor away?
⑤ <u>It</u> is impossible for me to hate cats.

15 다음 중 의미가 <u>다른</u> 하나를 고르시오.

① Make sure to send along a key.
② Make sure you send along a key.
③ Be sure you send along a key.
④ Don't forget to send along a key.
⑤ Remember sending along a key.

[16~18] 다음 글을 읽고 물음에 답하시오.

Jobs in the Movies
Ratatouille (2007) Everyone will love this movie.
Anton Ego is a food critic. After he eats the food Remy cooked, he realizes that anyone can cook.
Remy, a little mouse, dreams of becoming a cook. He goes into a restaurant and meets a boy named Linguini. Controlling Linguini, (A) <u>he</u> makes delicious food and ends up ____ⓐ____ a great cook.

16 위 글의 빈칸 ⓐ에 become을 알맞은 형태로 쓰시오.

➡ _____

17 주어진 영영풀이에 해당하는 단어를 본문에서 찾아 쓰시오.

> a person who writes about and expresses opinions about things such as books, films, music, or art

➡ _____

18 위 글의 밑줄 친 (A)he가 가리키는 것을 본문에서 찾아 쓰시오.

➡ _____

[19~21] 다음 글을 읽고 물음에 답하시오.

Ways to Make Your Town Better
Doing something nice for your neighbors can change your town. Start small. Here are some tips.
1. Say hello to your neighbors and smile.
2. (A)Don't forget saying, "Thank you."
3. Share your umbrella on a rainy day.

4. Laugh out loud when your neighbor tells a joke.

5. Make something for your neighbors.

6. Hold the door ___ⓐ___ the person behind you.

7. Invite your neighbors ___ⓑ___ your party.

If you just do one thing each day, you can make your town better.

19 위 글의 빈칸 ⓐ와 ⓑ에 들어갈 전치사가 바르게 짝지어진 것은?

	ⓐ ⓑ		ⓐ ⓑ
①	for – in	②	by – at
③	to – at	④	for – to
⑤	by – to		

20 위 글의 밑줄 친 (A)에서 어법상 틀린 부분을 찾아 고치시오.

➡ _____

21 위 글을 읽고 다음 중 마을을 더 좋게 만드는 방법에 해당하지 않는 것을 고르시오.

① 큰 실천 사항부터 시작하라.
② 이웃들에게 인사를 하고 미소를 지어라.
③ 비 오는 날에 당신의 우산을 함께 써라.
④ 이웃이 농담하면 크게 소리 내어 웃어라.
⑤ 이웃들을 위해 뭔가를 만들어라.

[22~24] 다음 글을 읽고 물음에 답하시오.

Be Kind to Books!

Do you know what books hate? They hate water, the sun, and dog ears. Why dog ears?

Water is bad for WITCHES and BOOKS! / The SUN also TURNs Books YELLOW / Don't DOG-EAR! Use a bookmark! / Be Kind to Books!

Stop folding dog ears in books. Use a bookmark instead. ⓐ여러분의 책을 구해 주는 것은 바로 책갈피입니다. Be kind to your books. The more you love your books, the happier your books will be. ⓑHow about making your own?

22 위 글의 밑줄 친 ⓐ의 우리말에 맞게 주어진 어휘를 이용하여 9 단어로 영작하시오.

> it, that, save

➡ _____

23 위 글의 밑줄 친 ⓑ와 바꿔 쓸 수 있는 말을 **모두** 고르시오.

① Why don't you make your own?
② How do you like your own?
③ What about making your own?
④ Why don't we make your own?
⑤ Why not make your own?

24 According to the passage, which is NOT true?

① The things which books hate are water, the sun, and dog ears.
② You should use dog ears instead of a bookmark.
③ A bookmark can save your books.
④ You should be kind to your books.
⑤ As you love your books more, your books will be happier.

[25~27] 다음 글을 읽고 물음에 답하시오.

Secret Messages

ⓐ다른 어떤 사람도 읽을 수 없는 메시지를 친구에게 보낼 수 있다고 상상해 봐라! It's not so difficult for you to learn how to read and write your own secret messages.

1. Read Backward

ⓑ

COME TO MY HOUSE AT TEN

This is easy ©to solve. Just read the words backward! It seems simple once you know the secret, but it can be a hard one when you don't.

25 위 글의 밑줄 친 ⓐ의 우리말에 맞게 주어진 어휘를 알맞게 배열하시오.

> your friend / else / messages / imagine / to / can / you / read / that / send / can / no one

➡ _____

_____

_____

26 위 글의 비밀 메시지 ⓑ의 내용을 영어로 쓰시오.

➡ _____

27 아래 〈보기〉에서 위 글의 밑줄 친 ©to solve와 to부정사의 용법이 같은 것의 개수를 고르시오.

> ┤ 보기 ├
> ① I need a pencil to write with.
> ② She stood up to go out.
> ③ It is very important to study English hard.
> ④ His job is to sing a song.
> ⑤ This water is not good to drink.

① 1개　② 2개　③ 3개　④ 4개　⑤ 5개

[28~30] 다음 글을 읽고 물음에 답하시오.

> **Jobs in the Movies**
>
> **Zootopia (2016)** It's the greatest movie ever!
> Flash is a public officer. He is very slow but works hard. You will be surprised to see what he does in his free time. ⓐIt's ⓑdriving a race car!
> Nick is a fox with a big mouth. ©Helping Judy, he gets closer to her. He later becomes a police officer like Judy.
> Judy is a small rabbit, but she's smart and strong. After a lot of effort, she becomes a police officer and solves many cases.

28 위 글의 밑줄 친 ⓐIt이 가리키는 것을 본문에서 찾아 쓰시오.

➡ _____

29 위 글의 밑줄 친 ⓑdriving과 문법적 쓰임이 같은 것을 모두 고르시오.

① He is good at playing tennis.
② Seeing is believing.
③ Do you know that boy playing the piano?
④ His job is selling cars.
⑤ She is writing a letter.

30 위 글의 밑줄 친 ©를 다음과 같이 고칠 때, 빈칸에 들어갈 알맞은 접속사를 모두 고르시오.

> _____ he helps Judy, he gets closer to her.

① Though　　② As
③ If　　　　④ Until
⑤ While

MEMO

INSIGHT
on the textbook

교과서 파헤치기

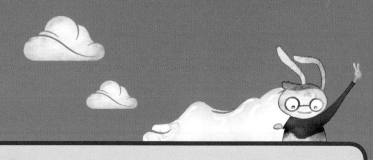

※ 다음 영어를 우리말로 쓰시오.

01 provide _____

02 recently _____

03 healthy _____

04 search _____

05 evidence _____

06 false _____

07 source _____

08 actually _____

09 artwork _____

10 support _____

11 seem _____

12 totally _____

13 sink _____

14 critically _____

15 funny _____

16 light _____

17 major _____

18 octopus _____

19 touching _____

20 site _____

21 attack _____

22 clown _____

23 offer _____

24 unique _____

25 comfortable _____

26 untrue _____

27 cleaner _____

28 perfect _____

29 performance _____

30 spread _____

31 unclear _____

32 complete _____

33 snake _____

34 prefer _____

35 turn out _____

36 give up _____

37 tell A from B _____

38 make sense _____

39 be based on _____

40 pass away _____

41 pay attention to _____

42 made up _____

43 laugh out loud _____

※ 다음 우리말을 영어로 쓰시오.

01 구하다

02 완벽한

03 가라앉다

04 선호하다

05 세제, 청소기

06 비판적으로

07 공격하다

08 최근에

09 거짓의, 잘못된

10 공연, 수행

11 편안한

12 실제로, 사실

13 전적으로

14 근원, 출처

15 증거

16 지지하다, 후원하다

17 완전한

18 제공하다

19 무서운

20 장소

21 광대

22 퍼진; 퍼지다

23 건강한

24 환호하다

25 사실이 아닌

26 가벼운

27 주요한, 주된

28 감동적인

29 문어

30 예술 작품

31 독특한

32 착용하다

33 지루한

34 찾다, 검색하다

35 포기하다

36 돌아가시다

37 ~에 바탕을 두다

38 의미가 통하다

39 큰 소리로 웃다

40 ~로부터 만들어지다

41 판명되다

42 ~에 주의를 기울이다

43 A와 B를 구별하다

※ 다음 영영풀이에 알맞은 단어를 <보기>에서 골라 쓴 후, 우리말 뜻을 쓰시오.

1 _____ : completely, absolutely: _____

2 _____ : an untrue statement: _____

3 _____ : having a strong emotional effect: _____

4 _____ : very important and serious: _____

5 _____ : incorrect, untrue, or mistaken: _____

6 _____ : to shout with joy, approval, or enthusiasm: _____

7 _____ : what you think or believe about something: _____

8 _____ : to supply something that is wanted or needed: _____

9 _____ : in a way that expresses disapproval: _____

10 _____ : to disappear below the surface of the water: _____

11 _____ : a soft sea creature with eight long arms: _____

12 _____ : anything that causes you to believe that something is true: _____

13 _____ : to open it out or arrange it over a place or surface: _____

14 _____ : to try to hurt or damage someone or something using physical violence:
_____

15 _____ : to give assistance, approval, comfort, or encouragement to someone:
_____

16 _____ : a performer in a circus who wears funny clothes and bright make-up,
and does silly things in order to make people laugh: _____

보기			
sink	cheer	attack	octopus
clown	touching	opinion	support
critically	false	totally	evidence
provide	lie	major	spread

※ 다음 우리말과 일치하도록 빈칸에 알맞은 말을 쓰시오.

해석

Get Ready 2

(1) **G:** There's no monkey _____ this in the world. Its nose is too
    big. _____ _____ it's _____.

   B: I don't _____. I saw that _____ of monkey on TV. It's
    _____.

(2) **G:** This animal has a long nose and two long, _____ _____.
    _____ _____ _____ it? Is it _____?

   B: Well, _____ _____ the Internet and _____ it together.

   G: That's a good idea.

(3) **B:** _____ do you _____ _____ this animal?

   G: It doesn't have legs, but it doesn't _____ _____ a snake.
    It's very _____.

   B: I think so, _____.

(4) **B:** _____ monkey is very small. Is it _____?

   G: I don't know. _____ visit some animal _____ _____
    and _____ it _____.

   B: That's a good idea.

Start Off - Listen & Talk A

1. **G:** Look at those shoes the girl is wearing. I think they're great.
    _____ _____ _____ _____ _____ them?

   B: I think they look _____ and _____.

   G: Right. I want _____ _____ them for the _____
    _____.

2. **G:** I like the coat the boy _____ _____. I think it's _____
    and _____.

   B: Well, I don't _____ _____ you. _____, I bought one last
    week. It's not so warm, and it's _____ _____ than it looks.

   G: Really? I don't _____ it.

Start Off - Listen & Talk B

G: _____ do you _____ about this drama?

B: I think it's very _____. The boy _____ _____ his life _____
    _____ his sister. It's _____ _____ _____ of this year.

G: I _____ _____. It's not a good drama.

B: Come on. _____ do you _____ _____ ?

G: It doesn't _____ _____. And it's _____ _____ _____.

Start Off - Speak Up

A: _____ do you feel _____ this _____?
B: I think it's great. It _____ the phone is strong.
A: I don't agree. We _____ _____ _____ every ad.

Step Up - Real-life Scene

Alex: Big Mouth's show is really _____. _____ _____ _____ _____ _____ it?
Somi: Well, I don't think it's _____ great.
Alex: Come on. I love Mr. Big Mouth. He always _____ me _____ _____ _____.
Somi: He's funny, but don't believe _____ he _____.
Alex: All right. Oh, look at his photo of an _____. He said it lives in a tree.
Somi: It doesn't _____ _____.
Alex: He took the photo _____ it was _____ the tree. I don't think he's _____. It's a great photo.
Somi: I don't _____ _____ you. It's a _____ photo. An octopus can't live _____ _____ the sea.

Express Yourself A

1. G: _____ do you _____ _____ these animals?
   B: They are very cute, but I think cats don't _____ _____ well _____ dogs.
   G: I don't agree. And _____ _____ are good friends. They are _____ the trip _____.
2. G: _____ do you _____ about this kid here?
   B: I think she is very pretty. _____ _____ _____, why did she cut her hair?
   G: Can you _____?
   B: Well, girls these days _____ short hair.
   G: I don't agree _____ that. Most girls like long hair _____ _____ short hair. And this kid here is not a girl. _____ _____, he is a boy.
   B: Really?
   G: Yes. He grew his hair _____ _____ sick children.
3. G: How do you _____ _____ the teddy bears?
   B: They are cute. Is there _____ _____ about them?
   G: They _____ _____ _____ of a police officer's _____.
   B: Oh, I see.
   G: This police officer made them for the kids. Their dad was a police officer, and he _____ _____ _____.
   B: That's very _____.

※ 다음 우리말에 맞도록 대화를 영어로 쓰시오.

Get Ready 2

(1) G: _____
_____

  B: _____

(2) G: _____
_____

  B: _____

  G: _____

(3) B: _____

  G: _____

  B: _____

(4) B: _____

  G: _____

  B: _____

(1) G: 세상에 이런 원숭이는 없어. 코가 너무 크잖아. 나는 그것이 가짜라고 생각해.
   B: 나는 동의하지 않아. 저런 종류의 원숭이를 TV에서 본 적이 있어. 그건 진짜야.
(2) G: 이 동물은 긴 코와 두 개의 길고 날카로운 이빨을 가지고 있어. 그것을 어떻게 생각해? 진짜일까?
   B: 음, 인터넷을 찾아보고 함께 확인해 보자.
   G: 좋은 생각이야.
(3) B: 이 동물을 어떻게 생각해?
   G: 그것은 다리가 없지만 뱀처럼 보이지는 않아. 정말 이상하네.
   B: 나도 그렇게 생각해.
(4) B: 이 원숭이는 정말 작다. 진짜일까?
   G: 모르겠어. 동물 사실 확인 사이트를 방문해서 함께 확인해 보자.
   B: 좋은 생각이야.

Start Off - Listen & Talk A

1. G: _____
_____

  B: _____

  G: _____

2. G: _____

  B: _____
_____

  G: _____

1. G: 저 여자애가 신고 있는 신발 좀 봐. 멋있는 것 같아. 너는 저 신발을 어떻게 생각해?
   B: 가볍고 편안해 보여.
   G: 맞아. 난 학교 체험 학습 때 신으려고 저걸 사고 싶어.
2. G: 저 남자애가 입고 있는 코트가 마음에 들어. 따뜻하고 가벼울 것 같아.
   B: 글쎄, 나는 동의하지 않아. 사실 나는 지난주에 저것을 샀어. 그렇게 따뜻하지도 않고 보기보다 훨씬 더 무거워.
   G: 정말로? 믿을 수가 없어.

Start Off - Listen & Talk B

G: _____

B: _____
_____

G: _____

B: _____

G: _____

G: 이 드라마를 어떻게 생각하니?
B: 난 아주 감동적이라고 생각해. 소년이 그의 여동생을 구하기 위해 자신의 생명을 포기했잖아. 올해 최고의 드라마야.
G: 난 동의하지 않아. 그건 좋은 드라마가 아니야.
B: 이런. 왜 그렇게 생각해?
G: 현실적으로 보이지 않아. 그리고 약간 지루해.

Start Off - Speak Up

A: _____

B: _____

A: _____

Step Up - Real-life Scene

Alex: _____

Somi: _____

Alex: _____

Somi: _____

Alex: _____

Somi: _____

Alex: _____

_____

Somi: _____

_____

Express Yourself A

1. G: _____

B: _____

G: _____

_____

2. G: _____

B: _____

G: _____

B: _____

G: _____

B: _____

G: _____

3. G: _____

B: _____

G: _____

B: _____

G: _____

B: _____

A: 이 광고를 어떻게 생각하니?
B: 굉장하다고 생각해. 그건 그 전화기가 튼튼하다는 것을 보여주고 있어.
A: 나는 동의하지 않아. 우리는 모든 광고를 믿어서는 안 돼.

Alex: Big Mouth 쇼는 정말 굉장해. 너는 어떻게 생각하니?
소미: 글쎄, 나는 그렇게 대단한 것 같지 않아.
Alex: 왜 그래. 나는 Big Mouth 씨를 진짜 좋아해. 그는 언제나 나를 큰 소리로 웃게 해 줘.
소미: 웃기긴 하지만, 그가 하는 모든 말을 믿지는 마.
Alex: 알았어. 오, 그가 찍은 문어 사진을 봐. 그가 말하기를 그건 나무에 산대.
소미: 말도 안 돼.
Alex: 그는 문어가 나무에 기어 올라갈 때 사진을 찍었대. 그가 거짓말하고 있는 것 같지는 않아. 대단한 사진이야.
소미: 나는 네 말에 동의하지 않아. 그건 가짜 사진이야. 문어는 바다 밖에서는 살 수 없다고.

1. G: 이 동물들을 어떻게 생각해?
   B: 아주 귀엽지만, 고양이는 개와 잘 어울리지 못한다고 생각해.
   G: 나는 동의하지 않아. 그리고 이 둘은 좋은 친구야. 그들은 함께 즐겁게 여행하고 있어.
2. G: 여기 이 아이를 어떻게 생각해?
   B: 매우 예쁘다고 생각해. 그런데 그녀는 왜 머리카락을 잘랐니?
   G: 짐작할 수 있어?
   B: 음, 요새 여자아이들은 짧은 머리를 더 좋아하더라.
   G: 난 그것에 동의하지 않아. 대부분의 여자아이는 짧은 머리보다 긴 머리를 좋아해. 그리고 여기 이 아이는 여자아이가 아니야. 사실, 이 아이는 남자아이야.
   B: 정말이니?
   G: 응. 그는 아픈 아이들을 돕기 위해 머리를 길렀어.
3. G: 곰 인형들을 어떻게 생각해?
   B: 귀여워. 뭔가 특별한 점이 있니?
   G: 그것들은 한 경찰관의 제복으로 만들어졌어.
   B: 아, 그렇구나.
   G: 이 경찰이 아이들을 위해 그것들을 만들어 줬어. 그들의 아빠는 경찰관이었고, 최근에 세상을 떠나셨어.
   B: 아주 감동적이야.

※ 다음 우리말과 일치하도록 빈칸에 알맞은 것을 골라 쓰시오.

1 How to Be a _____ _____ _____
    A. News   B. Smart   C. Reader

2 In October 2016, stories about _____ clowns _____ schools _____ the Washington area, but Danina Garcia-Fuller's students didn't believe them a _____.
    A. shook   B. bit   C. scary   D. across

3 "Some people were _____ _____ because they saw _____ on social media," said Patricia Visoso, _____ of Garcia-Fuller's students.
    A. scared   B. one   C. things   D. getting

4 "But they never _____ _____ _____ who was _____ this."
    A. saying   B. checked   C. on   D. up

5 The stories were _____ _____ _____ teenagers, not by major newspapers or TV _____.
    A. by   B. made   C. stations   D. actually

6 They offered no _____ _____ that clowns really were _____ to _____ students.
    A. attack   B. hard   C. trying   D. evidence

7 The story _____ _____ to be a _____ _____.
    A. out   B. turned   C. lie   D. complete

8 "I think a _____ of people just look _____ one _____ and believe it's _____," Patricia's classmate Ivy-Brooks said.
    A. true   B. thing   C. at   D. lot

9 "It's really important to look at the _____ and to pay attention to what is _____ and what is _____."
    A. sources   B. real   C. right   D. fake

10 _____ Garcia-Fuller's students, many _____ in America are learning to _____ _____ about information they're seeing in the news and on the Internet.
    A. critically   B. like   C. teenagers   D. think

11 This skill is _____ more important these days as stories can _____ very fast, and anyone can make a website _____ of _____ information.
    A. spread   B. false   C. getting   D. full

1 현명한 뉴스 독자가 되는 방법

2 2016년 10월, 무서운 광대들에 관한 이야기가 워싱턴 지역 전역의 학교에 충격을 안겼지만, Danina Garcia-Fuller의 학생들은 조금도 그 이야기들을 믿지 않았다.

3 "몇몇 사람들은 그들이 소셜 미디어에 올라온 것들을 봤기 때문에 무서워했어요."라고 Garcia-Fuller의 학생 중 한 명인 Patricia Visoso가 말했다.

4 "하지만 그들은 이것을 누가 말하고 있는지를 전혀 확인하지 않았어요."

5 그 이야기들은 실제로 주요 신문사나 TV 방송국이 아닌 10대들이 지어냈다.

6 그들은 광대들이 정말로 학생들을 공격하려고 한다는 명백한 증거를 하나도 제공하지 않았다.

7 그 이야기는 결국 완벽한 거짓말인 것으로 드러났다.

8 "많은 사람이 단지 한 가지만을 보고 그것이 사실이라고 믿는 것 같아요."라고 Patricia의 반 친구인 Ivy-Brooks가 말했다.

9 올바른 출처를 살펴보고, 무엇이 진짜이고 무엇이 가짜인지에 주의를 기울이는 것은 정말 중요해요."

10 Garcia-Fuller의 학생들처럼, 많은 미국의 10대들은 뉴스 속 그리고 인터넷상에서 보고 있는 정보에 관해 비판적으로 생각하는 것을 배워 나가고 있다.

11 이 기능은 최근 더 중요해지고 있는데, 이야기들은 아주 빠른 속도로 퍼져 나갈 수 있고 누구나 허위 정보로 가득 찬 웹사이트를 만들어 낼 수 있기 때문이다.

12 Garcia-Fuller said she was teaching her students _____ _____ _____ fake news _____ real news.

    A. tell   B. how   C. from   D. to

13 "_____ of the first _____ is to _____ _____.

    A. steps   B. down   C. one   D. slow

14 If a story or a photo seems _____ good _____ be _____, stop and _____.

    A. to   B. think   C. too   D. true

15 Is there any _____ that _____ _____ the writer _____?

    A. supports   B. evidence   C. what   D. says

16 And _____ is this _____ _____?"

    A. coming   B. where   C. from

17 Garcia-Fuller's students also learn how to _____ _____ _____ _____ in the news.

    A. fact   B. from   C. opinion   D. tell

18 "Opinions are good to read," said 15-year-old McKenzie Campbell, "but you also have to _____ if they are _____ _____ _____."

    A. based   B. facts   C. check   D. on

19 Garcia-Fuller also said sometimes it can be very _____ to be a _____ _____ _____.

    A. hard   B. reader   C. smart   D. news

20 She tests her students with a website that _____ to _____ information on an animal _____ a tree _____.

    A. called   B. appears   C. octopus   D. provide

21 The _____ is _____ of information on this animal, _____ with a few _____ photos of octopuses in trees.

    A. unclear   B. full   C. along   D. site

22 But like the story of _____ _____, it's totally _____.

    A. made   B. scary   C. up   D. clowns

23 The lesson, Garcia-Fuller tells her students, is to "check the information you're seeing _____ more _____" and to "question _____, _____ things that I say."

    A. carefully   B. even   C. everything   D. once

12 Garcia-Fuller는 그녀가 자신의 학생들에게 가짜 뉴스를 진짜 뉴스로부터 구분하는 방법을 가르치고 있다고 말했다.

13 "첫 단계 중 하나는 속도를 늦추는 것(천천히 생각하는 것)입니다.

14 만약 어떤 이야기나 어떤 사진이 진짜라고 하기엔 너무 좋아 보인다면, 멈춰서 생각해 보세요.

15 글쓴이가 말하고 있는 것을 뒷받침하는 어떠한 증거라도 있나요?

16 그리고 이 정보가 어디서 온 것인가요?"

17 Garcia-Fuller의 학생들은 또한 뉴스에서 사실을 의견과 구분하는 방법에 대해서도 배운다.

18 "의견들은 읽을 만한 가치가 있습니다."라고 15살인 McKenzie Campbell이 말했다. "하지만 여러분은 그것들이 사실에 기반을 둔 것인지를 확인해 보아야 합니다."

19 Garcia-Fuller는 또한 때때로 현명한 뉴스 독자가 되는 것이 아주 어려울 수도 있다고 말했다.

20 그녀는 자신의 학생들을 '나무 문어'라는 이름의 동물에 대한 정보를 제공하는 것처럼 보이는 웹사이트로 시험한다.

21 그 사이트는 나무 위에 있는 문어들의 몇몇 불확실한 사진과 함께, 이 동물에 대한 정보로 가득 차 있다.

22 하지만 무서운 광대들의 이야기와 마찬가지로, 그것은 완전히 꾸며진 것이다.

23 Garcia-Fuller가 그녀의 학생들에게 말하는 교훈은 '당신이 보고 있는 정보를 한 번만 더 신중하게 확인해 보라'는 것과 '모든 것, 심지어 내가 말하는 것에도 의문을 가져 보라'는 것이다.

※ 다음 우리말과 일치하도록 빈칸에 알맞은 것을 골라 쓰시오.

1 _____ _____ Be a _____ _____ _____

2 In October 2016, stories about scary clowns _____ _____ _____ the Washington area, but Danina Garcia-Fuller's students _____ _____ them _____ _____ .

3 "Some people were _____ _____ because they saw things on social media," said Patricia Visoso, _____ _____ Garcia-Fuller's students.

4 "But they never _____ _____ _____ who _____ _____ this."

5 The stories _____ _____ _____ _____ teenagers, not by _____ _____ or TV stations.

6 They offered _____ _____ _____ that clowns really were _____ _____ _____ students.

7 The story _____ _____ _____ _____ a _____ _____ .

8 "I think a lot of people _____ _____ _____ _____ and believe it's true," Patricia's classmate Ivy-Brooks said.

9 "It's really important _____ _____ _____ _____ _____ and to _____ _____ _____ _____ _____ and _____ _____ _____ ."

10 _____ Garcia-Fuller's students, many teenagers in America are learning _____ _____ _____ about information they're seeing in the news and _____ _____ _____ .

11 This skill is _____ _____ _____ these days as stories can _____ very fast, and anyone can make a website _____ _____ _____ _____ .

1 현명한 뉴스 독자가 되는 방법

2 2016년 10월, 무서운 광대들에 관한 이야기가 워싱턴 지역 전역의 학교에 충격을 안겼지만, Danina Garcia-Fuller의 학생들은 조금도 그 이야기들을 믿지 않았다.

3 "몇몇 사람들은 그들이 소셜 미디어에 올라온 것들을 봤기 때문에 무서워했어요."라고 Garcia-Fuller의 학생 중 한 명인 Patricia Visoso가 말했다.

4 "하지만 그들은 이것을 누가 말하고 있는지를 전혀 확인하지 않았어요."

5 그 이야기들은 실제로 주요 신문사나 TV 방송국이 아닌 10대들이 지어냈다.

6 그들은 광대들이 정말로 학생들을 공격하려고 한다는 명백한 증거를 하나도 제공하지 않았다.

7 그 이야기는 결국 완벽한 거짓말인 것으로 드러났다.

8 "많은 사람이 단지 한 가지만을 보고 그것이 사실이라고 믿는 것 같아요."라고 Patricia의 반 친구인 Ivy-Brooks가 말했다.

9 올바른 출처를 살펴보고, 무엇이 진짜이고 무엇이 가짜인지에 주의를 기울이는 것은 정말 중요해요."

10 Garcia-Fuller의 학생들처럼, 많은 미국의 10대들은 뉴스 속 그리고 인터넷상에서 보고 있는 정보에 관해 비판적으로 생각하는 것을 배워 나가고 있다.

11 이 기능은 최근 더 중요해지고 있는데, 이야기들은 아주 빠른 속도로 퍼져 나갈 수 있고 누구나 허위 정보로 가득 찬 웹사이트를 만들어 낼 수 있기 때문이다.

12 Garcia-Fuller said she was teaching her students _____ _____ _____ fake news _____ _____ _____.

13 " _____ _____ _____ _____ _____ is to _____ _____.

14 If a story or a photo seems _____ _____ _____ _____ _____, stop and think.

15 Is there any _____ that supports _____ _____ _____?

16 And where is this _____ _____?"

17 Garcia-Fuller's students also learn _____ _____ _____ fact _____ opinion in the news.

18 "Opinions are good to read," said 15-year-old McKenzie Campbell, "but you also _____ _____ check _____ they _____ _____ _____ _____."

19 Garcia-Fuller also said sometimes it can be very hard to be _____ _____ _____ _____.

20 She tests her students with a website that _____ _____ _____ information on an animal called a tree octopus.

21 The site _____ _____ _____ information on this animal, _____ _____ a few _____ _____ of octopuses in trees.

22 But _____ the story of _____ _____, it's totally _____ _____.

23 The lesson, Garcia-Fuller tells her students, is to "check the information you're seeing _____ _____ _____" and to " _____ _____, even things that I say."

12 Garcia-Fuller는 그녀가 자신의 학생들에게 가짜 뉴스를 진짜 뉴스로부터 구분하는 방법을 가르치고 있다고 말했다.

13 "첫 단계 중 하나는 속도를 늦추는 것(천천히 생각하는 것)입니다.

14 만약 어떤 이야기나 어떤 사진이 진짜라고 하기엔 너무 좋아 보인다면, 멈춰서 생각해 보세요.

15 글쓴이가 말하고 있는 것을 뒷받침하는 어떠한 증거라도 있나요?

16 그리고 이 정보가 어디서 온 것인가요?"

17 Garcia-Fuller의 학생들은 또한 뉴스에서 사실을 의견과 구분하는 방법에 대해서도 배운다.

18 "의견들은 읽을 만한 가치가 있습니다,"라고 15살인 McKenzie Campbell이 말했다. "하지만 여러분은 그것들이 사실에 기반을 둔 것인지를 확인해 보아야 합니다."

19 Garcia-Fuller는 또한 때때로 현명한 뉴스 독자가 되는 것이 아주 어려울 수도 있다고 말했다.

20 그녀는 자신의 학생들을 '나무 문어'라는 이름의 동물에 대한 정보를 제공하는 것처럼 보이는 웹사이트로 시험한다.

21 그 사이트는 나무 위에 있는 문어들의 몇몇 불확실한 사진과 함께, 이 동물에 대한 정보로 가득 차 있다.

22 하지만 무서운 광대들의 이야기와 마찬가지로, 그것은 완전히 꾸며진 것이다.

23 Garcia-Fuller가 그녀의 학생들에게 말하는 교훈은 '당신이 보고 있는 정보를 한 번만 더 신중하게 확인해 보라'는 것과 '모든 것, 심지어 내가 말하는 것에도 의문을 가져 보라'는 것이다.

※ 다음 문장을 우리말로 쓰시오.

1　How to Be a Smart News Reader

➡ _____

2　In October 2016, stories about scary clowns shook schools across the Washington area, but Danina Garcia-Fuller's students didn't believe them a bit.

➡ _____

_____

3　"Some people were getting scared because they saw things on social media," said Patricia Visoso, one of Garcia-Fuller's students.

➡ _____

_____

4　"But they never checked up on who was saying this."

➡ _____

5　The stories were actually made by teenagers, not by major newspapers or TV stations.

➡ _____

6　They offered no hard evidence that clowns really were trying to attack students.

➡ _____

7　The story turned out to be a complete lie.

➡ _____

8　"I think a lot of people just look at one thing and believe it's true," Patricia's classmate Ivy-Brooks said.

➡ _____

_____

9　"It's really important to look at the right sources and to pay attention to what is real and what is fake."

➡ _____

10　Like Garcia-Fuller's students, many teenagers in America are learning to think critically about information they're seeing in the news and on the Internet.

➡ _____

_____

11　This skill is getting more important these days as stories can spread very fast, and anyone can make a website full of false information.

➡ _____

_____

12 Garcia-Fuller said she was teaching her students how to tell fake news from real news.

➡ _____

13 "One of the first steps is to slow down.

➡ _____

14 If a story or a photo seems too good to be true, stop and think.

➡ _____

15 Is there any evidence that supports what the writer says?

➡ _____

16 And where is this coming from?"

➡ _____

17 Garcia-Fuller's students also learn how to tell fact from opinion in the news.

➡ _____

18 "Opinions are good to read," said 15-year-old McKenzie Campbell, "but you also have to check if they are based on facts."

➡ _____
_____

19 Garcia-Fuller also said sometimes it can be very hard to be a smart news reader.

➡ _____

20 She tests her students with a website that appears to provide information on an animal called a tree octopus.

➡ _____

21 The site is full of information on this animal, along with a few unclear photos of octopuses in trees.

➡ _____

22 But like the story of scary clowns, it's totally made up.

➡ _____

23 The lesson, Garcia-Fuller tells her students, is to "check the information you're seeing once more carefully" and to "question everything, even things that I say."

➡ _____
_____

※ 다음 괄호 안의 단어들을 우리말에 맞도록 바르게 배열하시오.

1   (to / How / a / Be / News / Smart / Reader)
➡ _____

2   (October / in / 2016, / about / stories / clowns / scary / schools / shook / the / across / area, / Washington / but / Garcia-Fuller's / Danina / students / believe / didn't / them / bit. / a)
➡ _____
_____
_____

3   (people / "some / were / scared / getting / because / saw / they / things / social / on / media, / Patricia / said / one / Visoso, / of / students. / Garcia-Fuller's)
➡ _____
_____

4   ("but / never / they / up / checked / who / on / was / this." / saying)
➡ _____

5   (stories / the / actually / were / by / made / teenagers, / by / not / newspapers / major / TV / or / stations.)
➡ _____

6   (offered / they / hard / no / that / evidence / clowns / were / really / trying / were / attack / to / students.)
➡ _____
_____

7   (story / the / out / turned / be / to / a / lie. / complete)
➡ _____

8   (think / "I / lot / a / people / of / look / just / one / at / and / thing / it's / believe / true," / classmate / Paricia's / said. / Ivy-Brooks)
➡ _____
_____

9   (really / "it's / to / important / look / at / right / the / and / sources / to / attention / pay / to / is / what / and / real / is / what / fake.")
➡ _____
_____

10   (Gracia-Fuller's / like / students, / teenagers / many / in / are / America / to / learning / critically / think / information / about / seeing / they're / the / in / and / news / on / Internet. / the)
➡ _____
_____
_____

11   (skill / this / getting / is / important / more / days / these / stories / as / spread / can / fast, / very / anyone / and / make / can / website / a / of / full / information. / false)
➡ _____
_____

---

1 현명한 뉴스 독자가 되는 방법

2 2016년 10월, 무서운 광대들에 관한 이야기가 워싱턴 지역 전역의 학교에 충격을 안겼지만, Danina Garcia-Fuller의 학생들은 조금도 그 이야기들을 믿지 않았다.

3 "몇몇 사람들은 그들이 소셜 미디어에 올라온 것들을 봤기 때문에 무서워했어요."라고 Garcia-Fuller의 학생 중 한 명인 Patricia Visoso가 말했다.

4 "하지만 그들은 이것을 누가 말하고 있는지를 전혀 확인하지 않았어요."

5 그 이야기들은 실제로 주요 신문사나 TV 방송국이 아닌 10대들이 지어냈다.

6 그들은 광대들이 정말로 학생들을 공격하려고 한다는 명백한 증거를 하나도 제공하지 않았다.

7 그 이야기는 결국 완벽한 거짓말인 것으로 드러났다.

8 "많은 사람이 단지 한 가지만을 보고 그것이 사실이라고 믿는 것 같아요."라고 Patricia의 반 친구인 Ivy-Brooks가 말했다.

9 올바른 출처를 살펴보고, 무엇이 진짜이고 무엇이 가짜인지에 주의를 기울이는 것은 정말 중요해요."

10 Garcia-Fuller의 학생들처럼, 많은 미국의 10대들은 뉴스 속 그리고 인터넷상에서 보고 있는 정보에 관해 비판적으로 생각하는 것을 배워 나가고 있다.

11 이 기능은 최근 더 중요해지고 있는데, 이야기들은 아주 빠른 속도로 퍼져 나갈 수 있고 누구나 허위 정보로 가득 찬 웹사이트를 만들어 낼 수 있기 때문이다.

12 (said / Garcia-Fuller / was / she / her / teaching / how / students / to / fake / tell / news / real / from / news.)

➡ _____

_____

13 (of / "one / first / the / is / steps / slow / to / down.)

➡ _____

14 (a / if / or / story / photo / a / too / seems / to / good / true, / be / and / think. / stop)

➡ _____

15 (there / is / evidence / any / supports / that / the / what / says? / writer)

➡ _____

16 (where / and / this / is / from?" / coming)

➡ _____

17 (students / Garcia-Fuller's / learn / also / to / how / fact / tell / from / in / opinion / news. / the)

➡ _____

_____

18 (are / "opinions / to / good / read," / 15-year-old / said / Campbell, / McKenzie / you / "but / also / you / to / have / if / check / are / they / on / based / facts.")

➡ _____

_____

19 (Garcia-Fuller / said / also / it / sometimes / be / can / hard / very / be / to / a / news / smart / reader.)

➡ _____

_____

20 (tests / she / students / her / a / with / that / website / to / appears / information / provide / an / on / called / animal / tree / octopus. / a)

➡ _____

_____

21 (site / the / full / is / information / of / this / on / animal, / with / along / few / a / photos / unclear / octopuses / of / trees. / in)

➡ _____

_____

22 (like / but / story / the / scary / of / clowns, / totally / it's / up. / made)

➡ _____

23 (lesson, / the / Garcia-Fuller / her / tells / students, / to / is / the / "check / information / seeing / you're / more / once / carefully" / to / and / everything / "question / even / that / things / say." / I)

➡ _____

_____

_____

12 Garcia-Fuller는 그녀가 자신의 학생들에게 가짜 뉴스를 진짜 뉴스로부터 구분하는 방법을 가르치고 있다고 말했다.

13 "첫 단계 중 하나는 속도를 늦추는 것(천천히 생각하는 것)입니다.

14 만약 어떤 이야기나 어떤 사진이 진짜라고 하기엔 너무 좋아 보인다면, 멈춰서 생각해 보세요.

15 글쓴이가 말하고 있는 것을 뒷받침하는 어떠한 증거라도 있나요?

16 그리고 이 정보가 어디서 온 것인가요?"

17 Garcia-Fuller의 학생들은 또한 뉴스에서 사실을 의견과 구분하는 방법에 대해서도 배운다.

18 "의견들은 읽을 만한 가치가 있습니다."라고 15살인 McKenzie Campbell이 말했다. "하지만 여러분은 그것들이 사실에 기반을 둔 것인지를 확인해 보아야 합니다."

19 Garcia-Fuller는 또한 때때로 현명한 뉴스 독자가 되는 것이 아주 어려울 수도 있다고 말했다.

20 그녀는 자신의 학생들을 '나무 문어'라는 이름의 동물에 대한 정보를 제공하는 것처럼 보이는 웹사이트로 시험한다.

21 그 사이트는 나무 위에 있는 문어들의 몇몇 불확실한 사진과 함께, 이 동물에 대한 정보로 가득 차 있다.

22 하지만 무서운 광대들의 이야기와 마찬가지로, 그것은 완전히 꾸며진 것이다.

23 Garcia-Fuller가 그녀의 학생들에게 말하는 교훈은 '당신이 보고 있는 정보를 한 번만 더 신중하게 확인해 보라'는 것과 '모든 것, 심지어 내가 말하는 것에도 의문을 가져 보라'는 것이다.

※ **다음 우리말을 영어로 쓰시오.**

1 현명한 뉴스 독자가 되는 방법

➡ _____

2 2016년 10월, 무서운 광대들에 관한 이야기가 워싱턴 지역 전역의 학교에 충격을 안겼지만,
Danina Garcia-Fuller의 학생들은 조금도 그 이야기들을 믿지 않았다.

➡ _____

_____

3 "몇몇 사람들은 그들이 소셜 미디어에 올라온 것들을 봤기 때문에 무서워했어요."라고 Garcia-Fuller의
학생 중 한 명인 Patricia Visoso가 말했다.

➡ _____

_____

4 "하지만 그들은 이것을 누가 말하고 있는지를 전혀 확인하지 않았어요."

➡ _____

5 그 이야기들은 실제로 주요 신문사나 TV 방송국이 아닌 10대들이 지어냈다.

➡ _____

6 그들은 광대들이 정말로 학생들을 공격하려고 한다는 명백한 증거를 하나도 제공하지 않았다.

➡ _____

7 그 이야기는 결국 완벽한 거짓말인 것으로 드러났다.

➡ _____

8 "많은 사람이 단지 한 가지만을 보고 그것이 사실이라고 믿는 것 같아요."라고 Patricia의
반 친구인 Ivy-Brooks가 말했다.

➡ _____

_____

9 "올바른 출처를 살펴보고, 무엇이 진짜이고 무엇이 가짜인지에 주의를 기울이는 것은 정말 중요해요."

➡ _____

_____

10 Garcia-Fuller의 학생들처럼, 많은 미국의 10대들은 뉴스 속 그리고 인터넷상에서 보고 있는 정보에 관해
비판적으로 생각하는 것을 배워 나가고 있다.

➡ _____

_____

11 이 기능은 최근 더 중요해지고 있는데, 이야기들은 아주 빠른 속도로 퍼져 나갈 수 있고 누구나 허위 정보로
가득 찬 웹사이트를 만들어 낼 수 있기 때문이다.

➡ _____

_____

12 Garcia-Fuller는 그녀가 자신의 학생들에게 가짜 뉴스를 진짜 뉴스로부터 구분하는 방법을 가르치고 있다고 말했다.

➡ _____

13 "첫 단계 중 하나는 속도를 늦추는 것(천천히 생각하는 것)입니다.

➡ _____

14 만약 어떤 이야기나 어떤 사진이 진짜라고 하기엔 너무 좋아 보인다면, 멈춰서 생각해 보세요.

➡ _____

15 글쓴이가 말하고 있는 것을 뒷받침하는 어떠한 증거라도 있나요?

➡ _____

16 그리고 이 정보가 어디서 온 것인가요?"

➡ _____

17 Garcia-Fuller의 학생들은 또한 뉴스에서 사실을 의견과 구분하는 방법에 대해서도 배운다.

➡ _____

18 "의견들은 읽을 만한 가치가 있습니다,"라고 15살인 McKenzie Campbell이 말했다. "하지만 여러분은 그것들이 사실에 기반을 둔 것인지를 확인해 보아야 합니다."

➡ _____
_____

19 Garcia-Fuller는 또한 때때로 현명한 뉴스 독자가 되는 것이 아주 어려울 수도 있다고 말했다.

➡ _____

20 그녀는 자신의 학생들을 '나무 문어'라는 이름의 동물에 대한 정보를 제공하는 것처럼 보이는 웹사이트로 시험한다.

➡ _____

21 그 사이트는 나무 위에 있는 문어들의 몇몇 불확실한 사진과 함께, 이 동물에 대한 정보로 가득 차 있다.

➡ _____

22 하지만 무서운 광대들의 이야기와 마찬가지로, 그것은 완전히 꾸며진 것이다.

➡ _____

23 Garcia-Fuller가 그녀의 학생들에게 말하는 교훈은 '당신이 보고 있는 정보를 한 번만 더 신중하게 확인해 보라'는 것과 '모든 것, 심지어 내가 말하는 것에도 의문을 가져 보라'는 것이다.

➡ _____
_____

※ 다음 우리말과 일치하도록 빈칸에 알맞은 말을 쓰시오.

After You Read A

1. In October 2016, stories about scary clowns _____ schools
_____ _____ _____ _____.

2. Garcia-Fuller's students also learn _____ _____ _____
_____ _____ _____ in the news.

3. The site _____ _____ _____ information on this animal,
_____ _____ a few _____ _____ _____ in
trees.

Do It Yourself

1. Team N W _____ _____ _____ _____ _____ the
school festival.

2. They _____ _____ the students and teachers _____ _____
_____ _____.

3. But they performed _____ _____ _____ _____
team.

4. A lot of students _____ _____ and _____ _____ when the
team danced.

5. Ms. Yu, the P.E. teacher, said it was _____ _____
_____ _____.

Link to the World

Fact

1. This drawing, *Don Quixote*, is _____ _____ _____ _____.

2. Picasso _____ it in 1955 _____ black lines _____
_____ _____.

Opinion

3. I don't know _____ the man on the horse is _____, but he
_____ _____ _____ and _____.

4. I think he _____ _____ _____ and _____.

5. I think this _____ _____ _____ _____ _____ _____
of Cervantes' novel *Don Quixote*.

1. 2016년 10월, 무서운 광대들에 관한 이야기가 워싱턴 지역 전역의 학교에 충격을 안겼다.
2. Garcia-Fuller의 학생들은 또한 뉴스에서 사실을 의견과 구분하는 방법에 대해서도 배운다.
3. 그 사이트는 나무 위에 있는 문어들의 몇몇 불확실한 사진과 함께, 이 동물에 대한 정보로 가득 차 있다.

1. NW 팀은 학교 축제 기간에 무대에서 춤을 선보였다.
2. 그들은 학생들과 선생님들이 그들의 춤을 좋아할지 확신이 서지 않았다.
3. 하지만 그들은 다른 어떠한 팀보다 훨씬 더 멋지게 공연을 해냈다.
4. 그 팀이 춤출 때 많은 학생이 일어서서 크게 환호했다.
5. 체육 선생님인 유 선생님은 그해 최고의 공연이라고 말씀하셨다.

사실
1. 이 그림 '돈키호테'는 피카소의 작품 중 하나이다.
2. 피카소는 이 그림을 1955년에 흰 배경과 대비를 이루는 검은 선들로 그렸다.
의견
3. 말 위에 올라탄 남자가 용감한지는 잘 모르겠지만, 그는 매우 피곤하고 굶주려 보인다.
4. 내 생각에는 그에게 약간의 음식과 물이 필요한 것 같다.
5. 나는 이 미술품이 세르반테스의 소설인 '돈키호테'의 가장 흥미로운 부분을 보여 주고 있다고 생각한다.

※ 다음 우리말을 영어로 쓰시오.

After You Read A

1. 2016년 10월, 무서운 광대들에 관한 이야기가 워싱턴 지역 전역의 학교에 충격을 안겼다.

➡ _____

2. Garcia-Fuller의 학생들은 또한 뉴스에서 사실을 의견과 구분하는 방법에 대해서도 배운다.

➡ _____

3. 그 사이트는 나무 위에 있는 뮤어들의 몇몇 불확실한 사진과 함께, 이 동물에 대한 정보로 가득 차 있다.

➡ _____

Do It Yourself

1. NW 팀은 학교 축제 기간에 무대에서 춤을 선보였다.

➡ _____

2. 그들은 학생들과 선생님들이 그들의 춤을 좋아할지 확신이 서지 않았다.

➡ _____

3. 하지만 그들은 다른 어떠한 팀보다 훨씬 더 멋지게 공연을 해냈다.

➡ _____

4. 그 팀이 춤출 때 많은 학생이 일어서서 크게 환호했다.

➡ _____

5. 체육 선생님인 유 선생님은 그해 최고의 공연이라고 말씀하셨다.

➡ _____

Link to the World

사실

1. 이 그림 '돈키호테'는 피카소의 작품 중 하나이다.

➡ _____

2. 피카소는 이 그림을 1955년에 흰 배경과 대비를 이루는 검은 선들로 그렸다.

➡ _____

의견

3. 말 위에 올라탄 남자가 용감한지는 잘 모르겠지만, 그는 매우 피곤하고 굶주려 보인다.

➡ _____

4. 내 생각에는 그에게 약간의 음식과 물이 필요한 것 같다.

➡ _____

5. 나는 이 미술품이 세르반테스의 소설인 '돈키호테'의 가장 흥미로운 부분을 보여 주고 있다고 생각한다.

➡ _____

※ 다음 영어를 우리말로 쓰시오.

01	pole	_____	22	look	_____
02	fix	_____	23	heater	_____
03	weapon	_____	24	order	_____
04	reason	_____	25	palace	_____
05	situation	_____	26	army	_____
06	instead	_____	27	bark	_____
07	knowing	_____	28	powerful	_____
08	approach	_____	29	gate	_____
09	military	_____	30	push	_____
10	warrior	_____	31	sword	_____
11	injured	_____	32	tie	_____
12	movement	_____	33	finally	_____
13	patience	_____	34	noise	_____
14	follow	_____	35	give up	_____
15	stand	_____	36	stand against	_____
16	suddenly	_____	37	let ~ go	_____
17	general	_____	38	focus on	_____
18	above	_____	39	calm down	_____
19	anymore	_____	40	sooner or later	_____
20	happen	_____	41	stand in line	_____
21	yell	_____	42	at that moment	_____
			43	in all possible ways	_____

※ 다음 우리말을 영어로 쓰시오.

01	정문, 대문	
02	군대, 군대의	
03	~보다 위에	
04	검, 칼	
05	인내심, 참을성	
06	수리하다	
07	상황	
08	명령하다	
09	마침내	
10	더 이상	
11	부상당한	
12	장군	
13	기둥, 막대, 장대	
14	일어나다, 발생하다	
15	대신에	
16	다가가다	
17	참다, 견디다	
18	단식하다	
19	따르다, 따라가다	
20	전사	
21	군대, 육군	

22	궁, 궁전	
23	(개가) 짖다	
24	다 안다는 듯한	
25	표정	
26	승리자, 우승자	
27	이유	
28	(사람들이 조직적으로 벌이는) 운동	
29	소음	
30	무기	
31	소리 지르다	
32	강력한	
33	갑자기	
34	묶다	
35	곤경에 처하다	
36	~에 집중하다	
37	조만간, 머지않아	
38	~을 풀어주다, 석방하다	
39	그 순간에	
40	진정하다	
41	포기하다	
42	~을 돌보다	
43	~을 편들어, ~의 면에	

※ 다음 영영풀이에 알맞은 단어를 <보기>에서 골라 쓴 후, 우리말 뜻을 쓰시오.

1 _____ : to shout loudly: _____

2 _____ : to repair or correct something: _____

3 _____ : a military officer of very high rank: _____

4 _____ : to eat no food for a period of time: _____

5 _____ : the armed forces of a country: _____

6 _____ : after a long period of time: _____

7 _____ : to tell someone to do something: _____

8 _____ : to become aware of a fact or to understand it: _____

9 _____ : having physical damage to a part of the body: _____

10 _____ : being able to stay calm and not get annoyed: _____

11 _____ : having a lot of power to control people and events: _____

12 _____ : someone or something that wins a contest, prize, etc.: _____

13 _____ : to make the short loud sound that a dog makes: _____

14 _____ : the emotions and feelings that can be seen in a person's face or eyes: _____

15 _____ : a fact or situation which explains why something happens: _____

16 _____ : a fighter or soldier, especially one in old times who was very brave and experienced in fighting: _____

보기			
reason	finally	patience	order
injured	fix	powerful	yell
bark	military	look	realize
warrior	general	winner	fast

※ 다음 우리말과 일치하도록 빈칸에 알맞은 말을 쓰시오.

Get Ready 2

(1) **M:** We'_____ _____ _____ _____ one hour, and we're still waiting.

    W: _____ down! We're _____ there.

(2) **G:** Brrr.... _____ a cold day! I _____ standing _____ _____ in _____ _____.

    B: _____ _____! Drink this _____ _____.

    G: Oh, thank you so much.

(3) **G:** Look! That man didn't _____ _____ _____! I'm very angry.

    B: _____ _____! He _____ here.

(4) **B:** The boy _____ me _____ _____ me. I _____ it.

    G: _____ _____. He's _____ a child.

Start Off - Listen & Talk A

1. **B:** What's that _____ _____?

    G: They're _____ the _____.

    B: I can't _____ _____ my studies _____ _____. I _____ _____ _____.

    G: Calm _____! They will finish it soon.

2. **G:** I _____ _____ my pencil case. Have you _____ it?

    B: No, I _____. Where did you _____ it?

    G: I put it on my desk, but now it's _____. I'm really _____.

    B: _____ down! I'll help you _____ it.

Start Off - Listen & Talk B

B: Ouch! He _____ _____ my _____ again.

G: Are you _____?

B: No. This is the _____ time he _____ _____ today. I _____ _____ it. I'll go and talk to him.

G: _____ _____! He's not _____ his _____ today, so he can't see well.

B: What _____ _____ his glasses?

G: He _____ his glasses _____ a soccer game this morning.

B: I see, but he _____ _____ _____ more careful.

(1) **M:** 우리 한 시간 이상 기다렸는데 아직도 기다리고 있네.
    W: 진정해! 거의 다 되어 가.

(2) **G:** 부르르…. 정말 추운 날이네! 나는 추운 날씨에 줄 서는 게 싫어.
    B: 진정해! 이 뜨거운 우유를 마셔 봐.
    G: 와, 정말 고마워.

(3) **G:** 저것 봐! 저 남자가 줄을 서지 않았어! 정말 화가 나.
    B: 진정해! 저 사람은 여기서 일하는 사람이야.

(4) **B:** 내 뒤에 있는 남자아이가 자꾸 밀어. 참을 수가 없어.
    G: 진정해. 아직 어린아이야.

1. **B:** 밖에서 나는 저 소음은 뭐지?
    G: 히터를 고치고 있어.
    B: 공부에 전혀 집중할 수가 없잖아. 참을 수가 없어.
    G: 진정해! 곧 끝날 거야.

2. **G:** 내 필통을 찾을 수가 없어. 내 필통 봤니?
    B: 아니, 못 봤어. 어디에 뒀어?
    G: 내 책상 위에 뒀는데 사라졌어. 정말 화가 나.
    B: 진정해! 내가 그걸 찾는 걸 도와줄게.

B: 아! 그 애가 또 내 발을 밟았어.
G: 괜찮니?
B: 아니. 이번이 오늘 그 애가 내 발을 세 번째로 밟은 거야. 참을 수가 없어. 가서 말해야겠어.
G: 진정해! 그 애는 오늘 안경을 안 쓰고 있어서 잘 볼 수가 없어.
B: 안경이 어떻게 됐는데?
G: 오늘 아침에 축구 경기를 하다가 안경을 깨뜨렸어.
B: 그렇구나. 하지만 그 애는 더 조심했어야 했어.

Start Off - Speak Up

A: I _____ _____ this place. It's too _____.

B: _____ _____! We're at the _____. Let's _____ it.

A: 나는 이 장소를 참을 수가 없어. 너무 사람이 많아.
B: 진정해! 우리는 축제에 와 있잖아. 축제를 즐기자.

Step Up - Real-life Scene

Minji: Minsu, there is no cup _____ _____ _____. _____ _____ _____ do the _____?

Minho: Sorry, but I _____ _____ _____ them.

Minji: What? You always forget _____ you _____ _____. _____ _____ _____ _____ it. I _____ the living room all morning.

Minho: Calm down! I'm _____ _____ my homework.

Minji: _____ the _____ first, and then do your homework.

Minho: I can't. I don't think I can _____ my homework today. Science is _____ _____ for me.

Minji: Science? You know I'_____ _____ _____ science. _____ _____ _____ you.

Minho: Great. Thanks. I'll wash your cup _____ _____ and I'll do _____ _____ of the dishes _____ _____ this.

민지: 민수야, 내가 사용할 컵이 없어. 왜 설거지를 안 했니?
민수: 미안하지만, 설거지하는 걸 잊었어.
민지: 뭐라고? 너는 항상 해야 할 일을 잊어버리는구나. 참을 수가 없어. 나는 아침 내내 거실 청소를 했어.
민수: 진정해! 나는 숙제하느라 바빠.
민지: 설거지를 먼저 하고 난 뒤에 숙제해.
민수: 안 돼! 오늘 숙제를 끝낼 수가 없을 것 같아. 과학은 나에게 너무 어려워.
민지: 과학이라고? 너도 알겠지만 내가 과학을 잘하잖아. 내가 도와줄게.
민수: 잘됐다. 고마워. 당장 누나 컵부터 씻을게. 그리고 나머지 설거지는 숙제 끝낸 후에 할게.

Express Yourself A

1. M1: The king _____ me here. Open the door.

   M2: Wait there. The door will open _____ a _____ days.

   M1: What? A hundred days? I can't _____ a hundred days _____ _____. I _____ _____ _____ _____.

   M2: _____ _____! _____ is an important _____ _____ in this school.

2. M1: Why did you _____ _____ _____ here? Please _____ _____.

   M2: How can you _____ _____? Think.

   M1: I _____ _____ this _____. I'm not _____ or bad.

   M2: Calm down. _____ _____ you'll find a _____.

1. M1: 왕이 나를 여기에 보냈소. 문을 여시오.
   M2: 거기서 기다리시오. 100일 후 문이 열릴 것이오.
   M1: 뭐라고요? 100일이라고요? 아무것도 하지 않고 100일을 보낼 수는 없소. 참을 수가 없소.
   M2: 진정하시오! 그것이 이 학교에 들어오기 위한 중요한 규칙이오.

2. M1: 저를 왜 여기에 묶어 두셨습니까? 저를 풀어 주십시오.
   M2: 어떻게 풀려날 수 있겠느냐? 생각해 보아라.
   M1: 저는 이 푯말을 참을 수가 없습니다. 저는 위험하지도 나쁘지도 않습니다.
   M2: 진정하거라. 나는 네가 방법을 찾을 것이라고 확신한다.

Check yourself

G: What's that _____ _____?

B: A dog is _____.

G: I _____ _____ my studies at all. I can't _____ _____.

B: _____ _____! He will be _____ soon.

G: 밖에서 나는 저 소음은 뭐지?
B: 개가 짖고 있는 거야.
G: 공부에 전혀 집중할 수가 없어. 참을 수가 없어.
B: 진정해! 곧 조용해질 거야.

※ 다음 우리말에 맞도록 대화를 영어로 쓰시오.

Get Ready 2

(1) M: _____

W: _____

(2) G: _____

B: _____

G: _____

(3) G: _____

B: _____

(4) B: _____

G: _____

해석

(1) M: 우리 한 시간 이상 기다렸는데 아직도 기다리고 있네.
W: 진정해! 거의 다 되어 가.

(2) G: 부르르…. 정말 추운 날이네! 나는 추운 날씨에 줄 서는 게 싫어.
B: 진정해! 이 뜨거운 우유를 마셔 봐.
G: 와, 정말 고마워.

(3) G: 저것 봐! 저 남자가 줄을 서지 않았어! 정말 화가 나.
B: 진정해! 저 사람은 여기서 일하는 사람이야.

(4) B: 내 뒤에 있는 남자아이가 자꾸 밀어. 참을 수가 없어.
G: 진정해. 아직 어린아이야.

Start Off - Listen & Talk A

1. B: _____

G: _____

B: _____

G: _____

2. G: _____

B: _____

G: _____

B: _____

1. B: 밖에서 나는 저 소음은 뭐지?
G: 히터를 고치고 있어.
B: 공부에 전혀 집중할 수가 없잖아. 참을 수가 없어.
G: 진정해! 곧 끝날 거야.

2. G: 내 필통을 찾을 수가 없어. 내 필통 봤니?
B: 아니, 못 봤어. 어디에 뒀어?
G: 내 책상 위에 뒀는데 사라졌어. 정말 화가 나.
B: 진정해! 내가 그걸 찾는 걸 도와줄게.

Start Off - Listen & Talk B

B: _____

G: _____

B: _____

G: _____

B: _____

G: _____

B: _____

B: 아! 그 애가 또 내 발을 밟았어.
G: 괜찮니?
B: 아니. 이번이 오늘 그 애가 내 발을 세 번째로 밟은 거야. 참을 수가 없어. 가서 말해야겠어.
G: 진정해! 그 애는 오늘 안경을 안 쓰고 있어서 잘 볼 수가 없어.
B: 안경이 어떻게 됐는데?
G: 오늘 아침에 축구 경기를 하다가 안경을 깨뜨렸어.
B: 그렇구나. 하지만 그 애는 더 조심했어야 했어.

Start Off - Speak Up

A: _____

B: _____

A: 나는 이 장소를 참을 수가 없어. 너무 사람이 많아.
B: 진정해! 우리는 축제에 와 있잖아. 축제를 즐기자.

Step Up - Real-life Scene

Minji: _____
Minho: _____
Minji: _____
_____
Minho: _____
Minji: _____
Minho: _____
_____
Minji: _____
Minho: _____
_____

민지: 민수야, 내가 사용할 컵이 없어. 왜 설거지를 안 했니?
민수: 미안하지만, 설거지하는 걸 잊었어.
민지: 뭐라고? 너는 항상 해야 할 일을 잊어버리는구나. 참을 수가 없어. 나는 아침 내내 거실 청소를 했어.
민수: 진정해! 나는 숙제하느라 바빠.
민지: 설거지를 먼저 하고 난 뒤에 숙제해.
민수: 안 돼! 오늘 숙제를 끝낼 수가 없을 것 같아. 과학은 나에게 너무 어려워.
민지: 과학이라고? 너도 알겠지만 내가 과학을 잘하잖아. 내가 도와줄게.
민수: 잘됐다. 고마워. 당장 누나 컵부터 씻을게. 그리고 나머지 설거지는 숙제 끝낸 후에 할게.

Express Yourself A

1. M1: _____
   M2: _____
   M1: _____
   _____
   M2: _____
2. M1: _____
   M2: _____
   M1: _____
   M2: _____

1. M1: 왕이 나를 여기에 보냈소. 문을 여시오.
   M2: 거기서 기다리시오. 100일 후 문이 열릴 것이오.
   M1: 뭐라고요? 100일이라고요? 아무것도 하지 않고 100일을 보낼 수는 없소. 참을 수가 없소.
   M2: 진정하시오! 그것이 이 학교에 들어오기 위한 중요한 규칙이오.

2. M1: 저를 왜 여기에 묶어 두셨습니까? 저를 풀어 주십시오.
   M2: 어떻게 풀려날 수 있겠느냐? 생각해 보아라.
   M1: 저는 이 푯말을 참을 수가 없습니다. 저는 위험하지도 나쁘지도 않습니다.
   M2: 진정하거라. 나는 네가 방법을 찾을 것이라고 확신한다.

Check yourself

G: _____
B: _____
G: _____
B: _____

G: 밖에서 나는 저 소음은 뭐지?
B: 개가 짖고 있는 거야.
G: 공부에 전혀 집중할 수가 없어. 참을 수가 없어.
B: 진정해! 곧 조용해질 거야.

※ 다음 우리말과 일치하도록 빈칸에 알맞은 것을 골라 쓰시오.

1 Corky, _____ _____ _____
A. Warrior   B. Best   C. the

2 Corky was a _____ _____ _____ .
A. young   B. brave   C. man

3 He wanted to be a _____ , but the king said, "You're the _____ man in my _____ , but you have _____ to learn."
A. strongest   B. general   C. army   D. much

4 He _____ Corky _____ go to a _____ _____ school.
A. military   B. ordered   C. famous   D. to

5 "Wait there. in a _____ days, your _____ will start," a _____ said from inside the school _____ .
A. training   B. gate   C. hundred   D. voice

6 Corky _____ _____ .
A. angry   B. got

7 But then he _____ there _____ be a _____ , so he _____ .
A. reason   B. thought   C. might   D. waited

8 On the _____ and _____ day, the _____ _____ .
A. first   B. opened   C. hundred   D. gate

9 An old man said, "You have _____ to _____ your first _____ : _____ .
A. patience   B. learned   C. weapon   D. use

10 _____ is the _____ important _____ to _____ a war."
A. win   B. patience   C. thing   D. most

11 _____ , the teacher told Corky to _____ _____ a _____ .
A. against   B. then   C. pole   D. stand

12 _____ , he _____ Corky _____ the _____ .
A. pole   B. suddenly   C. to   D. tied

13 _____ his head, he _____ a sign that _____ " _____ and Bad."
A. dangerous   B. above   C. read   D. put

14 Many people _____ _____ .
A. by   B. passed

1 최고의 전사, Corky

2 Corky는 용감한 청년이었다.

3 그는 장군이 되기를 원했지만 왕은 이렇게 말했다. "자네는 우리 군대에서 가장 강한 전사이네. 하지만 자네는 아직도 배울 게 많아."

4 왕은 Corky에게 유명한 군사 학교에 갈 것을 명령했다.

5 "거기서 기다려라. 훈련은 100일 후에 시작할 것이다." 군사 학교 안에서 이렇게 외치는 목소리가 들렸다.

6 Corky는 화가 났다.

7 하지만 이유가 있을 것으로 생각하고 기다렸다.

8 101일째 되던 날, 문이 열렸다.

9 한 노인이 이렇게 말했다. "너는 첫 번째 무기인 '인내'를 사용하는 법을 배운 것이다.

10 인내는 전쟁에서 이기기 위해 가장 중요한 것이다."

11 그리고 난 뒤, 스승은 Corky에게 기둥 앞에 서라고 말했다.

12 갑자기 그는 Corky를 기둥에 묶었다.

13 그의 머리 위에는 '위험하고 나쁨'이라는 푯말을 붙였다.

14 많은 사람이 지나갔다.

15 _____ gave Corky angry _____, and _____ _____ at him.

    A. others   B. some   C. looks   D. shouted

16 Corky _____ _____.

    A. back   B. shouted

17 He _____, "_____ me _____, or you all will be in big _____!"

    A. trouble   B. yelled   C. free   D. set

18 That _____ the _____ _____.

    A. worse   B. made   C. situation

19 "I need to _____ _____ _____," he _____.

    A. thought   B. another   C. try   D. way

20 _____, Corky began to _____ _____.

    A. speak   B. then   C. softly

21 He said he was _____ _____ or _____ _____ was a good man.

    A. but   B. bad   C. dangerous   D. not

22 He _____ _____ this in all _____ _____.

    A. possible   B. kept   C. ways   D. saying

23 Finally, the people _____ _____ _____.

    A. let   B. go   C. him

24 "Now you control _____ _____ _____ _____: words.

    A. weapon   B. most   C. the   D. powerful

25 Soft _____ are _____ _____ sharp _____," said the teacher.

    A. swords   B. words   C. than   D. stronger

26 Next, the teacher _____ Corky _____ a large hall _____ a chair in the _____.

    A. with   B. took   C. middle   D. to

27 There were 19 _____ who _____ _____ their tests.

    A. warriors   B. passed   C. other   D. had

28 "The _____ _____ _____ _____ in the chair will be the winner," the teacher said.

    A. to   B. one   C. sit   D. first

29 Corky and _____ _____ began _____.

    A. fighting   B. others   C. the

30 They _____, _____, ran, and _____.

    A. jumped   B. pulled   C. pushed

---

15 몇몇은 Corky를 화난 표정으로 쳐다봤고, 다른 몇몇은 그에게 소리를 질렀다.

16 Corky도 그들에게 소리를 질렀다.

17 그는 "나를 풀어 줘. 그러지 않으면 모두 혼쭐날 줄 알아!"라고 외쳤다.

18 그것은 상황을 더 악화시켰다.

19 그는 '다른 방법을 써야겠어.'라고 생각했다.

20 그러고 나서 Corky는 부드럽게 말하기 시작했다.

21 그는 자신이 위험하거나 나쁘지 않고 좋은 사람이라고 말했다.

22 그는 모든 방법을 동원해 계속해서 이렇게 말했다.

23 마침내 사람들은 그를 풀어 주었다.

24 "이제 너는 가장 강력한 무기인 '말'을 통제하게 되었다.

25 부드러운 말은 날카로운 칼보다 강하니라."라고 스승은 말했다.

26 다음 단계로 스승은 Corky를 중앙에 의자가 놓여 있는 커다란 홀로 데리고 갔다.

27 그곳에는 시험에 통과한 19명의 다른 전사들이 있었다.

28 "저 의자에 가장 먼저 앉는 사람이 승자가 될 것이다."라고 스승이 말했다.

29 Corky와 나머지 전사들은 싸우기 시작했다.

30 그들은 밀고 당기고 달리고 뛰어올랐다.

31 They _____ harder and _____, so Corky _____ _____.

    A. harder   B. tired   C. fought   D. became

32 _____, he said, "I will not _____ _____.

    A. anymore   B. finally   C. fight

33 _____, I will _____ _____ of the _____."

    A. injured   B. instead   C. care   D. take

34 The _____ _____ saw this and fought _____ _____.

    A. harder   B. warriors   C. even   D. other

35 _____ they _____, more _____ became tired and _____.

    A. warriors   B. fought   C. as   D. hurt

36 Corky took good _____ _____ them, _____ they _____ him.

    A. followed   B. care   C. so   D. of

37 Soon, _____ the _____ _____ Thunder were _____ Corky.

    A. following   B. all   C. except   D. warriors

38 Thunder _____ _____ the chair to _____ _____ it.

    A. toward   B. sit   C. walked   D. in

39 Then, he _____ Corky _____ _____ his 18 _____.

    A. followers   B. saw   C. with   D. standing

40 Thunder _____ he was _____ _____.

    A. all   B. realized   C. alone

41 "I _____ _____. You're the _____ _____," Thunder said to Corky.

    A. winner   B. up   C. real   D. give

42 At that _____, the teacher _____ and said. "Of all the great _____, peace is my _____.

    A. appeared   B. weapons   C. moment   D. favorite

43 _____ or _____, everyone wants to stand on the _____ of _____."

    A. side   B. later   C. sooner   D. peace

44 Corky _____ to the _____ after his _____ _____.

    A. palace   B. ended   C. returned   D. training

45 When the king saw him _____, he gave Corky a _____ and _____ smile and said, "What's _____, General?"

    A. knowing   B. up   C. approach   D. wise

31 그들은 점점 더 격렬히 싸웠고, Corky는 지쳤다.

32 마침내 그가 말했다. "나는 더는 싸움을 하지 않겠다.

33 대신에 부상당한 자들을 돌볼 것이다."

34 나머지 전사들은 이것을 보고 더 심하게 싸움을 했다.

35 그들이 싸움을 할수록 더 많은 전사들이 지치고 다쳤다.

36 Corky는 그들을 잘 돌봐 주었고, 그들은 Corky를 따르게 되었다.

37 곧 Thunder를 제외한 모든 전사들이 Corky를 따르고 있었다.

38 Thunder는 의자로 걸어가 그곳에 앉으려 했다.

39 그러다 그는 Corky가 18명의 추종자들과 함께 서 있는 것을 봤다.

40 Thunder는 자신이 혼자라는 사실을 깨달았다.

41 "나는 포기하겠다. 네가 진정한 승자다."라고 Thunder가 Corky에게 말했다.

42 그때 스승이 나타나 말했다. "모든 훌륭한 무기 중에서 평화는 내가 가장 좋아하는 것이다.

43 조만간 모든 사람은 평화의 편에 서기를 원한다."

44 Corky는 훈련을 마친 후 성으로 돌아갔다.

45 Corky가 다가오는 것을 본 왕은 그에게 이미 모든 것을 알고 있다는 듯한 현명한 미소를 띠며 말했다. "안녕하시오, 장군?"

※ 다음 우리말과 일치하도록 빈칸에 알맞은 것을 골라 쓰시오.

1 Corky, _____ _____ _____

2 Corky was a _____ _____ _____ .

3 He wanted to be a _____ , but the king said, "You're _____ _____ _____ in my army, but you _____ _____ _____ ."

4 He _____ Corky _____ _____ to a famous military school.

5 "Wait there. _____ _____ _____ _____ , your training will start," a _____ _____ from inside the school gate.

6 Corky _____ _____ .

7 But then he thought there _____ _____ _____ _____ , _____ he _____ .

8 _____ _____ _____ _____ _____ _____ , the gate opened.

9 An old man said, "You _____ _____ to use your _____ _____ : _____ .

10 Patience is the most important thing _____ _____ _____ _____ ."

11 Then, the teacher told Corky _____ _____ _____ a pole.

12 _____ , he _____ Corky _____ the pole.

13 _____ his head, he put a sign _____ _____ "Dangerous and Bad."

14 Many people _____ _____ .

1 최고의 전사, Corky

2 Corky는 용감한 청년이었다.

3 그는 장군이 되기를 원했지만 왕은 이렇게 말했다. "자네는 우리 군대에서 가장 강한 전사이네. 하지만 자네는 아직도 배울 게 많아."

4 왕은 Corky에게 유명한 군사 학교에 갈 것을 명령했다.

5 "거기서 기다려라. 훈련은 100일 후에 시작할 것이다." 군사 학교 안에서 이렇게 외치는 목소리가 들렸다.

6 Corky는 화가 났다.

7 하지만 이유가 있을 것으로 생각하고 기다렸다.

8 101일째 되던 날, 문이 열렸다.

9 한 노인이 이렇게 말했다. "너는 첫 번째 무기인 '인내'를 사용하는 법을 배운 것이다.

10 인내는 전쟁에서 이기기 위해 가장 중요한 것이다."

11 그리고 난 뒤, 스승은 Corky에게 기둥 앞에 서라고 말했다.

12 갑자기 그는 Corky를 기둥에 묶었다.

13 그의 머리 위에는 '위험하고 나쁨'이라는 푯말을 붙였다.

14 많은 사람이 지나갔다.

15 _____ gave Corky _____ _____, and _____ shouted at him.

16 Corky _____ _____.

17 He yelled, "_____ _____ _____, _____ you all will be _____ _____ _____!"

18 That _____ the situation _____.

19 "I need to try _____ way," he _____.

20 Then, Corky _____ _____ _____ _____.

21 He said he was _____ dangerous or bad _____ was a good man.

22 He _____ _____ this in _____ _____ _____.

23 _____, the people _____ _____ _____.

24 "Now you control _____ _____ _____ _____: words.

25 Soft words are _____ _____ _____ _____," said the teacher.

26 Next, the teacher _____ Corky _____ a large hall with a chair _____ _____ _____.

27 There were 19 _____ warriors who _____ _____ their tests.

28 "_____ _____ _____ _____ sit in the chair will be the _____," the teacher said.

29 Corky and _____ _____ _____ _____.

30 They _____, _____, ran, and _____.

---

15 몇몇은 Corky를 화난 표정으로 쳐다봤고, 다른 몇몇은 그에게 소리를 질렀다.

16 Corky도 그들에게 소리를 질렀다.

17 그는 "나를 풀어 줘. 그러지 않으면 모두 혼쭐날 줄 알아!"라고 외쳤다.

18 그것은 상황을 더 악화시켰다.

19 그는 '다른 방법을 써야겠어.'라고 생각했다.

20 그러고 나서 Corky는 부드럽게 말하기 시작했다.

21 그는 자신이 위험하거나 나쁘지 않고 좋은 사람이라고 말했다.

22 그는 모든 방법을 동원해 계속해서 이렇게 말했다.

23 마침내 사람들은 그를 풀어 주었다.

24 "이제 너는 가장 강력한 무기인 '말'을 통제하게 되었다.

25 부드러운 말은 날카로운 칼보다 강하니라."라고 스승은 말했다.

26 다음 단계로 스승은 Corky를 중앙에 의자가 놓여 있는 커다란 홀로 데리고 갔다.

27 그곳에는 시험에 통과한 19명의 다른 전사들이 있었다.

28 "저 의자에 가장 먼저 앉는 사람이 승자가 될 것이다."라고 스승이 말했다.

29 Corky와 나머지 전사들은 싸우기 시작했다.

30 그들은 밀고 당기고 달리고 뛰어올랐다.

31 They fought _____ _____ _____, so Corky _____ _____.

32 Finally, he said, "I will not fight _____.

33 Instead, I will _____ _____ _____ _____ _____ _____."

34 The _____ _____ saw this and fought _____ _____.

35 _____ they fought, more warriors _____ _____ and _____.

36 Corky _____ _____ _____ _____ them, so they followed him.

37 Soon, all the warriors _____ Thunder were _____ Corky.

38 Thunder _____ _____ the chair _____ _____ _____ _____.

39 Then, he saw Corky _____ _____ his 18 followers.

40 Thunder realized he was _____ _____.

41 "I _____ _____. You're _____ _____ _____ _____," Thunder said to Corky.

42 _____ _____ _____, the teacher _____ and said. "Of all the great weapons, peace is _____ _____.

43 _____ _____ _____, everyone wants to stand _____ _____ _____ _____ peace."

44 Corky _____ _____ the palace after his training ended.

45 When the king saw him _____, he gave Corky a wise and _____ smile and said, "_____ _____, General?"

---

31 그들은 점점 더 격렬히 싸웠고, Corky는 지쳤다.

32 마침내 그가 말했다. "나는 더는 싸움을 하지 않겠다.

33 대신에 부상당한 자들을 돌볼 것이다."

34 나머지 전사들은 이것을 보고 더 심하게 싸움을 했다.

35 그들이 싸움을 할수록 더 많은 전사들이 지치고 다쳤다.

36 Corky는 그들을 잘 돌봐 주었고, 그들은 Corky를 따르게 되었다.

37 곧 Thunder를 제외한 모든 전사들이 Corky를 따르고 있었다.

38 Thunder는 의자로 걸어가 그곳에 앉으려 했다.

39 그러다 그는 Corky가 18명의 추종자들과 함께 서 있는 것을 봤다.

40 Thunder는 자신이 혼자라는 사실을 깨달았다.

41 "나는 포기하겠다. 네가 진정한 승자다."라고 Thunder가 Corky에게 말했다.

42 그때 스승이 나타나 말했다. "모든 훌륭한 무기 중에서 평화는 내가 가장 좋아하는 것이다.

43 조만간 모든 사람은 평화의 편에 서기를 원한다."

44 Corky는 훈련을 마친 후 성으로 돌아갔다.

45 Corky가 다가오는 것을 본 왕은 그에게 이미 모든 것을 알고 있다는 듯한 현명한 미소를 띠며 말했다. "안녕하시오, 장군?"

※ 다음 문장을 우리말로 쓰시오.

1 ▶ Corky, the Best Warrior

➡ _____

2 ▶ Corky was a brave young man.

➡ _____

3 ▶ He wanted to be a general, but the king said, "You're the strongest man in my army, but you
have much to learn."

➡ _____

_____

4 ▶ He ordered Corky to go to a famous military school.

➡ _____

5 ▶ "Wait there. In a hundred days, your training will start," a voice said from inside the school gate.

➡ _____

6 ▶ Corky got angry.

➡ _____

7 ▶ But then he thought there might be a reason, so he waited.

➡ _____

8 ▶ On the hundred and first day, the gate opened.

➡ _____

9 ▶ An old man said, "You have learned to use your first weapon: patience.

➡ _____

10 ▶ Patience is the most important thing to win a war."

➡ _____

11 ▶ Then, the teacher told Corky to stand against a pole.

➡ _____

12 ▶ Suddenly, he tied Corky to the pole.

➡ _____

13 ▶ Above his head, he put a sign that read "Dangerous and Bad."

➡ _____

14 Many people passed by.
➡ _____

15 Some gave Corky angry looks, and others shouted at him.
➡ _____

16 Corky shouted back.
➡ _____

17 He yelled, "Set me free, or you all will be in big trouble!"
➡ _____

18 That made the situation worse.
➡ _____

19 "I need to try another way," he thought.
➡ _____

20 Then, Corky began to speak softly.
➡ _____

21 He said he was not dangerous or bad but was a good man.
➡ _____

22 He kept saying this in all possible ways.
➡ _____

23 Finally, the people let him go.
➡ _____

24 "Now you control the most powerful weapon: words.
➡ _____

25 Soft words are stronger than sharp swords," said the teacher.
➡ _____

26 Next, the teacher took Corky to a large hall with a chair in the middle.
➡ _____

27 There were 19 other warriors who had passed their tests.
➡ _____

28 "The first one to sit in the chair will be the winner," the teacher said.
➡ _____

29 Corky and the others began fighting.
➡ _____

30 They pushed, pulled, ran, and jumped.
➡ _____

31 They fought harder and harder, so Corky became tired.

➡ _____

32 Finally, he said, "I will not fight anymore.

➡ _____

33 Instead, I will take care of the injured."

➡ _____

34 The other warriors saw this and fought even harder.

➡ _____

35 As they fought, more warriors became tired and hurt.

➡ _____

36 Corky took good care of them, so they followed him.

➡ _____

37 Soon, all the warriors except Thunder were following Corky.

➡ _____

38 Thunder walked toward the chair to sit in it.

➡ _____

39 Then, he saw Corky standing with his 18 followers.

➡ _____

40 Thunder realized he was all alone.

➡ _____

41 "I give up. You're the real winner," Thunder said to Corky.

➡ _____

42 At that moment, the teacher appeared and said. "Of all the great weapons, peace is my favorite.

➡ _____

43 Sooner or later, everyone wants to stand on the side of peace."

➡ _____

44 Corky returned to the palace after his training ended.

➡ _____

45 When the king saw him approach, he gave Corky a wise and knowing smile and said, "What's up, General?"

➡ _____

※ 다음 괄호 안의 단어들을 우리말에 맞도록 바르게 배열하시오.

1 (the / Corky, / Warrior / Best)
➡ _____

2 (was / Corky / brave / a / man. / young)
➡ _____

3 (wanted / he / be / to / general, / a / the / but / said, / king / the / "you're / man / strongest / my / in / army, / you / but / much / have / learn." / to)
➡ _____
_____

4 (ordered / he / to / Corky / to / go / famous / a / school. / military)
➡ _____

5 (there. / "wait // a / in / days, / hundred / training / your / start," / will / voice / a / from / said / inside / school / the / gate.)
➡ _____
_____

6 (got / Corky / angry.)
➡ _____

7 (then / but / thought / he / might / there / a / be / reason, / he / so / waited.)
➡ _____

8 (the / on / hundred / first / and / day, / gate / the / opened.)
➡ _____

9 (old / an / said, / man / have / "you / learned / use / to / first / your / patience. / weapon:)
➡ _____

10 (is / patience / most / the / thing / important / win / to / war." / a)
➡ _____

11 (the / then, / told / teacher / to / Corky / against / stand / pole. / a)
➡ _____

12 (he / suddenly, / Corky / tied / to / pole. / the)
➡ _____

13 (his / above / head, / put / he / sign / a / read / that / Bad." / and / "Dangerous)
➡ _____

14 (people / many / by. / passed)
➡ _____

15 (gave / some / angry / Corky / looks, / others / and / at / shouted / him.)

➡ _____

16 (shouted / Corky / back.)

➡ _____

17 (yelled, / he / me / "set / or / free, / all / you / be / will / big / in / trouble!")

➡ _____

18 (made / that / situation / the / worse.)

➡ _____

19 (need / "I / to / another / try / way," / thought. / he)

➡ _____

20 (Corky / then, / to / began / softly. / speak)

➡ _____

21 (said / he / was / he / not / or / dangerous / but / bad / a / was / man. / good)

➡ _____

22 (kept / he / this / saying / all / in / ways. / possible)

➡ _____

23 (the / finally, / let / people / go. / him)

➡ _____

24 (you / "now / the / control / powerful / most / words. / weapon:)

➡ _____

25 (words / soft / stronger / are / sharp / than / said / swords," / teacher. / the)

➡ _____

26 (the / next, / took / teacher / to / Corky / a / hall / large / with / chair / a / the / in / middle.)

➡ _____

27 (were / there / other / 19 / who / warriors / passed / had / tests. / their)

➡ _____

28 (first / "the / to / one / in / sit / chair / the / be / will / winner," / the / teacher / the / said.)

➡ _____

29 (Corky / the / and / others / fighting. / began)

➡ _____

30 (pushed, / they / ran, / pulled, / jumped. / and)

➡ _____

15 몇몇은 Corky를 화난 표정으로 쳐다봤고, 다른 몇몇은 그에게 소리를 질렀다.

16 Corky도 그들에게 소리를 질렀다.

17 그는 "나를 풀어 줘. 그러지 않으면 모두 혼쭐날 줄 알아!"라고 외쳤다.

18 그것은 상황을 더 악화시켰다.

19 그는 '다른 방법을 써야겠어.'라고 생각했다.

20 그러고 나서 Corky는 부드럽게 말하기 시작했다.

21 그는 자신이 위험하거나 나쁘지 않고 좋은 사람이라고 말했다.

22 그는 모든 방법을 동원해 계속해서 이렇게 말했다.

23 마침내 사람들은 그를 풀어 주었다.

24 "이제 너는 가장 강력한 무기인 '말'을 통제하게 되었다.

25 부드러운 말은 날카로운 칼보다 강하니라."라고 스승은 말했다.

26 다음 단계로 스승은 Corky를 중앙에 의자가 놓여 있는 커다란 홀로 데리고 갔다.

27 그곳에는 시험에 통과한 19명의 다른 전사들이 있었다.

28 "저 의자에 가장 먼저 앉는 사람이 승자가 될 것이다."라고 스승이 말했다.

29 Corky와 나머지 전사들은 싸우기 시작했다.

30 그들은 밀고 당기고 달리고 뛰어올랐다.

31 (fought / they / and / harder / so / harder, / became / Corky / tired.)

➡ _____

32 (he / finally, / said, / will / "I / fight / not / anymore.)

➡ _____

33 (I / instead, / take / will / of / care / injured."/ the)

➡ _____

34 (other / the / saw / warriors / this / and / even / fought / harder.)

➡ _____

35 (they / as / fought, / warriors / more / tired / became / hurt. / and)

➡ _____

36 (took / Corky / care / good / them, / of / they / so / him. / followed)

➡ _____

37 (all / soon, / the / except / warriors / were / Thunder / Corky. / following)

➡ _____

38 (walked / Thunder / the / toward / to / chair / sit / it. / in)

➡ _____

39 (he / then, / Corky / saw / with / standing / 18 / his / followers.)

➡ _____

40 (realized / Thunder / was / he / alone. / all)

➡ _____

41 (give / "I / up. // the / you're / winner," / real / said / Thunder / Corky. / to)

➡ _____

42 (that / at / moment, / teacher / the / and / appeared / said. // "of / the / all / weapons, / great / is / peace / favorite. / my)

➡ _____

_____

43 (later, / or / sooner / wants / everyone / stand / to / the / on / of / side / peace.")

➡ _____

44 (returned / Corky / the / to / after / palace / training / his / ended.)

➡ _____

45 (the / when / saw / king / approach, / him / gave / he / Corky / wise / a / knowing / and / and / smile / said, / up, / General?" / "what's)

➡ _____

_____

31 그들은 점점 더 격렬히 싸웠고, Corky는 지쳤다.

32 마침내 그가 말했다. "나는 더는 싸움을 하지 않겠다.

33 대신에 부상당한 자들을 돌볼 것이다."

34 나머지 전사들은 이것을 보고 더 심하게 싸움을 했다.

35 그들이 싸움을 할수록 너 많은 전사들이 지치고 다쳤다.

36 Corky는 그들을 잘 돌봐 주었고, 그들은 Corky를 따르게 되었다.

37 곧 Thunder를 제외한 모든 전사들이 Corky를 따르고 있었다.

38 Thunder는 의자로 걸어가 그곳에 앉으려 했다.

39 그러다 그는 Corky가 18명의 추종자들과 함께 서 있는 것을 봤다.

40 Thunder는 자신이 혼자라는 사실을 깨달았다.

41 "나는 포기하겠다. 네가 진정한 승자다."라고 Thunder가 Corky에게 말했다.

42 그때 스승이 나타나 말했다. "모든 훌륭한 무기 중에서 평화는 내가 가장 좋아하는 것이다.

43 조만간 모든 사람은 평화의 편에 서기를 원한다."

44 Corky는 훈련을 마친 후 성으로 돌아갔다.

45 Corky가 다가오는 것을 본 왕은 그에게 이미 모든 것을 알고 있다는 듯한 현명한 미소를 띠며 말했다. "안녕하시오, 장군?"

※ 다음 우리말을 영어로 쓰시오.

1 최고의 전사, Corky

➡ _____

2 Corky는 용감한 청년이었다.

➡ _____

3 그는 장군이 되기를 원했지만 왕은 이렇게 말했다. "자네는 우리 군대에서 가장 강한 전사이네.
하지만 자네는 아직도 배울 게 많아."

➡ _____

_____

4 왕은 Corky에게 유명한 군사 학교에 갈 것을 명령했다.

➡ _____

5 "거기서 기다려라. 훈련은 100일 후에 시작할 것이다." 군사 학교 안에서 이렇게 외치는 목소리가 들렸다.

➡ _____

6 Corky는 화가 났다.

➡ _____

7 하지만 이유가 있을 것으로 생각하고 기다렸다.

➡ _____

8 101일째 되던 날, 문이 열렸다.

➡ _____

9 한 노인이 이렇게 말했다. "너는 첫 번째 무기인 '인내'를 사용하는 법을 배운 것이다.

➡ _____

10 인내는 전쟁에서 이기기 위해 가장 중요한 것이다."

➡ _____

11 그리고 난 뒤, 스승은 Corky에게 기둥 앞에 서라고 말했다.

➡ _____

12 갑자기 그는 Corky를 기둥에 묶었다.

➡ _____

13 그의 머리 위에는 '위험하고 나쁨'이라는 푯말을 붙였다.

➡ _____

14 많은 사람이 지나갔다.

➡ _____

15 몇몇은 Corky를 화난 표정으로 쳐다봤고, 다른 몇몇은 그에게 소리를 질렀다.

➡ _____

16 Corky도 그들에게 소리를 질렀다.

➡ _____

17 그는 "나를 풀어 줘. 그러지 않으면 모두 혼쭐날 줄 알아!"라고 외쳤다.

➡ _____

18 그것은 상황을 더 악화시켰다.

➡ _____

19 그는 '다른 방법을 써야겠어.'라고 생각했다.

➡ _____

20 그러고 나서 Corky는 부드럽게 말하기 시작했다.

➡ _____

21 그는 자신이 위험하거나 나쁘지 않고 좋은 사람이라고 말했다.

➡ _____

22 그는 모든 방법을 동원해 계속해서 이렇게 말했다.

➡ _____

23 마침내 사람들은 그를 풀어 주었다.

➡ _____

24 "이제 너는 가장 강력한 무기인 '말'을 통제하게 되었다.

➡ _____

25 부드러운 말은 날카로운 칼보다 강하니라."라고 스승은 말했다.

➡ _____

26 다음 단계로 스승은 Corky를 중앙에 의자가 놓여 있는 커다란 홀로 데리고 갔다.

➡ _____

27 그곳에는 시험에 통과한 19명의 다른 전사들이 있었다.

➡ _____

28 "저 의자에 가장 먼저 앉는 사람이 승자가 될 것이다."라고 스승이 말했다.

➡ _____

29 Corky와 나머지 전사들은 싸우기 시작했다.

➡ _____

30 그들은 밀고 당기고 달리고 뛰어올랐다.

➡ _____

31 그들은 점점 더 격렬히 싸웠고, Corky는 지쳤다.

➡ _____

32 마침내 그가 말했다. "나는 더는 싸움을 하지 않겠다.

➡ _____

33 대신에 부상당한 자들을 돌볼 것이다."

➡ _____

34 나머지 전사들은 이것을 보고 더 심하게 싸움을 했다.

➡ _____

35 그들이 싸움을 할수록 더 많은 전사들이 지치고 다쳤다.

➡ _____

36 Corky는 그들을 잘 돌봐 주었고, 그들은 Corky를 따르게 되었다.

➡ _____

37 곧 Thunder를 제외한 모든 전사들이 Corky를 따르고 있었다.

➡ _____

38 Thunder는 의자로 걸어가 그곳에 앉으려 했다.

➡ _____

39 그러다 그는 Corky가 18명의 추종자들과 함께 서 있는 것을 봤다.

➡ _____

40 Thunder는 자신이 혼자라는 사실을 깨달았다.

➡ _____

41 "나는 포기하겠다. 네가 진정한 승자다."라고 Thunder가 Corky에게 말했다.

➡ _____

42 그때 스승이 나타나 말했다. "모든 훌륭한 무기 중에서 평화는 내가 가장 좋아하는 것이다.

➡ _____

_____

43 조만간 모든 사람은 평화의 편에 서기를 원한다."

➡ _____

44 Corky는 훈련을 마친 후 성으로 돌아갔다.

➡ _____

45 Corky가 다가오는 것을 본 왕은 그에게 이미 모든 것을 알고 있다는 듯한 현명한 미소를 띠며 말했다. "안녕하시오, 장군?"

➡ _____

_____

※ 다음 우리말과 일치하도록 빈칸에 알맞은 말을 쓰시오.

After You Read A

1. Corky _____ _____ _____ _____ _____ in the army.

2. Corky went to _____ _____ _____ and waited _____ _____ _____ _____.

3. Corky _____ _____ he was not _____, so people finally _____ him _____.

4. Corky _____ _____ and took care of _____ _____.

Inside the Story

1. Two people _____ _____ in the hall. _____ is the king, and _____ _____ is Corky.

2. The king _____ Corky _____ _____ _____ _____ _____ _____.

3. Many people are standing around Corky. _____ is talking to Corky, _____ _____ _____ _____ _____ _____.

4. The teacher _____ _____ _____ _____ _____ and _____ there.

5. Two men are standing inside the gate. _____ is holding a _____, and _____ _____ _____ _____ _____ _____ _____.

6. _____ _____ _____ _____ _____ _____ tells Corky _____ _____ there for 100 days.

7. Many warriors are listening to the teacher. _____ are standing, and _____ _____ _____ _____.

8. The teacher wants them _____ _____ _____ _____ _____ the chair.

Link to the World

1. Mahatma Gandhi led a _____ _____ _____ _____ _____ _____.

2. He _____ his people _____ _____ England.

3. He _____ for a long time _____ _____ _____ _____ with weapons.

4. "_____ _____ _____ _____ _____ will only _____ the whole world _____," he said.

1. Corky는 군대에서 장군이 되기를 원했다.
2. Corky는 군사 학교에 가서 100일 동안 기다렸다.
3. Corky는 계속해서 자신이 위험하지 [나쁘지] 않다고 말해서, 사람들이 마침내 그를 풀어 주었다.
4. Corky는 싸움을 멈추고 부상당한 자들을 돌보아주었다.

1. 두 사람이 홀에서 말하고 있다. 한 사람은 왕이고 나머지 한 사람은 Corky이다.
2. 왕은 Corky에게 군사 학교로 가라고 명령한다.
3. 많은 사람이 Corky 주변에 서 있다. 한 사람은 Corky에게 말하고 있고 나머지 사람들은 듣고 있다.
4. 스승은 Corky에게 조용히 하고 거기 있으라고 말한다.
5. 두 남자가 문 안에서 서 있다. 한 명은 칼을 들고 있고 나머지 한 명은 곤봉을 들고 있다.
6. 칼을 들고 있는 남자는 Corky에게 100일 동안 거기서 기다리라고 말한다.
7. 많은 전사가 스승의 말을 듣고 있다. 몇몇은 서 있고 나머지는 무릎을 꿇고 있다.
8. 스승은 그들이 의자에 앉기 위해 계속 싸우기를 원한다.

1. 마하트마 간디는 인도를 해방하기 위한 평화 운동을 이끌었다.
2. 그는 그의 국민들에게 영국에 대항하여 평화롭게 싸울 것을 요청했다.
3. 그는 무기를 들고 싸우는 대신 오랫동안 단식 투쟁을 했다.
4. "눈에는 눈이라는 식의 복수는 오직 전 세계를 눈멀게 할 뿐이다."라고 그는 말했다.

※ 다음 우리말을 영어로 쓰시오.

After You Read A

1. Corky는 군대에서 장군이 되기를 원했다.

➡ _____

2. Corky는 군사 학교에 가서 100일 동안 기다렸다.

➡ _____

3. Corky는 계속해서 자신이 위험하지[나쁘지] 않다고 말해서, 사람들이 마침내 그를 풀어 주었다.

➡ _____

4. Corky는 싸움을 멈추고 부상당한 자들을 돌보아주었다.

➡ _____

Inside the Story

1. 두 사람이 홀에서 말하고 있다. 한 사람은 왕이고 나머지 한 사람은 Corky이다.

➡ _____

2. 왕은 Corky에게 군사 학교로 가라고 명령한다.

➡ _____

3. 많은 사람이 Corky 주변에 서 있다. 한 사람은 Corky에게 말하고 있고 나머지 사람들은 듣고 있다.

➡ _____

4. 스승은 Corky에게 조용히 하고 거기 있으라고 말한다.

➡ _____

5. 두 남자가 문 안에 서 있다. 한 명은 칼을 들고 있고 나머지 한 명은 곤봉을 들고 있다.

➡ _____

6. 칼을 들고 있는 남자는 Corky에게 100일 동안 거기서 기다리라고 말한다.

➡ _____

7. 많은 전사가 스승의 말을 듣고 있다. 몇몇은 서 있고 나머지는 무릎을 꿇고 있다.

➡ _____

8. 스승은 그들이 의자에 앉기 위해 계속 싸우기를 원한다.

➡ _____

Link to the World

1. 마하트마 간디는 인도를 해방하기 위한 평화 운동을 이끌었다.

➡ _____

2. 그는 그의 국민들에게 영국에 대항하여 평화롭게 싸울 것을 요청했다.

➡ _____

3. 그는 무기를 들고 싸우는 대신 오랫동안 단식 투쟁을 했다.

➡ _____

4. "눈에는 눈이라는 식의 복수는 오직 전 세계를 눈멀게 할 뿐이다."라고 그는 말했다.

➡ _____

※ 다음 영어를 우리말로 쓰시오.

01 instead _____

02 average _____

03 control _____

04 tip _____

05 critic _____

06 effort _____

07 public _____

08 realize _____

09 about _____

10 fake _____

11 fold _____

12 forest _____

13 shape _____

14 million _____

15 backward _____

16 case _____

17 hold _____

18 imagine _____

19 share _____

20 tiny _____

21 joke _____

22 neighbor _____

23 shout _____

24 once _____

25 own _____

26 peace _____

27 public officer _____

28 save _____

29 hate _____

30 bookmark _____

31 officer _____

32 piece _____

33 solve _____

34 race car _____

35 end up -ing _____

36 would rather A than B _____

37 get closer to _____

38 keep ~ away _____

39 laugh out loud _____

40 cut ~ into small pieces _____

41 stop+-ing _____

42 say hello to _____

43 rain cats and dogs _____

※ 다음 우리말을 영어로 쓰시오.

01 비평가

02 노력

03 평균; 평균의

04 가짜의

05 조언, 도움말

06 접다

07 통제하다, 조종하다

08 공유하다, 나누다

09 대략

10 농담

11 공공의

12 숲

13 해결하다

14 일단 ~하기만 하면

15 경주용 차

16 깨닫다

17 구하다

18 소리치다

19 작은

20 뒤에서부터, 역방향으로
   (주로 소유격 뒤에서)
21 ~ 자신의

22 평화

23 사건

24 백만

25 창조하다, 만들어 내다

26 모양, 형태

27 책갈피

28 공무원

29 잡다

30 이웃, 옆집 사람

31 관리, 관료

32 대신에

33 조각

34 상상하다

35 큰 소리로 웃다

36 ~하는 것을 멈추다

37 틀림없이 ~하다

38 B하느니 A하겠다

39 결국 ~가 되다

40 ~와 가까워지다

41 ~를 멀리하게 하다

42 ~에게 인사하다

43 비가 억수같이 오다

※ 다음 영영풀이에 알맞은 단어를 <보기>에서 골라 쓴 후, 우리말 뜻을 쓰시오.

1 _____ : an attempt to do something: _____

2 _____ : someone who lives near you: _____

3 _____ : in the direction behind you: _____

4 _____ : very good to eat or drink: _____

5 _____ : a large area of trees growing close together: _____

6 _____ : to rain very heavily: _____

7 _____ : in the place of someone or something else: _____

8 _____ : to ask someone to come to your house, to a party, etc.: _____

9 _____ : to make an idea or picture of something in your mind: _____

10 _____ : a situation in which there is no war, violence, or arguing: _____

11 _____ : to have or use something at the same time as someone else: _____

12 _____ : to bend something so that one part of it lies flat on top of another part:
  _____

13 _____ : to keep someone or something safe from death, harm, loss, etc.: _____

14 _____ : someone whose job is to give their opinion of a book, play, movie, etc.:
  _____

15 _____ : to notice or understand something that you did not notice or understand
  before: _____

16 _____ : to take action so that you are certain that something happens, is true, etc.:
  _____

보기

fold	neighbor	imagine	backward
make sure	instead	realize	invite
share	delicious	peace	effort
save	forest	critic	rain cats and dogs

※ 다음 우리말과 일치하도록 빈칸에 알맞은 것을 골라 쓰시오.

1 _____ _____
A. Magazine   B. Teens'

2 _____ to _____ Your Town
A. Make   B. Ways   C. Better

3 Doing _____ _____ for your neighbors can _____ your town. Start small. Here are some _____.
A. change   B. something   C. tips   D. nice

4 1. _____ to your _____ and _____.
A. smile   B. hello   C. neighbors   D. say

5 2. Don't _____ _____ _____, "Thank you."
A. forget   B. say   C. to

6 3. Share your umbrella _____ _____ _____ _____.
A. rainy   B. on   C. day   D. a

7 4. _____ _____ _____ when your neighbor tells a _____.
A. joke   B. out   C. laugh   D. loud

8 5. Make _____ _____ your _____.
A. for   B. something   C. neighbors

9 6. _____ the _____ for the _____ _____ you.
A. behind   B. hold   C. person   D. door

10 7. _____ your _____ _____ your party.
A. to   B. invite   C. neighbors

11 If you just do one thing _____ day, you can _____ your _____ _____.
A. better   B. each   C. make   D. town

12 _____ for _____
A. Peace   B. Messages

13 On World Peace Day, we _____ our peace _____ the _____.
A. on   B. put   C. board   D. messages

14 Peace means _____ _____ _____ the world. - Kim Jimin
A. around   B. having   C. friends

15 I'd _____ have _____ on Earth _____ _____ of Earth. - Seo Eunji
A. pieces   B. rather   C. than   D. peace

16 I want peace every _____ I go _____ there is always someone _____ or _____. - Park Hansol
A. shouting   B. fighting   C. because   D. place

17 Peace _____ _____ _____.- Yang Miran
A. everyone   B. makes   C. smile

---

1 십대들의 잡지

2 마을을 더 좋게 만드는 방법들

3 이웃들을 위해 뭔가 좋은 일을 하면 여러분의 마을을 변화시킬 수 있다. 작은 것부터 시작하라. 여기 몇 가지 도움말이 있다.

4 1. 이웃들에게 인사를 하고 미소를 지어라.

5 2. 잊지 말고 "고맙습니다."라고 말해라.

6 3. 비 오는 날에 당신의 우산을 함께 써라.

7 4. 이웃이 농담하면 크게 소리 내어 웃어라.

8 5. 이웃들을 위해 뭔가를 만들어라.

9 6. 뒤에 오는 사람을 위해 문을 잡아 줘라.

10 7. 이웃을 당신의 파티에 초대해라.

11 만약 당신이 매일 한 가지씩 하기만 하면, 당신의 마을을 더 좋게 만들 수 있다.

12 평화 메시지

13 우리는 세계 평화의 날에 게시판에 평화 메시지를 붙였다.

14 평화는 세상 어디에서나 친구가 있다는 것을 의미한다. - 김지민

15 나는 지구의 조각들을 갖느니 지구 위의 평화를 갖겠다. - 서은지

16 항상 싸우거나 소리치는 누군가가 있으므로 나는 내가 가는 모든 곳에서 평화를 원한다. - 박한솔

17 평화는 모든 사람을 미소 짓게 만든다. - 양미란

18 Peace is _____ all of us. We just _____ _____ _____ it. - Jang Jaehee

    A. share   B. inside   C. to   D. need

19 _____ _____

    A. LAUGH   B. LET'S

20 _____ apple _____ _____

    A. a   B. an   C. day

21 Jake came in to see his dad. "Dad!" he said, "Is it _____ _____ an apple a day _____ the doctor _____?"

    A. keeps   B. true   C. away   D. that

22 "That's _____ _____ _____," said his dad.

    A. say   B. they   C. what

23 "Well, give me an _____ quickly! I _____ _____ the doctor's _____!"

    A. apple   B. window   C. broke   D. just

24 _____ _____ _____ Books!

    A. to   B. Be   C. Kind

25 Do you know _____ _____ _____? They hate water, the sun, and dog ears. _____ dog ears?

    A. what   B. hate   C. why   D. books

26 Water is _____ for _____ and BOOKS! / The SUN also _____ Books YELLOW / Don't DOG-EAR! Use a _____! / Be Kind to Books!

    A. bookmark   B. bad   C. TURNs   D. WITCHES

27 _____ _____ dog ears in books. Use a _____ _____.

    A. instead   B. folding   C. stop   D. bookmark

28 _____ is a bookmark _____ can _____ your books. _____ kind to your books.

    A. save   B. that   C. be   D. it

29 The _____ you love your books, the _____ your books will be. _____ _____ making your own?

    A. about   B. more   C. happier   D. how

30 _____ That Sound _____

    A. Fake   B. Facts

31 1. _____ 7% of all people who _____ _____ _____ are living on the Earth today.

    A. lived   B. about   C. ever   D. have

32 About 108,200 million people _____ _____ _____ in the history of the world. And about 7,442 million are living on the Earth today.

    A. ever   B. born   C. been   D. have

33 2. Bangladesh _____ _____ _____ _____ Russia.

    A. than   B. has   C. people   D. more

18 평화는 우리 모두의 내면에 있다. 우리는 단지 그것을 공유할 필요가 있을 뿐이다. – 장재희

19 웃읍시다

20 하루에 사과 한 개

21 Jake가 아빠를 보러 들어왔다. "아빠!" 그는 "하루에 사과 한 개가 의사를 멀리하게 만든다는 것이 사실이에요?"라고 말했다.

22 "사람들이 그렇게 말하지," 아빠가 말했다.

23 "자, 저에게 빨리 사과 한 개를 주세요! 제가 방금 의사 선생님의 유리창을 깨뜨렸어요!"

24 책들을 친절하게 대해 주세요!

25 여러분은 책들이 무엇을 싫어하는지 아나요? 그들은 물, 햇빛, 그리고 강아지 귀를 싫어합니다. 왜 강아지 귀일까요?

26 물은 마녀와 책에 해롭다! / 햇빛도 책을 누렇게 뜨게 한다. / 강아지 귀처럼 책을 접지 마라! 책갈피를 사용해라! / 책들을 친절하게 대해 주세요!

27 강아지 귀 모양으로 책을 접는 것을 멈춰 주세요. 대신에 책갈피를 이용하세요.

28 여러분의 책을 구해 주는 것은 바로 책갈피입니다. 여러분의 책들을 친절하게 대해 주세요.

29 여러분이 책을 더 많이 사랑하면 할수록 여러분의 책들은 더 행복해질 겁니다. 여러분 자신의 책갈피를 만들어 보는 게 어떨까요?

30 가짜 같은 사실

31 1 지금까지 살아온 모든 사람의 약 7%가 오늘날 지구상에 살고 있다.

32 세계 역사에서 약 1천8십억 명의 사람들이 지금까지 태어났다. 그리고 약 7십4억 4천2백만 명이 오늘날 지구상에 살고 있다.

33 2 방글라데시는 러시아보다 인구가 더 많다.

34 Russia is the world's _____ _____, but _____ Bangladesh has 166.3 million people _____ 2018. Russia has 143.9 million people.

    A. tiny   B. in   C. country   D. largest

35 3. A banyan tree _____ Kolkata, India, is _____ _____ the _____ Walmart.

    A. average   B. near   C. than   D. bigger

36 The average Walmart store _____ about 104,000 _____ feet. The Great Banyan Tree in Kolkata, India, is about the _____ of a forest, _____ 155,000 square feet.

    A. covering   B. covers   C. size   D. square

37 4. Baby carrots _____ _____ _____ 1986.

    A. invented   B. in   C. were

38 Baby carrots are not actually baby carrots. Big ugly carrots are cut _____ small _____ that have the _____ of a baby carrot. Farmer Mike Yurosek invented them in 1986 as a way to use ugly carrots that weren't _____.

    A. into   B. sold   C. shape   D. pieces

39 _____ _____ the _____

    A. Movies   B. in   C. Jobs

40 Zootopia (2016) It's _____ _____ _____ _____ !

    A. movie   B. the   C. ever   D. greatest

41 Flash is a _____ officer. He is very slow but works hard. You will be _____ to see _____ he does in his _____ time. It's driving a race car!

    A. free   B. surprised   C. public   D. what

42 Nick is a fox _____ a big mouth. Helping Judy, he _____ _____ to her. He _____ becomes a police officer like Judy.

    A. closer   B. with   C. later   D. gets

43 Judy is a small rabbit, but she's smart and strong. After a _____ of _____, she becomes a police officer and _____ many _____.

    A. cases   B. effort   C. solves   D. lot

44 Ratatouille (2007) Everyone _____ _____ movie.

    A. love   B. will   C. this

45 Anton Ego is a food _____. After he eats the food Remy _____, he _____ that _____ can cook.

    A. critic   B. cooked   C. anyone   D. realizes

---

34 러시아는 세계에서 가장 큰 나라이지만, 아주 작은 방글라데시에는 2018년 기준으로 1억 6천6백3십만 명의 인구가 있다. 러시아는 1억 4천3백9십만 명의 인구가 있다.

35 3 인도 Kolkata 부근의 한 바니안(banyan) 나무는 평균적인 월마트보다 크다.

36 평균적인 월마트 상점은 약 10만4천 평방피트의 넓이이다. 인도 Kolkata에 있는 그레이트 바니안 나무는 대략 숲 하나의 크기로 15만5천 평방피트를 차지한다.

37 4 베이비 당근은 1986년 발명되었다.

38 베이비 당근은 실제로 아기처럼 작은 당근이 아니다. 크고 못생긴 당근들이 베이비 당근 모양을 가진 작은 조각으로 잘린다. 농부 Mike Yurosek이 팔리지 않는 못생긴 당근을 사용할 하나의 방편으로 1986년에 그것을 발명하였다.

39 영화 속 직업들

40 주토피아(2016) 그것은 이제까지 가장 대단한 영화이다!

41 Flash는 공무원이다. 그는 아주 느리지만 열심히 일한다. 여러분은 그가 여가 시간에 무엇을 하는지 알게 되면 놀랄 것이다. 그것은 경주용 자동차를 운전하는 것이다!

42 Nick은 커다란 입을 가진 여우이다. Judy를 도우면서 그녀와 가까워진다. 나중에 Judy처럼 경찰관이 된다.

43 Judy는 작은 토끼지만, 영리하고 강하다. 많은 노력을 한 후에, 그녀는 경찰관이 되었고 많은 사건을 해결한다.

44 라따뚜이(2007) 누구라도 이 영화를 사랑할 것이다.

45 Anton Ego는 음식 비평가이다. Remy가 요리한 음식을 먹은 후에, 그는 "누구라도 요리할 수 있다."라는 것을 깨닫는다.

46 Remy, a little mouse, dreams of becoming a cook. He goes into a restaurant and meets a boy _____ Linguini. _____ Linguini, he makes delicious food and _____ up _____ a great cook.

    A. ends   B. named   C. becoming   D. controlling

47 _____ _____ _____ Emojis

    A. with   B. Say   C. It

48 Do you know _____ _____ _____ _____ ?

    A. mean   B. these   C. emojis   D. what

49 Killing two birds with one _____ . / The apple of your eyes. / Don't play games with fire. / Once in a blue moon. / Let's call it a day. / Money does not _____ on trees. / It's raining _____ and dogs. / A _____ of cake.

    A. grow   B. stone   C. cats   D. piece

50 _____ _____

    A. Songe   B. Emoji

51 Now, _____ _____ a Christmas song together! The _____, the _____!

    A. louder   B. sing   C. happier   D. let's

52 _____ _____

    A. Messages   B. Secret

53 _____ you can send messages to your friend that no one _____ can read! It's not so _____ for you to learn how to read and write your own _____ messages.

    A. else   B. secret   C. imagine   D. difficult

54 1. _____ _____

    A. Backward   B. Read

55 This is easy to _____ . Just read the words _____ ! It seems _____ once you know the secret, but it can be a _____ one when you don't.

    A. backward   B. hard   C. simple   D. solve

56 2. Read _____ _____ _____

    A. Letter   B. Second   C. Every

57 Read _____ second letter _____ with the first letter, and when you _____, start again on the letters you _____ .

    A. finish   B. missed   C. starting   D. every

58 3. Pig-pen

59 The Pig-pen is _____ than it _____ . The lines _____ each letter mean the letter _____ the lines.

    A. looks   B. around   C. inside   D. easier

60 Now create your own set of secret letters and write secret messages to send to your friends. _____ _____ you _____ a key so your friends can understand your messages!

    A. sure   B. along   C. make   D. send

46 작은 쥐 Remy는 요리사가 되기를 꿈꾼다. 그는 식당에 들어가서 Linguini라는 이름의 소년을 만난다. Linguini를 통제하면서 그는 맛있는 음식을 만들고 결국에는 훌륭한 요리사가 된다.

47 이모지로 말하자

48 이 이모지들이 무엇을 의미하는지 아니?

49 돌 하나로 새 두 마리 잡기. (일석이조.) / 당신이 가장 사랑하는 사람. (눈에 넣어도 안 아플 사람.) / 불을 가지고 장난치지 마라. / 극히 드물게. / 오늘은 이만하자. / 돈이 나무에서 자라는 것은 아니다. (돈이 그냥 생기는 건 아니다.) / 비가 억수같이 온다. / 케이크 한 조각. (누워서 떡 먹기.)

50 이모지 노래

51 자, 함께 크리스마스 노래를 불러 봅시다! 더 크게 부를수록, 더 행복해집니다!

52 비밀 메시지

53 다른 어떤 사람도 읽을 수 없는 메시지를 친구에게 보낼 수 있다고 상상해 봐! 여러분 자신의 비밀 메시지를 읽고 쓰는 법을 배우는 것이 그렇게 어렵지는 않다.

54 1. 거꾸로 읽어라

55 이것은 풀기 쉽다 - 그냥 단어들을 거꾸로 읽어라! 일단 여러분이 비밀을 알면 간단하지만, 그렇지 못하면 어려울 수 있다.

56 2. 두 번째 글자마다 읽어라

57 첫 번째 글자에서 시작해서 두 번째 글자마다 읽어라. 그리고 끝나면 여러분이 빠뜨린 글자로 다시 시작하라.

58 3. 피그펜

59 피그펜(돼지우리)은 보기보다 쉽다. 각 글자 주변의 선들은 그 선들 안에 있는 글자를 의미한다.

60 이제 여러분은 자신만의 비밀 문자 세트를 만들어서 친구들에게 보낼 비밀 메시지를 써 보아라. 친구들이 메시지를 이해할 수 있도록 해결의 열쇠도 함께 보내도록 해라.

※ 다음 우리말과 일치하도록 빈칸에 알맞은 것을 골라 쓰시오.

1 _____ Magazine

2 _____ _____ _____ Your Town _____

3 Doing _____ _____ for your neighbors can change your town. Start small. Here are _____ _____ .

4 1. _____ _____ _____ your neighbors and _____ .

5 2. Don't _____ _____ _____ , "Thank you."

6 3. Share your umbrella _____ _____ _____ _____ .

7 4. _____ _____ _____ when your neighbor tells a joke.

8 5. Make something _____ your neighbors.

9 6. _____ the door for the person _____ _____ .

10 7. _____ your neighbors _____ your party.

11 If you just do one thing _____ _____ , you can _____ your town _____ .

12 Messages for _____

13 On World Peace Day, we _____ our peace messages _____ the board.

14 Peace means _____ _____ around the world. - Kim Jimin

15 _____ _____ have peace on Earth _____ _____ of Earth. - Seo Eunji

16 I want peace _____ _____ I go because there is always someone _____ or _____ . - Park Hansol

17 Peace _____ everyone _____ .- Yang Miran

18 Peace is _____ all of us. We just need to share it. - Jang Jaehee

19 LET'S _____

20 An apple _____ _____

1 십대들의 잡지

2 마을을 더 좋게 만드는 방법들

3 이웃들을 위해 뭔가 좋은 일을 하면 여러분의 마을을 변화시킬 수 있다. 작은 것부터 시작하라. 여기 몇 가지 도움말이 있다.

4 1. 이웃들에게 인사를 하고 미소를 지어라.

5 2. 잊지 말고 "고맙습니다."라고 말해라.

6 3. 비 오는 날에 당신의 우산을 함께 써라.

7 4. 이웃이 농담하면 크게 소리 내어 웃어라.

8 5. 이웃들을 위해 뭔가를 만들어라.

9 6. 뒤에 오는 사람을 위해 문을 잡아 줘라.

10 7. 이웃을 당신의 파티에 초대해라.

11 만약 당신이 매일 한 가지씩 하기만 하면, 당신의 마을을 더 좋게 만들 수 있다.

12 평화 메시지

13 우리는 세계 평화의 날에 게시판에 평화 메시지를 붙였다.

14 평화는 세상 어디에서나 친구가 있다는 것을 의미한다. – 김지민

15 나는 지구의 조각들을 갖느니 지구 위의 평화를 갖겠다. – 서은지

16 항상 싸우거나 소리치는 누군가가 있으므로 나는 내가 가는 모든 곳에서 평화를 원한다. – 박한솔

17 평화는 모든 사람을 미소 짓게 만든다. – 양미란

18 평화는 우리 모두의 내면에 있다. 우리는 단지 그것을 공유할 필요가 있을 뿐이다. – 장재희

19 웃읍시다

20 하루에 사과 한 개

21 Jake came in to see his dad. "Dad!" he said, "Is _____ true _____ an apple a day _____ the doctor _____?"

22 "That's _____ _____ _____," said his dad.

23 "Well, give me an apple quickly! I _____ _____ the doctor's window!"

24 _____ _____ to Books!

25 Do you know _____ _____ _____? They hate water, the sun, and dog ears. _____ dog ears?

26 Water is bad for _____ and BOOKS! / The SUN also _____ Books YELLOW / _____ DOG-EAR! Use a _____ ! / _____ _____ to Books!

27 Stop _____ dog ears in books. Use a bookmark _____.

28 _____ _____ a bookmark _____ _____ _____ your books. Be kind to your books.

29 _____ _____ you love your books, _____ _____ your books will be. _____ _____ making _____ _____?

30 _____ That _____ _____ _____

31 1. About 7% of all people who _____ _____ _____ are _____ _____ the Earth today.

32 About 108,200 million people _____ _____ _____ _____ in the history of the world. And _____ 7,442 million are living on the Earth today.

33 2. Bangladesh has _____ people _____ Russia.

34 Russia is the world's _____ country, but tiny Bangladesh has 166.3 million people in 2018. Russia has 143.9 million people.

35 3. A banyan tree near Kolkata, India, is _____ _____ the _____ Walmart.

36 The average Walmart store _____ about 104,000 square feet. The Great Banyan Tree in Kolkata, India, is about _____ _____ a forest, _____ 155,000 square feet.

37 4. Baby carrots _____ _____ _____ 1986.

38 Baby carrots are not actually baby carrots. Big ugly carrots _____ _____ _____ small _____ that have the shape of a baby carrot. Farmer Mike Yurosek invented them in 1986 as a _____ _____ _____ ugly carrots that _____ _____.

39 _____ in the Movies

40 Zootopia (2016) It's _____ _____ _____ ever!

21 Jake가 아빠를 보러 들어왔다. "아빠!" 그는 "하루에 사과 한 개가 의사를 멀리하게 만든다는 것이 사실이에요?"라고 말했다.

22 "사람들이 그렇게 말하지," 아빠가 말했다.

23 "자, 저에게 빨리 사과 한 개를 주세요! 제가 방금 의사 선생님의 유리창을 깨뜨렸어요!"

24 책들을 친절하게 대해 주세요!

25 여러분은 책들이 무엇을 싫어하는지 아나요? 그들은 물, 햇빛 그리고 강아지 귀를 싫어합니다. 왜 강아지 귀일까요?

26 물은 마녀와 책에 해롭다! / 햇빛도 책을 누렇게 뜨게 한다. / 강아지 귀처럼 책을 접지 마라! 책갈피를 사용해라! / 책들을 친절하게 대해 주세요!

27 강아지 귀 모양으로 책을 접는 것을 멈춰 주세요. 대신에 책갈피를 이용하세요.

28 여러분의 책을 구해 주는 것은 바로 책갈피입니다. 여러분의 책들을 친절하게 대해 주세요.

29 여러분이 책을 더 많이 사랑하면 할수록 여러분의 책들은 더 행복해질 겁니다. 여러분 자신의 책갈피를 만들어 보는 게 어떨까요?

30 가짜 같은 사실

31 1 지금까지 살아온 모든 사람의 약 7%가 오늘날 지구상에 살고 있다.

32 세계 역사에서 약 1천8십2억 명의 사람들이 지금까지 태어났다. 그리고 약 7십4억 4천2백만 명이 오늘날 지구상에 살고 있다.

33 2 방글라데시는 러시아보다 인구가 더 많다.

34 러시아는 세계에서 가장 큰 나라이지만, 아주 작은 방글라데시에는 2018년 기준으로 1억 6천6백3십만 명의 인구가 있다. 러시아는 1억 4천3백9십만 명의 인구가 있다.

35 3 인도 Kolkata 부근의 한 바니안(banyan) 나무는 평균적인 월마트보다 크다.

36 평균적인 월마트 상점은 약 10만4천 평방피트의 넓이이다. 인도 Kolkata에 있는 그레이트 바니안 나무는 대략 숲 하나의 크기로 15만5천 평방피트를 차지한다.

37 4 베이비 당근은 1986년 발명되었다.

38 베이비 당근은 실제로 아기처럼 작은 당근이 아니다. 크고 못생긴 당근들이 베이비 당근 모양을 가진 작은 조각으로 잘린다. 농부 Mike Yurosek이 팔리지 않는 못생긴 당근을 사용할 하나의 방편으로 1986년에 그것을 발명하였다.

39 영화 속 직업들

40 주토피아(2016) 그것은 이제까지 가장 대단한 영화이다!

41 Flash is a _____ _____. He is very slow but works hard. You will be _____ _____ _____ _____ _____ _____ in his free time. It's driving a race car!

42 Nick is a fox _____ a big mouth. _____ _____, he gets closer to her. He _____ becomes a police officer like Judy.

43 Judy is a small rabbit, but she's smart and strong. After _____ _____ _____ _____, she becomes a police officer and _____ _____ _____.

44 Ratatouille (2007) _____ _____ _____ this movie.

45 Anton Ego is a _____ _____. After he eats the food Remy cooked, he _____ that _____ can cook.

46 Remy, a little mouse, _____ _____ _____ a cook. He goes into a restaurant and meets a boy _____ Linguini. _____ Linguini, he makes delicious food and _____ _____ _____ a great cook.

47 Say It _____ Emojis

48 Do you know _____ _____ _____ _____ _____?

49 Killing two birds with one stone. / The apple of your eyes. / Don't play games with fire. / _____ _____ _____ blue moon. / Let's call it a day. / Money does not grow on trees. / It's raining _____ and _____. / _____ _____ _____ cake.

50 Emoji Song

51 Now, _____ _____ a Christmas song together! _____ _____, _____ _____!

52 _____ Messages

53 Imagine you can send messages to your friend that _____ _____ _____ _____ _____! It's not so difficult for you to learn how to read and write your own secret messages.

54 1. Read _____

55 This is _____ _____ _____. Just read the words _____! It seems simple _____ you know the secret, but it can be a hard one when you don't.

56 2. Read _____ Second Letter

57 Read every second letter _____ _____ the first letter, and when you finish, start again on the letters you _____.

58 3. Pig-pen

59 The Pig-pen is _____ _____ _____ _____. The lines around _____ _____ mean the letter inside the lines.

60 Now create your own set of _____ _____ and write secret messages _____ _____ your friends. _____ _____ you _____ _____ a key so your friends can understand your messages!

41 Flash는 공무원이다. 그는 아주 느리지만 열심히 일한다. 여러분은 그가 여가 시간에 무엇을 하는지 알게 되면 놀랄 것이다. 그것은 경주용 자동차를 운전하는 것이다!

42 Nick은 커다란 입을 가진 여우이다. Judy를 도우면서 그녀와 가까워진다. 나중에 Judy처럼 경찰관이 된다.

43 Judy는 작은 토끼지만, 영리하고 강하다. 많은 노력을 한 후에, 그녀는 경찰관이 되었고 많은 사건을 해결한다.

44 라따뚜이(2007) 누구라도 이 영화를 사랑할 것이다.

45 Anton Ego는 음식 비평가이다. Remy가 요리한 음식을 먹은 후에, 그는 "누구라도 요리할 수 있다."라는 것을 깨닫는다.

46 작은 쥐 Remy는 요리사가 되기를 꿈꾼다. 그는 식당에 들어가서 Linguini라는 이름의 소년을 만난다. Linguini를 통제하면서 그는 맛있는 음식을 만들고 결국에는 훌륭한 요리사가 된다.

47 이모지로 말하자

48 이 이모지들이 무엇을 의미하는지 아니?

49 돌 하나로 새 두 마리 잡기. (일석이조.) / 당신이 가장 사랑하는 사람. (눈에 넣어도 안 아플 사람.) / 불을 가지고 장난치지 마라. / 극히 드물게. / 오늘은 이만하자. / 돈이 나무에서 자라는 것은 아니다. (돈이 그냥 생기는 건 아니다.) / 비가 억수같이 온다. / 케이크 한 조각. (누워서 떡 먹기.)

50 이모지 노래

51 자, 함께 크리스마스 노래를 불러 봅시다! 더 크게 부를수록, 더 행복해집니다!

52 비밀 메시지

53 다른 어떤 사람도 읽을 수 없는 메시지를 친구에게 보낼 수 있다고 상상해 봐라! 여러분 자신의 비밀 메시지를 읽고 쓰는 법을 배우는 것이 그렇게 어렵지는 않다.

54 1. 거꾸로 읽어라

55 이것은 풀기 쉽다 – 그냥 단어들을 거꾸로 읽어라! 일단 여러분이 비밀을 알면 간단하지만, 그렇지 못하면 어려울 수 있다.

56 2. 두 번째 글자마다 읽어라

57 첫 번째 글자에서 시작해서 두 번째 글자마다 읽어라. 그리고 끝나면 여러분이 빠뜨린 글자로 다시 시작하라.

58 3. 피그펜

59 피그펜(돼지우리)은 보기보다 쉽다. 각 글자 주변의 선들은 그 선들 안에 있는 글자를 의미한다.

60 이제 여러분은 자신만의 비밀 문자 세트를 만들어서 친구들에게 보낼 비밀 메시지를 써 보아라. 친구들이 메시지를 이해할 수 있도록 해결의 열쇠도 함께 보내도록 해라.

※ 다음 문장을 우리말로 쓰시오.

1 Teens' Magazine
➡ _____

2 Ways to Make Your Town Better
➡ _____

3 Doing something nice for your neighbors can change your town. Start small. Here are some tips.
➡ _____

4 1. Say hello to your neighbors and smile.
➡ _____

5 2. Don't forget to say, "Thank you."
➡ _____

6 3. Share your umbrella on a rainy day.
➡ _____

7 4. Laugh out loud when your neighbor tells a joke.
➡ _____

8 5. Make something for your neighbors.
➡ _____

9 6. Hold the door for the person behind you.
➡ _____

10 7. Invite your neighbors to your party.
➡ _____

11 If you just do one thing each day, you can make your town better.
➡ _____

12 Messages for Peace
➡ _____

13 On World Peace Day, we put our peace messages on the board.
➡ _____

14 Peace means having friends around the world. - Kim Jimin
➡ _____

15 I'd rather have peace on Earth than pieces of Earth. - Seo Eunji
➡ _____

16 I want peace every place I go because there is always someone fighting or shouting. - Park Hansol
➡ _____

17 Peace makes everyone smile.- Yang Miran
➡ _____

18 Peace is inside all of us. We just need to share it. - Jang Jaehee
➡ _____

19 LET'S LAUGH
➡ _____

20 An apple a day
➡ _____

21 Jake came in to see his dad. "Dad!" he said, "Is it true that an apple a day keeps the doctor away?"
➡ _____

22 "That's what they say," said his dad.
➡ _____

23 "Well, give me an apple quickly! I just broke the doctor's window!"
➡ _____

24 Be Kind to Books!
➡ _____

25 Do you know what books hate? They hate water, the sun, and dog ears. Why dog ears?
➡ _____

26 Water is bad for WITCHES and BOOKS! / The SUN also TURNs Books YELLOW / Don't DOG-EAR! Use a bookmark! / Be Kind to Books!
➡ _____
_____

27 Stop folding dog ears in books. Use a bookmark instead.
➡ _____

28 It is a bookmark that can save your books. Be kind to your books.
➡ _____

29 The more you love your books, the happier your books will be. How about making your own?
➡ _____

30 Facts That Sound Fake
➡ _____

31 1. About 7% of all people who have ever lived are living on the Earth today.
➡ _____

32 About 108,200 million people have ever been born in the history of the world. And about 7,442 million are living on the Earth today.
➡ _____

33 2. Bangladesh has more people than Russia.
➡ _____

34 Russia is the world's largest country, but tiny Bangladesh has 166.3 million people in 2018. Russia has 143.9 million people.
➡ _____

35 3. A banyan tree near Kolkata, India, is bigger than the average Walmart.
➡ _____

36 The average Walmart store covers about 104,000 square feet. The Great Banyan Tree in Kolkata, India, is about the size of a forest, covering 155,000 square feet.
➡ _____

37 4. Baby carrots were invented in 1986.
➡ _____

38 Baby carrots are not actually baby carrots. Big ugly carrots are cut into small pieces that have the shape of a baby carrot. Farmer Mike Yurosek invented them in 1986 as a way to use ugly carrots that weren't sold.
➡ _____
_____

39 Jobs in the Movies
➡ _____

40 Zootopia (2016) It's the greatest movie ever!
➡ _____

41 Flash is a public officer. He is very slow but works hard. You will be surprised to see what he does in his free time. It's driving a race car!
➡ _____

42 Nick is a fox with a big mouth. Helping Judy, he gets closer to her. He later becomes a police officer like Judy.
➡ _____

43 Judy is a small rabbit, but she's smart and strong. After a lot of effort, she becomes a police officer and solves many cases.
➡ _____

44 Ratatouille (2007) Everyone will love this movie.
➡ _____

45 Anton Ego is a food critic. After he eats the food Remy cooked, he realizes that anyone can cook.
➡ _____

46 Remy, a little mouse, dreams of becoming a cook. He goes into a restaurant and meets a boy named Linguini. Controlling Linguini, he makes delicious food and ends up becoming a great cook.
➡ _____

47 Say It with Emojis
➡ _____

48 Do you know what these emojis mean?
➡ _____

49 Killing two birds with one stone. / The apple of your eyes. / Don't play games with fire. / Once in a blue moon. / Let's call it a day. / Money does not grow on trees. / It's raining cats and dogs. / A piece of cake.
➡ _____
_____
_____

50 Emoji Song
➡ _____

51 Now, let's sing a Christmas song together! The louder, the happier!
➡ _____

52 Secret Messages
➡ _____

53 Imagine you can send messages to your friend that no one else can read! It's not so difficult for you to learn how to read and write your own secret messages.
➡ _____
_____

54 1. Read Backward
➡ _____

55 This is easy to solve. Just read the words backward! It seems simple once you know the secret, but it can be a hard one when you don't.
➡ _____

56 2. Read Every Second Letter
➡ _____

57 Read every second letter starting with the first letter, and when you finish, start again on the letters you missed.
➡ _____

58 3. Pig-pen
➡ _____

59 The Pig-pen is easier than it looks. The lines around each letter mean the letter inside the lines.
➡ _____

60 Now create your own set of secret letters and write secret messages to send to your friends. Make sure you send along a key so your friends can understand your messages!
➡ _____
_____

※ 다음 괄호 안의 단어들을 우리말에 맞도록 바르게 배열하시오.

1 (Magazine / Teens')
➡ _____

2 (to / Ways / Your / Make / Better / Town)
➡ _____

3 (something / doing / for / nice / neighbors / your / change / can / town. / your // small. / start // are / here / tips. / some)
➡ _____
_____

4 (1. / hello / say / your / to / and / smile. / neighbors)
➡ _____

5 (2. / forget / don't / say, / to / you." / "thank)
➡ _____

6 (3. / your / share / on / umbrella / day. / rainy / a)
➡ _____

7 (4. / out / laugh / when / loud / neighbor / your / a / joke. / tells)
➡ _____

8 (5. / something / make / your / for / neighbors.)
➡ _____

9 (6. / the / hold / for / door / person / the / you. / behind)
➡ _____

10 (7. / your / invite / neighbors / to / party. / your)
➡ _____

11 (you / if / do / just / thing / one / day, / each / can / you / make / town / your / better.)
➡ _____

12 (for / Messages / Peace)
➡ _____

13 (World / On / Day, / Peace / put / we / peace / our / on / messages / board. / the)
➡ _____

14 (means / peace / friends / having / the / around / world. / - / Jimin / Kim)
➡ _____

15 (rather / I'd / peace / have / Earth / on / pieces / than / Earth. / of / - / Eunji / Seo)
➡ _____

16 (want / I / every / peace / I / place / because / go / is / there / someone / always / shouting. / or / fighting / - / Hansol / Park)
➡ _____

17 (peace / everyone / smile. / makes / - / Miran / Yang)
➡ _____

1 십대들의 잡지

2 마을을 더 좋게 만드는 방법들

3 이웃들을 위해 뭔가 좋은 일을 하면 여러분의 마을을 변화시킬 수 있다. 작은 것부터 시작하라. 여기 몇 가지 도움말이 있다.

4 1. 이웃들에게 인사를 하고 미소를 지어라.

5 2. 잊지 말고 "고맙습니다."라고 말해라.

6 3. 비 오는 날에 당신의 우산을 함께 써라.

7 4. 이웃이 농담하면 크게 소리 내어 웃어라.

8 5. 이웃들을 위해 뭔가를 만들어라.

9 6. 뒤에 오는 사람을 위해 문을 잡아 줘라.

10 7. 이웃을 당신의 파티에 초대해라.

11 만약 당신이 매일 한 가지씩 하기만 하면, 당신의 마을을 더 좋게 만들 수 있다.

12 평화 메시지

13 우리는 세계 평화의 날에 게시판에 평화 메시지를 붙였다.

14 평화는 세상 어디에서나 친구가 있다는 것을 의미한다. – 김지민

15 나는 지구의 조각들을 갖느니 지구 위의 평화를 갖겠다. – 서은지

16 항상 싸우거나 소리치는 누군가가 있으므로 나는 내가 가는 모든 곳에서 평화를 원한다. – 박한솔

17 평화는 모든 사람을 미소 짓게 만든다. – 양미란

18 (is / peace / all / inside / us. / of // we / need / just / share / to / it. / Jaehee / Jang)

➡ _____

19 (LAUGH / LET'S)

➡ _____

20 (apple / an / day / a)

➡ _____

21 (came / Jake / to / in / his / see / dad. // he / "dad!" / said, / it / "is / that / true / apple / an / day / a / keeps / doctor / the / away?")

➡ _____

➡ _____

22 ("that's / they / what / say," / his / said / dad.)

➡ _____

23 (give / "well, / me / apple / an / quickly! // just / I / the / broke / window!" / doctor's)

➡ _____

➡ _____

24 (Kind / Be / Books! / to)

➡ _____

25 (you / do / what / know / hate? / books // hate / they / water, / sun, / the / and / ears. / dog // dog / why / ears?)

➡ _____

➡ _____

26 (is / water / for / bad / BOOKS! / and / WITCHES // SUN / the / also / Books / TURNs / YELLOW // DOG-EAR! / Don't // a / use / bookmark! // Kind / Be / Books! / to)

➡ _____

➡ _____

27 (folding / stop / ears / dog / books. / in // a / use / instead. / bookmark)

➡ _____

28 (is / it / bookmark / a / can / that / your / save / books. // kind / be / your / to / books.)

➡ _____

29 (more / the / love / you / books, / your / happier / the / books / your / be. / will // about / how / own? / your / making)

➡ _____

➡ _____

30 (That / Facts / Fake / Sound)

➡ _____

31 (1. / 7% / about / all / of / who / people / ever / have / are / lived / living / the / on / today. / Earth)

➡ _____

➡ _____

32 (108,200 / about / people / million / ever / have / born / been / the / in / of / history / world. / the // about / and / million / 7,442 / living / are / the / on / today. / Earth)

➡ _____

➡ _____

33 (2. / has / Bangladesh / more / than / people / Russia.)

➡ _____

18 평화는 우리 모두의 내면에 있다. 우리는 단지 그것을 공유할 필요가 있을 뿐이다. — 장재희

19 웃읍시다

20 하루에 사과 한 개

21 Jake가 아빠를 보러 들어왔다. "아빠!" 그는 "하루에 사과 한 개가 의사를 멀리하게 만든다는 것이 사실이에요?"라고 말했다.

22 "사람들이 그렇게 말하지," 아빠가 말했다.

23 "자, 저에게 빨리 사과 한 개를 주세요! 제가 방금 의사 선생님의 유리창을 깨뜨렸어요!"

24 책들을 친절하게 대해 주세요!

25 여러분은 책들이 무엇을 싫어하는지 아나요? 그들은 물, 햇빛, 그리고 강아지 귀를 싫어합니다. 왜 강아지 귀일까요?

26 물은 마녀와 책에 해롭다! / 햇빛도 책을 누렇게 뜨게 한다. / 강아지 귀처럼 책을 접지 마라! 책갈피를 사용해라! / 책들을 친절하게 대해 주세요!

27 강아지 귀 모양으로 책을 접는 것을 멈춰 주세요. 대신에 책갈피를 이용하세요.

28 여러분의 책을 구해 주는 것은 바로 책갈피입니다. 여러분의 책들을 친절하게 대해 주세요.

29 여러분이 책을 더 많이 사랑하면 할수록 여러분의 책들은 더 행복해질 겁니다. 여러분 자신의 책갈피를 만들어 보는 게 어떨까요?

30 가짜 같은 사실

31 1 지금까지 살아온 모든 사람의 약 7%가 오늘날 지구상에 살고 있다.

32 세계 역사에서 약 1천8십억 명의 사람들이 지금까지 태어났다. 그리고 약 7십4억 4천2백만 명이 오늘날 지구상에 살고 있다.

33 2 방글라데시는 러시아보다 인구가 더 많다.

34 (is / Russia / world's / the / country, / largest / tiny / but / has / Bangladesh / 166.3 / people / million / 2018 / in // has / Russia / million / 143.9 / people.)
➡ _____

_____

35 (3. / banyan / a / near / tree / India, / Kolkata, / is / than / bigger / average / the / Walmart.)
➡ _____

36 (average / the / store / Walmart / covers / 104,000 / about / feet. / square // Great / The / Banyan / in / Tree / India, / Kolkata, / about / is / the / of / size / forest, / a / 155,000 / covering / feet. / square)
➡ _____

37 (4. / carrots / baby / invented / were / 1986. / in)
➡ _____

38 (carrots / baby / not / are / baby / actually / carrots. // ugly / big / are / carrots / into / cut / pieces / small / have / that / shape / the / a / of / carrot. / baby // Mike / Farmer / Yurosek / them / invented / 1986 / in / a / as / to / way / ugly / use / that / carrots / sold. / weren't)
➡ _____

_____

_____

39 (in / Jobs / Movies / the)
➡ _____

40 ((2016) / Zootopia // the / it's / movie / greatest / ever!)
➡ _____

41 (is / Flash / a / officer. / public // is / he / very / but / slow / hard. / works // will / you / surprised / be / see / to / he / what / does / free / in / time. / his // driving / it's / race / a / car!)
➡ _____

_____

42 (is / Nick / fox / a / with / mouth / big / a // Judy, / helping / gets / he / to / closer / her. // later / he / becomes / police / a / officer / Judy. / like)
➡ _____

_____

43 (is / Judy / a / rabbit, / small / she's / but / strong. / and / smart // a / after / of / lot / effort, / becomes / she / police / a / officer / solves / and / cases. / many)
➡ _____

_____

44 ((2007) / Ratatouille // will / everyone / this / love / movie.)
➡ _____

45 (Ego / Anton / a / is / critic. / food // he / after / the / eats / food / cooked, / Remy / realizes / he / that / can / anyone / cook.)
➡ _____

_____

34 러시아는 세계에서 가장 큰 나라이지만, 아주 작은 방글라데시에는 2018년 기준으로 1억 6천6백3십만 명의 인구가 있다. 러시아는 1억 4천3백9십만 명의 인구가 있다.

35 3 인도 Kolkata 부근의 한 바니안(banyan) 나무는 평균적인 월마트보다 크다.

36 평균적인 월마트 상점은 약 10만4천 평방피트의 넓이이다. 인도 Kolkata에 있는 그레이트 바니안 나무는 대략 숲 하나의 크기로 15만5천 평방피트를 차지한다.

37 4 베이비 당근은 1986년 발명되었다.

38 베이비 당근은 실제로 아기처럼 작은 당근이 아니다. 크고 못생긴 당근들이 베이비 당근 모양을 가진 작은 조각으로 잘린다. 농부 Mike Yurosek이 팔리지 않는 못생긴 당근을 사용할 하나의 방편으로 1986년에 그것을 발명하였다.

39 영화 속 직업들

40 주토피아(2016) 그것은 이제까지 가장 대단한 영화이다!

41 Flash는 공무원이다. 그는 아주 느리지만 열심히 일한다. 여러분은 그가 여가 시간에 무엇을 하는지 알게 되면 놀랄 것이다. 그것은 경주용 자동차를 운전하는 것이다!

42 Nick은 커다란 입을 가진 여우이다. Judy를 도우면서 그녀와 가까워진다. 나중에 Judy처럼 경찰관이 된다.

43 Judy는 작은 토끼지만, 영리하고 강하다. 많은 노력을 한 후에, 그녀는 경찰관이 되었고 많은 사건을 해결한다.

44 라따뚜이(2007) 누구라도 이 영화를 사랑할 것이다.

45 Anton Ego는 음식 비평가이다. Remy가 요리한 음식을 먹은 후에, 그는 "누구라도 요리할 수 있다."라는 것을 깨닫는다.

46 (a / Remy / little / mouse, / of / dreams / a / becoming / cook. // goes / he / a / into / restaurant / and / a / meets / named / boy / Linguini. // Linguini, / controlling / makes / he / food / delicious / and / up / ends / a / becoming / cook. / great)

➡ _____

_____

47 (It / Say / Emojis / with)

➡ _____

48 (you / do / what / know / emojis / these / mean?)

➡ _____

49 (two / killing / with / birds / stone. / one // apple / the / your / of / eyes. // play / don't / with / games / fire. // in / once / blue / a / moon. // call / let's / a / it / day. // does / money / grow / not / trees. / on // raining / it's / dogs. / and / cats // / piece / a / cake. / of)

➡ _____

_____

50 (Song / Emoji)

➡ _____

51 (let's / now, / sing / Christmas / a / together! / song // louder, / the / happier! / the)

➡ _____

52 (Messages / Secret)

➡ _____

53 (you / imagine / send / can / messages / your / to / that / friend / no / else / one / read! / can // not / it's / difficult / so / you / for / learn / to / to / how / read / and / your / write / own / messages. / secret)

➡ _____

_____

54 (1. / Backward / Read)

➡ _____

55 (is / this / to / easy / solve. // read / just / words / the / backward! // seems / it / once / simple / know / the / you / secret, / it / but / be / can / one / hard / a / when / don't / you)

➡ _____

_____

56 (2. / Every / Read / Letter / Second)

➡ _____

57 (every / read / letter / second / with / starting / first / the / letter, / and / you / when / finish, / again / start / the / on / letters / missed. / you)

➡ _____

58 (Pig-pen / 3.)

➡ _____

59 (Pig-pen / the / easier / is / it / than / looks. // lines / the / each / around / letter / the / mean / letter / the / inside / lines.)

➡ _____

60 (create / now / own / your / of / set / letters / secret / and / secret / write / messages / send / to / your / to / friends. // sure / make / send / you / along / key / a / so / friends / your / can / your / understand / messages!)

➡ _____

_____

46 작은 쥐 Remy는 요리사가 되기를 꿈꾼다. 그는 식당에 들어가서 Linguini라는 이름의 소년을 만난다. Linguini를 통제하면서 그는 맛있는 음식을 만들고 결국에는 훌륭한 요리사가 된다.

47 이모지로 말하자

48 이 이모지들이 무엇을 의미하는지 아니?

49 돌 하나로 새 두 마리 잡기. (일석이조.) / 당신이 가장 사랑하는 사람. (눈에 넣어도 안 아플 사람.) / 불을 가지고 장난치지 마라. / 극히 드물게. / 오늘은 이만하자. / 돈이 나무에서 자라는 것은 아니다. (돈이 그냥 생기는 건 아니다.) / 비가 억수같이 온다. / 케이크 한 조각. (누워서 떡 먹기.)

50 이모지 노래

51 자, 함께 크리스마스 노래를 불러 봅시다! 더 크게 부를수록, 더 행복해집니다!

52 비밀 메시지

53 다른 어떤 사람도 읽을 수 없는 메시지를 친구에게 보낼 수 있다고 상상해 봐라! 여러분 자신의 비밀 메시지를 읽고 쓰는 법을 배우는 것이 그렇게 어렵지는 않다.

54 1. 거꾸로 읽어라

55 이것은 풀기 쉽다 – 그냥 단어들을 거꾸로 읽어라! 일단 여러분이 비밀을 알면 간단하지만, 그렇지 못하면 어려울 수 있다.

56 2. 두 번째 글자마다 읽어라

57 첫 번째 글자에서 시작해서 두 번째 글자마다 읽어라. 그리고 끝나면 여러분이 빠뜨린 글자로 다시 시작하라.

58 3. 피그펜

59 피그펜(돼지우리)은 보기보다 쉽다. 각 글자 주변의 선들은 그 선들 안에 있는 글자를 의미한다.

60 이제 여러분은 자신만의 비밀 문자 세트를 만들어서 친구들에게 보낼 비밀 메시지를 써 보아라. 친구들이 메시지를 이해할 수 있도록 해결의 열쇠도 함께 보내도록 해라.

※ 다음 우리말을 영어로 쓰시오.

1 십대들의 잡지

➡ _____

2 마을을 더 좋게 만드는 방법들

➡ _____

3 이웃들을 위해 뭔가 좋은 일을 하면 여러분의 마을을 변화시킬 수 있다. 작은 것부터 시작하라. 여기 몇 가지 도움말이 있다.

➡ _____

4 1. 이웃들에게 인사를 하고 미소를 지어라.

➡ _____

5 2. 잊지 말고 "고맙습니다."라고 말해라.

➡ _____

6 3. 비 오는 날에 당신의 우산을 함께 써라.

➡ _____

7 4. 이웃이 농담하면 크게 소리 내어 웃어라.

➡ _____

8 5. 이웃들을 위해 뭔가를 만들어라.

➡ _____

9 6. 뒤에 오는 사람을 위해 문을 잡아 줘라.

➡ _____

10 7. 이웃을 당신의 파티에 초대해라.

➡ _____

11 만약 당신이 매일 한 가지씩 하기만 하면, 당신의 마을을 더 좋게 만들 수 있다.

➡ _____

12 평화 메시지

➡ _____

13 우리는 세계 평화의 날에 게시판에 평화 메시지를 붙였다.

➡ _____

14 평화는 세상 어디에서나 친구가 있다는 것을 의미한다. – 김지민

➡ _____

15 나는 지구의 조각들을 갖느니 지구 위의 평화를 갖겠다. – 서은지

➡ _____

16 항상 싸우거나 소리치는 누군가가 있으므로 나는 내가 가는 모든 곳에서 평화를 원한다. – 박한솔

➡ _____

17 평화는 모든 사람을 미소 짓게 만든다. – 양미란

➡ _____

18 평화는 우리 모두의 내면에 있다. 우리는 단지 그것을 공유할 필요가 있을 뿐이다. – 장재희

➡ _____

19 웃읍시다

➡ _____

20 하루에 사과 한 개

➡ _____

21 Jake가 아빠를 보러 들어왔다. "아빠!" 그는 "하루에 사과 한 개가 의사를 멀리하게 만든다는 것이 사실이에요?"라고 말했다.
➡

22 "사람들이 그렇게 말하지," 아빠가 말했다.
➡

23 "자, 저에게 빨리 사과 한 개를 주세요! 제가 방금 의사 선생님의 유리창을 깨뜨렸어요!"
➡

24 책들을 친절하게 대해 주세요!
➡

25 여러분은 책들이 무엇을 싫어하는지 아나요? 그들은 물, 햇빛, 그리고 강아지 귀를 싫어합니다. 왜 강아지 귀일까요?
➡

26 물은 마녀와 책에 해롭다! / 햇빛도 책을 누렇게 뜨게 한다. / 강아지 귀처럼 책을 접지 마라! 책갈피를 사용해라! / 책들을 친절하게 대해 주세요!
➡

27 강아지 귀 모양으로 책을 접는 것을 멈춰 주세요. 대신에 책갈피를 이용하세요.
➡

28 여러분의 책을 구해 주는 것은 바로 책갈피입니다. 여러분의 책들을 친절하게 대해 주세요.
➡

29 여러분이 책을 더 많이 사랑하면 할수록 여러분의 책들은 더 행복해질 겁니다. 여러분 자신의 책갈피를 만들어 보는 게 어떨까요?
➡

30 가짜 같은 사실
➡

31 1. 지금까지 살아온 모든 사람의 약 7%가 오늘날 지구상에 살고 있다.
➡

32 세계 역사에서 약 1천8십2억 명의 사람들이 지금까지 태어났다. 그리고 약 7십4억 4천2백만 명이 오늘날 지구상에 살고 있다.
➡

33 2. 방글라데시는 러시아보다 인구가 더 많다.
➡

34 러시아는 세계에서 가장 큰 나라이지만, 아주 작은 방글라데시에는 2018년 기준으로 1억 6천6백3십만 명의 인구가 있다. 러시아는 1억 4천3백9십만 명의 인구가 있다.
➡

35 3. 인도 Kolkata 부근의 한 바니안(banyan) 나무는 평균적인 월마트보다 크다.
➡

36 평균적인 월마트 상점은 약 10만4천 평방피트의 넓이이다. 인도 Kolkata에 있는 그레이트 바니안 나무는 대략 숲 하나의 크기로 15만5천 평방피트를 차지한다.
➡

37 4. 베이비 당근은 1986년 발명되었다.
➡

38 베이비 당근은 실제로 아기처럼 작은 당근이 아니다. 크고 못생긴 당근들이 베이비 당근 모양을 가진 작은 조각으로 잘린다. 농부 Mike Yurosek이 팔리지 않는 못생긴 당근을 사용할 하나의 방편으로 1986년에 그것을 발명하였다.
➡

39 영화 속 직업들
➡

40 주토피아(2016) 그것은 이제까지 가장 대단한 영화이다!
➡

41 Flash는 공무원이다. 그는 아주 느리지만 열심히 일한다. 여러분은 그가 여가 시간에 무엇을 하는지 알게 되면 놀랄 것이다. 그것은 경주용 자동차를 운전하는 것이다!
➡ _____

42 Nick은 커다란 입을 가진 여우이다. Judy를 도우면서 그녀와 가까워진다. 나중에 Judy처럼 경찰관이 된다.
➡ _____

43 Judy는 작은 토끼지만, 영리하고 강하다. 많은 노력을 한 후에, 그녀는 경찰관이 되었고 많은 사건을 해결한다.
➡ _____

44 라따뚜이(2007) 누구라도 이 영화를 사랑할 것이다.
➡ _____

45 Anton Ego는 음식 비평가이다. Remy가 요리한 음식을 먹은 후에, 그는 "누구라도 요리할 수 있다." 라는 것을 깨닫는다.
➡ _____

46 작은 쥐 Remy는 요리사가 되기를 꿈꾼다. 그는 식당에 들어가서 Linguini라는 이름의 소년을 만난다. Linguini를 통제하면서 그는 맛있는 음식을 만들고 결국에는 훌륭한 요리사가 된다.
➡ _____

47 이모지로 말하자
➡ _____

48 이 이모지들이 무엇을 의미하는지 아니?
➡ _____

49 돌 하나로 새 두 마리 잡기. (일석이조.) / 당신이 가장 사랑하는 사람. (눈에 넣어도 안 아플 사람.) / 불을 가지고 장난치지 마라. / 극히 드물게. / 오늘은 이만하자. / 돈이 나무에서 자라는 것은 아니다. (돈이 그냥 생기는 건 아니다.) / 비가 억수같이 온다. / 케이크 한 조각. (누워서 떡 먹기.)
➡ _____
_____

50 이모지 노래
➡ _____

51 자, 함께 크리스마스 노래를 불러 봅시다! 더 크게 부를수록, 더 행복해집니다!
➡ _____

52 비밀 메시지
➡ _____

53 다른 어떤 사람도 읽을 수 없는 메시지를 친구에게 보낼 수 있다고 상상해 봐라! 여러분 자신의 비밀 메시지를 읽고 쓰는 법을 배우는 것이 그렇게 어렵지는 않다.
➡ _____

54 1. 거꾸로 읽어라
➡ _____

55 이것은 풀기 쉽다 – 그냥 단어들을 거꾸로 읽어라! 일단 여러분이 비밀을 알면 간단하지만, 그렇지 못하면 어려울 수 있다.
➡ _____

56 2. 두 번째 글자마다 읽어라
➡ _____

57 첫 번째 글자에서 시작해서 두 번째 글자마다 읽어라. 그리고 끝나면 여러분이 빠뜨린 글자로 다시 시작하라.
➡ _____

58 3. 피그펜
➡ _____

59 피그펜(돼지우리)은 보기보다 쉽다. 각 글자 주변의 선들은 그 선들 안에 있는 글자를 의미한다.
➡ _____

60 이제 여러분은 자신만의 비밀 문자 세트를 만들어서 친구들에게 보낼 비밀 메시지를 써 보아라. 친구들이 메시지를 이해할 수 있도록 해결의 열쇠도 함께 보내도록 해라.
➡ _____
_____

영어 기출 문제집

2학기

정답 및 해설

천재 | 정사열

적중100

중 3

Fact, Opinion or Fake

시험대비 실력평가

01 opinion	02 ④	03 ⑤	04 ②
05 ③	06 ①	07 turned out	
08 false			

01 내 생각에 영어는 가장 어려운 과목이다. <영어 설명> 사물 또는 사람에 대한 생각이나 믿음

02 'appear'는 '~처럼 보이다', '나타나다'의 의미를 가지고 있다. • 이 새로운 추세는 한 동안 계속될 것으로 보인다. • 도쿄의 한 지하철역에 새로운 자판기가 등장할 것이다.

03 (A) 내 숙제가 완벽하지(complete) 않아서 선생님은 화가 나셨다. (B) 우리는 우선 정보의 출처(source)를 찾아야 한다. critical: 비평의, 비판적인, complex: 복잡한, 착잡한, resource: 자원, 역량

04 '물리적인 폭력을 사용하여 어떤 사람이나 어떤 것을 다치게 하거나 손상을 주려고 하다'의 의미로 'attack(공격하다)'이 적절하다.

05 '서커스에서 우스운 옷을 입고 밝은 화장을 하고 사람들을 웃게 하려고 어리석은 행동을 하는 공연자'란 의미로 'clown(광대)'이 적절하다. 'crown'은 '왕관'이다.

06 나머지는 모두 '명사-형용사'관계이고, ①번은 '동사-명사'관계이다.

07 '~로 밝혀지다'는 'turn out'을 이용하여 과거형 turned를 쓰는 것이 적절하다.

08 유의어 관계다. 증거 : 거짓의

서술형 시험대비

01 (1) spread (2) critically (3) scared (4) sink
02 touching
03 (1) (c)omfortable (2) (b)oring
   (3) (m)ajor (4) (S)low
04 (1) support, 지지하다 (2) spread, 퍼지다
   (3) sink, 가라앉다 (4) octopus, 문어
05 (1) pay attention to (2) tell, from (3) made up

01 (1) '그 이야기는 빠르게 모든 사람에게 퍼졌다.' 'spread'의 과거형은 'spread'다. (2) '노동자들은 문제를 해결하기 위해 비판적으로 생각해야 한다.' 동사를 수식하기 위해 부사 'critically'로 바꾸어야 한다. (3) '그 어린 소년은 괴물을 무서워한다.'

'scare'는 동사로 be동사 뒤에 사용되기 위해 과거분사 형태로 바뀌어야 한다. (4) '만약 배에 구멍이 생기면, 배는 가라앉을 것이다.'

02 '연민, 동정, 슬픔 등을 느끼게 하는'의 의미로 'touching(감동적인)'이 적절하다.

03 (1) comfortable: 편안한 (2) boring: 지루한 (3) major: 주요한 (4) slow down: 속도를 줄이다

04 (1) 어떤 사람에게 도움, 동의, 위로, 격려 등을 주다 (2) 한 장소나 표면 위에 펼치거나 배열하다 (3) 수면 아래로 사라지다 (4) 여덟 개의 긴 다리를 가진 연한 바다 생물

05 (1) 학생들은 선생님에게 집중해야 한다. (2) 그의 부모님은 그에게 옳고 그른 것을 구별하는 법을 가르쳐 주셨다. (3) 분홍 말에 관한 이야기는 꾸며낸 것이었다.

[교과서] Conversation

핵심 Check

1 How do you feel about them?   2 ③

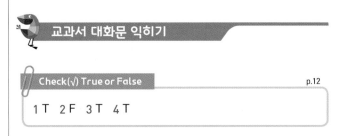

교과서 대화문 익히기

Check(√) True or False

1 T 2 F 3 T 4 T

교과서 확인학습

Get Ready 2
(1) like, I think, fake / agree, kind, real
(2) sharp teeth, What do you think of, real / search, check
(3) What / look like, strange / too
(4) This, real / Let's, fact

Start Off – Listen & Talk A
1. How do you feel about / light, comfortable / to buy, school field trip
2. is wearing / agree with, Actually, much heavier / believe

Start Off – Listen & Talk B
How, feel / touching, gave up, to save / Why / seem

real, a little boring

Start Off – Speak Up

How, about, ad / shows / should not

Step Up – Real-life Scene

cool, How do you feel about / that / makes, laugh, loud / octopus / make sense / when, climbing, lying / agree with, fake, out of

Express Yourself A

1. How, about / get along, with / these two, enjoying, together
2. By the way / guess / prefer / with, better than, In fact / to help
3. feel about / anything special / were made, uniform / passed away / touching

---

시험대비 기본평가 p.16

01 What, think of[about] 02 ④ 03 ③
04 ②

01 'What do you think of[about] ~?'는 '~에 대하여 어떻게 생각하니?'라는 표현이다.

02 상대방에게 어떤 대상에 대한 의견을 물을 때 사용하는 표현으로 'How do you feel about ~?', 'What do you think about ~?(~에 대하여 어떻게 생각하니?)', 'What's your opinion about ~?(~에 대한 의견이 무엇이니?)', 'What do you say about ~?(~에 대하여 어떻게 생각하십니까?)' 등을 사용할 수 있다. ④번의 'What do you know about ~?'은 '~에 대해 무엇을 알고 있어?'라는 뜻으로 특정 대상에 대해 무엇을 알고 있는지 물을 때 사용하는 표현이다.

03 ④번의 'I couldn't agree more.'는 '전적으로 동의해.'라는 표현이다.

04 'I don't agree with you.(나는 동의하지 않아요.)'는 상대와 의견이 달라서 동의하지 않고 상대의 의견에 이의를 제기하는 말이다.

시험대비 실력평가 p.17~18

01 ④   02 (a) touching (b) boring   03 ⑤
04 ③   05 ③   06 ②
07 get along, with   08 ⑤   09 ④
10 ①   11 ③

01 B의 '이 드라마가 올해 최고의 드라마다.'라는 말에 대해 G가 '그것은 좋은 드라마가 아니다.'라고 말하고 있으므로 ④가 적절하다. 나머지는 모두 동의하는 표현이다.

02 (a)는 '감동적인'의 뜻을 가지는 'touching'이 적절하고, (b)는 '지루한'의 뜻을 가진 'boring'이 적절하다.

03 Alex가 문어에 대해 많이 알고 있는지는 알 수 없다.

04 나머지는 'An octopus'를 가리키고, (c)는 앞 문장의 '문어가 나무에 사는 것'을 가리킨다.

05 빈칸 앞의 동의하지 않는다는 말에 대해 더 구체적으로 '강조, 첨가'하는 표현을 가진 'Actually(사실)'가 적절하다.

06 비교급을 강조하는 말은 'much, even, still, far, a lot'이다. 'very'는 원급(형용사나 부사)을 강조하는 말이다.

07 '사이좋게 지내다'라는 의미로 'get along (well) with'를 사용한다.

08 (A)는 상대방의 의견을 묻는 표현으로 'What do you think about ~?(~에 대하여 어떻게 생각하니?)', 'What's your opinion about ~?(~에 대한 의견이 무엇이니?)', 'What do you say about ~?(~에 대하여 어떻게 생각하십니까?)' 등으로 바꾸어 말할 수 있다.

09 대화에서 Fact에 해당하는 내용은 '아이가 아픈 아이들을 돕기 위해 머리를 잘랐다'는 것이다. 나머지는 '의견'이나 '거짓' 정보에 해당한다. ① 의견 ② 의견 ③ 거짓 정보 ⑤ 거짓 정보

10 상대방에게 어떤 대상에 대한 의견을 물을 때 사용하는 표현으로 '~에 대해 어떻게 생각하니?'라고 묻는 ①이 적절하다.

11 (a)는 이상한 동물을 보고 '진짜일까?' 또는 '가짜일까?'라고 물을 수 있다. (b)는 다리가 없고 뱀처럼 보이지는 않는 동물을 보고 '이것은 매우 이상해.'라고 말하는 것이 자연스럽다.

서술형 시험대비 p.19

01 (A) How do you feel about it?
   (B) I don't agree with you.
02 Because he always makes him laugh out loud.
03 (A) What do you think about
   (B) I think cats don't get along well with dogs
04 I don't agree with you

01 (A) 'How do you feel about ~?'은 '~을[~에 대해] 어떻게 생각해?'라는 의미로 상대방에게 어떤 대상에 대한 의견을 물을 때 사용하는 표현이다. (B) 'I don't agree with you.(나는 동의하지 않아요.)'는 상대와 의견이 달라서 동의하지 않고 상대의 의견에 이의를 제기하는 말이다.

02 질문: 왜 Alex는 Mr. Big Mouth를 좋아하는가?

03 (A) 'What do you think about ~?(~에 대하여 어떻게 생각하니?)', (B) 'I think+주어+동사 ~' 어순으로 쓴다.

04 G가 코트가 따뜻하고 가벼울 것 같아서 마음에 든다는 말에 대해 B가 '그렇게 따뜻하지도 않고 보기보다 훨씬 더 무거워.'라고 말하는 것으로 보아 G의 말에 동의하지 않는 표현이 들어가는 것이 적절하다.

핵심 Check
p.20~21

1 (1) told　(2) was
2 (1) Whether　(2) whether

시험대비 기본평가
p.22

01 (1) he is very tall
　(2) she was very happy to meet him
　(3) she was not crying
　(4) she looked great

02 (1) I wonder if[whether] she will like my present.
　(2) I don't know if he will give me flowers or not.
　(3) I want to know if he will throw the ball.
　(4) The question is whether they believe what I said or not.

---

01 전달동사가 과거이므로 따옴표 안의 현재시제는 과거시제로 바꾸고 따옴표 속 'I'는 문장의 주어, 따옴표 속 'you'는 듣는 이로 바꾼다. (1)은 키가 큰 것이 현재의 사실이므로 시제의 일치 원칙에 적용되지 않는다.

02 (1) 동사 wonder의 목적절로는 if 또는 whether절이 적절하다. (2) 'if'는 'or not'을 함께 사용할 때 문장 끝에만 사용 가능하며, 'whether'는 바로 다음이나 문장 끝에 'or not'을 붙여 쓸 수도 있다. (3) 접속사 if 다음에 '주어+동사'의 어순으로 쓴다. (4) 'whether'는 주어, 보어, 동사의 목적어, 전치사의 목적어 자리에 모두 쓰일 수 있지만, 'if'는 동사의 목적어 자리에 주로 쓰인다. 이 글에서는 명사절이 보어로 쓰이고 있으므로 if가 아닌 whether를 쓰는 것이 적절하다.

시험대비 실력평가
p.23~25

01 ④　　　　02 I wonder if he will catch my ball.
03 ⑤　　　04 ④　　　05 ④
06 (1) I told Amy that I wanted to play with her then.
　(2) Mom asked me if I was finished with my homework.
07 ③　　　08 ①　　　09 ③
10 I am not sure if I do well on the test.　11 ③
12 I'm not sure if[whether] they will give me a big hand.
13 My sister doubts if I cheated on the test (or not).
14 ②　　　15 ⑤　　　16 ⑤　　　17 ②
18 ③　　　19 (1) asked (2) says (3) if (4) felt (5) is

---

01 ④ 전달동사가 과거일 경우, 시제의 일치 법칙에 맞게 따옴표(" ") 안의 동사가 과거시제라면 과거완료로 바꾸어야 한다. (has eaten → had eaten)

02 wonder가 원형이므로 주절의 주어는 he가 아닌 I로 하고, 동사 wonder의 목적절로 'if+주어+동사+목적어'로 한다.

03 ①~④는 동사의 목적어로 쓰인 명사절의 접속사 if이고, ⑤는 조건을 나타내는 부사절의 접속사이다. 해석: 그 동물이 기분이 좋다면, 너는 그것을 볼 수 있을 거야.

04 ④ 전달동사(said)와 that절의 내용이 과거(would be)이므로, tomorrow를 the next day로 쓰는 것이 적절하다.

05 동사 asked의 목적어 자리에 질문을 나타내는 명사절의 접속사이면서 or not과 함께 쓸 수 있는 접속사는 whether이다.

06 (1) 부사를 전달자의 관점에 맞게 고쳐야 하므로 now는 then으로 쓰는 것이 적절하다. (2) 따옴표 안의 내용이 의문문인 화법전환은 전달동사를 ask로 바꾸어 쓴다.

07 ③은 목적절이 질문이 아닌 주어가 알고 있는 내용이므로, 명사절의 접속사 'that'이 적절하다. ①, ④는 조건을 나타내는 접속사 if가 적절하고 ②, ⑤는 목적어가 되는 명사절의 접속사 if를 쓰는 것이 적절하다.

08 의문문을 간접화법으로 전환할 때 전달동사 say 또는 say to를 ask로 바꿔야 한다.

09 첫 번째 문장은 동사 wonder의 목적절로 내용상 if 또는 whether가 적절하고, 두 번째 문장은 be동사의 보어절로 접속사 if는 쓸 수 없고 whether를 쓰는 것이 적절하다. 단, 두 문장 모두 질문하는 내용이므로 접속사 that의 사용은 어색하다.

10 am not sure(확실하지 않다)의 목적어 자리에 명사절의 접속사 if를 사용하여 목적절을 넣는다.

11 전달동사 said to는 told로 바꾼다. 직접화법을 간접화법으로 바꿀 때 따옴표 속 'I'는 문장의 주어로 바꾸고 따옴표 속 'you'는 듣는 이로 바꾼다. 전달동사가 과거이므로, 시제의 일치 법칙에 맞게 따옴표(" ") 안의 현재시제 동사는 과거시제로 바꾼다.

12 I'm not sure의 목적어 자리에 의문문을 넣어야 하므로, 명사절의 접속사 if 또는 whether를 넣어 연결한다. 이때, 이 의문문은 평서문의 어순으로 바꾸어 쓴다.

13 문장의 주어에 맞게 동사 doubt를 3인칭 단수형으로 쓰고 목적절로 if절을 쓴다. 단, 목적절의 내용이 과거이므로 if절의 동사 cheat는 과거시제로 쓴다.

14 ② 시제의 일치의 법칙에 맞게 My sister told me that she had met Tom by chance the day before.로 쓴다.

15 첫 번째 문장은 주어로 쓰인 명사절의 접속사이면서 or not과 함께 쓸 수 있는 whether가 적절하고, 두 번째 문장에서는 find out의 의미상 단정적 내용의 접속사 that이 아닌, 의문의 내용을 위한 접속사 if 또는 whether가 적절하다.

16 to keep과 함께 쓸 수 있는 전달동사로 made는 사용할 수 없다. 해석: 그 할머니는 나에게 그녀의 개를 지켜보라고 요청했다[말했다, 명령했다].

17 '내가 ~할게'의 의미로 'let me+동사원형'을 쓰고 동사 check의 목적절로 '~인지 아닌지'의 if절을 쓰는 것이 적절하다. 단, 접속사 if 바로 뒤에 or not을 쓰지 않고 문장 맨 끝에 써야 한다.

18 b. 듣는 이가 없으므로 전달동사를 told가 아닌 said로 쓴다. c. 전달동사를 said가 아닌 told로 쓴다. d. 명령문을 간접화법으로 쓸 때 부정명령문은 to not이 아닌 not to 동사원형으로 쓴다.

19 (1) 의문문을 간접화법으로 쓸 때 전달동사는 asked가 적절하다. (2) 듣는 이가 없으므로 전달동사는 says가 적절하다. (3) 목적절에 질문하는 내용이 적절하므로 접속사 if를 쓴다. (4) 전달하는 내용이 과거이므로 felt가 적절하다. (5) 전달동사는 과거이나 명사절의 내용이 과학적 사실이므로 현재시제를 쓴다.

서술형 시험대비
p.26~27

01 (1) I wonder if[whether] the plane arrived on time.
(2) I asked if[whether] she was married.
(3) The question is whether the meeting is ready.
(4) I think that he is very honest.
(5) Whether she will attend the audition depends on her physical condition.

02 (1) He told me (that) he really appreciated my help.
(2) My roommate told me (that) she[he] would be late that night.

03 (1) he knew (2) I want (3) he would help me

04 (1) John said to Mary, "I love you."
(2) She told him that she was sorry.
(3) I told my dad that I would call him later.
(4) Mr. Brown told me that he wanted me to study more.
(5) My mom said that dish tasted good.

05 He asked her what the weather was like in New York that day.

06 (1) I understand that you don't want to talk about it.
(2) Whether you are a boy or a girl makes no difference to me.
(3) Whether you will succeed or not depends on your efforts.
(4) I am not sure if[whether] there is life on other planets.
(5) Tell me if[whether] you have any plans for your future.

07 (1) whether we have enough money to buy the new car
(2) that he had lied to his family
(3) if she would have a garage sale in her backyard

08 (1) was hungry, why she looked angry
(2) was very cute, if she liked that food

01 (1), (2) 의문사가 없는 의문문을 목적절로 만들어야 하므로 접속사 if 또는 whether를 사용한다. (3) 의문문을 보어로 만들어야 하므로 접속사 if는 사용할 수 없고 whether를 사용한다. (4) 평서문을 목적절로 만들 때는 접속사 that을 사용한다. (5) 의문문을 주절로 만들어야 하므로 접속사 if는 사용할 수 없고 whether를 사용한다.

02 (1) 간접화법을 쓸 때 전달동사가 과거라면, 시제의 일치 법칙에 맞게 따옴표(" ") 안의 현재동사를 과거시제로 바꾼다. 또한 따옴표 속 'I'는 문장의 주어로 바꾸고, 따옴표 속 'you'는 듣는 이로 바꾼다. (2) 부사 tonight는 시제에 맞게 that night으로 바꾼다.

03 (1) 직접화법을 간접화법으로 바꿀 때 따옴표 속 'I'는 문장의 주어로 바꾸고, 전달동사가 과거라면, 시제의 일치 법칙에 맞게 따옴표(" ") 안의 동사가 현재시제라면 과거시제로 바꾼다. (2) 주절의 주어와 that절의 주어가 같다면 직접화법에서 'I'가 되고 본동사의 시제와 that절의 시제가 과거로 같으므로 따옴표(" ") 안에서는 현재시제로 쓰는 것이 적절하다. (3) 직접화법을 간접화법으로 바꿀 때 따옴표 속 'I'는 문장의 주어로 바꾸고 따옴표 속 'you'는 듣는 이로 바꾼다.

04 (1) 직접화법의 전달동사는 듣는 이가 있을 때 said to로 쓴다. (2) 전달동사가 과거이므로 that절의 동사 is는 was로 쓴다. (3) 주어가 아버지에게 말한 내용이므로 that절의 you는 him으로 쓴다. (4) 간접화법의 전달동사는 듣는 이가 있을 때 told로 쓴다. (5) 간접화법이므로 지시형용사 this는 that으로 쓴다.

05 의문문을 간접화법으로 전환할 때 전달동사 said to를 asked로 바꿔야 한다. 전달동사가 과거이므로, 시제의 일치 법칙에 맞게 따옴표(" ") 안의 현재동사를 과거시제로 바꾼다. 이때 부사 today는 의미상 적절하게 that day로 쓴다.

06 (1) 동사 understand의 목적어로는 질문을 나타내는 if는 적절하지 않으므로 접속사 that을 쓴다. (2) 명사절이 주어일 때 단수로 취급하므로 동사 make를 makes로 쓴다. (3) if절은 주어로 쓰이지 않으므로 whether를 쓰는 것이 적절하다. (4) I am not sure(나는 확실하지 않다)와 어울리는 접속사는 질문의 의미를 가진 if나 whether가 적절하다. (5) 동사 Tell의 목적어로 if 또는 whether절을 쓰는 것이 적절하다.

07 (1) 문장의 보어 자리이고 내용상 질문이므로 접속사 whether를 쓴다. (2) 동사 admit와 어울리는 접속사는 that이다. (3) 동사 ask의 목적절로 질문을 나타내는 if를 쓰는 것이 적절하다. 해석: 나는 할머니에게 그녀의 뒷마당에서 중고물품 판매를 할 것인지 물었다.

08 (1) 전달동사가 과거이므로 그림 속 대화의 현재는 과거시제로 질문은 간접의문문으로 바꾼다. (2) 지시형용사를 적절히 바꾼다. (this → that)

Reading

확인문제   p.28

1 T   2 F   3 T   4 F

확인문제   p.29

1 T   2 F   3 T   4 F

교과서 확인학습 A   p.30~31

01 Smart News Reader

02 shook schools, didn't believe, a bit

03 getting scared   04 checked up on

05 were actually made   06 no hard evidence

07 turned out to be   08 just look at one thing

09 to look at the right sources, what is real, what is fake

10 Like, to think critically, on the Internet

11 getting more important   12 how to tell, from

13 One of the first steps   14 too good to be true

15 what the writer says   16 coming from

17 how to tell, from   18 if, are based on

19 a smart news reader   20 appears to provide

21 along with   22 like, made up

23 once more carefully, question everything

교과서 확인학습 B   p.32~33

1 How to Be a Smart News Reader

2 In October 2016, stories about scary clowns shook schools across the Washington area, but Danina Garcia-Fuller's students didn't believe them a bit.

3 "Some people were getting scared because they saw things on social media," said Patricia Visoso, one of Garcia-Fuller's students.

4 "But they never checked up on who was saying this."

5 The stories were actually made by teenagers, not by major newspapers or TV stations.

6 They offered no hard evidence that clowns really were trying to attack students.

7 The story turned out to be a complete lie.

8 "I think a lot of people just look at one thing and believe it's true," Patricia's classmate Ivy-Brooks

said.

9 "It's really important to look at the right sources and to pay attention to what is real and what is fake."

10 Like Garcia-Fuller's students, many teenagers in America are learning to think critically about information they're seeing in the news and on the Internet.

11 This skill is getting more important these days as stories can spread very fast, and anyone can make a website full of false information.

12 Garcia-Fuller said she was teaching her students how to tell fake news from real news.

13 "One of the first steps is to slow down.

14 If a story or a photo seems too good to be true, stop and think.

15 Is there any evidence that supports what the writer says?

16 And where is this coming from?"

17 Garcia-Fuller's students also learn how to tell fact from opinion in the news.

18 "Opinions are good to read," said 15-year-old McKenzie Campbell, "but you also have to check if they are based on facts."

19 Garcia-Fuller also said sometimes it can be very hard to be a smart news reader.

20 She tests her students with a website that appears to provide information on an animal called a tree octopus.

21 The site is full of information on this animal, along with a few unclear photos of octopuses in trees.

22 But like the story of scary clowns, it's totally made up.

23 The lesson, Garcia-Fuller tells her students, is to "check the information you're seeing once more carefully" and to "question everything, even things that I say."

시험대비 실력평가   p.34~37

01 ⑤   02 The stories 03 ④   04 ④

05 (A) sources   (B) Like   (C) false

06 look at everything → just look at one thing

07 is appeared → appears   08 together with

09 ⑤   10 ①, ④   11 ②, ⑤   12 ③

13 which[that] is   14 ⑤

15 Is there any evidence that supports what the

01 ⓐ on social media: 소셜 미디어에 올라온, ⓑ check up on: ~을 확인하다

02 '그 이야기들'을 가리킨다.

03 무서운 광대들에 관한 이야기들은 실제로 '주요 신문사나 TV 방송국'이 아닌 '10대들'이 지어냈다.

04 올바른 출처를 살펴보고, 무엇이 진짜이고 무엇이 가짜인지에 주의를 기울이는 것이 정말 중요하다고 생각하는 Garcia-Fuller의 학생들처럼, 많은 미국의 10대들은 '비판적으로' 생각하는 것을 배워 나가고 있다고 하는 것이 적절하다. ① 무비판적으로, ② 순응하여, ③ 적응하여, 순응하여, ⑤ 무조건적으로, 절대적으로

05 (A) 올바른 '출처'를 살펴보라고 해야 하므로 sources가 적절하다. source: 자료, 출처 resource: 자원, (B) Garcia-Fuller의 학생들'처럼'이라고 해야 하므로 Like가 적절하다. alike: [명사 앞에는 안 씀] (아주) 비슷한, like: ~와 비슷한, ~같은(전치사), (C) 누구나 '허위' 정보로 가득 찬 웹사이트를 만들어 낼 수 있기 때문에 이 기능이 최근 더 중요해지고 있다고 해야 하므로 false가 적절하다.

06 Patricia의 반 친구인 Ivy-Brooks는 많은 사람이 '단지 한 가지만을 보고' 그것이 사실이라고 믿는 것 같다고 했다.

07 appear는 수동태로 쓸 수 없기 때문에, is appeared를 appears로 고치는 것이 적절하다.

08 along with = together with: ~와 함께

09 누가 '나무 문어'에 대한 정보를 꾸며냈는지는 알 수 없다. ① Sometimes it can be very hard to be a smart news reader. ② No. ③ Information on an animal called a tree octopus. ④ Information on the animal called a tree octopus, along with a few unclear photos of octopuses in trees.

10 ⓐ와 ①, ④ tell(know/distinguish) A from B: A와 B를 구분하다

11 ⓑ와 ②, ⑤: 주격 관계대명사, ① so ... that ~: 너무 …해서 ~하다(접속사), ③ 동격의 접속사, ④ 목적어를 이끄는 접속사

12 이 글은 'Garcia-Fuller가 자신의 학생들에게 가짜 뉴스를 진짜 뉴스로부터 구분하는 방법과 뉴스에서 사실을 의견과 구분하는 방법에 대해서 가르치는' 내용의 글이므로, 주제로는 ③번 '가짜 뉴스와 진짜 뉴스를, 그리고 뉴스에서 사실을 의견과 구분하는 방법'이 적절하다.

13 주격 관계대명사 which[that]와 be동사인 is가 생략되어 있다.

14 '사람들이 왜 허위 정보로 가득 찬 웹사이트를 만드는지'의 대답

할 수 없다. ① They just look at one thing. ② They are learning to think critically about information they're seeing in the news and on the Internet. ③ They're seeing it in the news and on the Internet. ④ Yes.

15 주격 관계대명사 'that'이 선행사 'any evidence'를 수식하도록 하고, 선행사를 포함한 관계대명사 'what'이 이끄는 명사절이 동사 'supports'의 목적어가 되도록 쓰는 것이 적절하다.

16 '의견들'을 가리킨다.

17 주어진 문장의 they에 주목한다. ②번 앞 문장의 Some people을 받고 있으므로 ②번이 적절하다.

18 ⓐ와 ①, ③: 동격절을 이끄는 접속사, ② 목적절을 이끄는 접속사, ④ 주절을 이끄는 접속사, ⑤ 보어절을 이끄는 접속사

19 이 글은 '몇몇 사람들은 명백한 증거를 하나도 제공하지 못한 완벽한 거짓말로 드러난 무서운 광대들에 관한 이야기를 누가 말하고 있는지 전혀 확인하지도 않고 단지 소셜 미디어에 올라온 것만을 보고 무서워했지만, Danina Garcia-Fuller의 학생들은 조금도 그 이야기들을 믿지 않았다'는 내용의 글이므로, 제목으로는 ③번 '이봐, 소셜 미디어에 올라온 것들을 믿을 때는 신중해야 해!'가 적절하다.

20 '나무 문어'라고 불리는 동물이라고 해야 하므로 과거분사 called로 쓰는 것이 적절하다.

21 ⓑ와 ②: 교훈, ①, ④, ⑤: 수업[교습/교육] (시간), ③ (교과서의) 과(課)

서술형 시험대비   p.38~39

01 student → students   02 not, but

03 It turned out that the story was a complete lie.

04 (A) on social media   (B) a complete lie

05 to think critically about information they're seeing in the news and on the Internet

06 filled with

07 It is really important to look at the right sources and to pay attention to what is real and what is fake.

08 (A) I am   (B) my

09 (A) is   (B) too good   (C) supports

10 they should

11 (A) slow down   (B) stop   (C) any evidence

12 a tree octopus   13 what

14 (A) once more carefully   (B) question everything

01 one+of+소유격+복수명사: ~ 중의 하나

02 B, not A = not A but B: A가 아니라 B

03 the story를 that절의 주어로 바꾸고, to be를 was로 바꾸는

것이 적절하다.

04 몇몇 사람들은 그들이 '소셜 미디어에 올라온' 것들을 봤기 때문에 무서운 광대들에 관한 이야기를 무서워했지만 그들은 누가 그 이야기를 말하고 있는지를 전혀 확인하지 않았는데, 그 이야기는 결국 완벽한 거짓말인 것으로 드러났다.

05 '뉴스에서 그리고 인터넷상에서 보고 있는 정보에 관해 비판적으로 생각하는 것'을 가리킨다.

06 be full of = be filled with: ~로 가득 차 있다. full of 앞에 which[that] is가 생략되어 있다.

07 올바른 출처를 살펴보고, 무엇이 진짜이고 무엇이 가짜인지에 주의를 기울이는 것이 정말 중요하다.

08 직접화법으로 고치면 'she was'를 'I am'으로, 'her' students를 'my' students로 고치는 것이 적절하다.

09 (A) 주어가 One이므로 is가 적절하다. (B) '만약 어떤 이야기나 어떤 사진이 진짜라고 하기엔 너무 좋아 보인다면'이라고 해야 하므로 too good이 적절하다. too+형용사/부사+to부정사: '너무 …해서 ~할 수 없다', 형용사/부사+enough to부정사: ~할 만큼 충분히 …한, (C) 글쓴이가 말하고 있는 것을 '뒷받침하는' 어떠한 증거라도 있는가라고 해야 하므로 supports가 적절하다. deny: (무엇이) 사실이 아니라고 말하다, 부인[부정]하다

10 의문사+to부정사 = 의문사+주어+should+동사원형

11 첫 단계 중 하나는 '속도를 늦추는 것'이다. 만약 어떤 이야기나 어떤 사진이 진짜라고 하기엔 너무 좋아 보일 때, '멈춰서' 글쓴이의 말을 뒷받침하는 '어떠한 증거'라도 있는지와 이 정보의 출처에 대해 생각해야 한다.

12 '나무 문어'를 가리킨다.

13 선행사를 포함하는 관계대명사 'what'으로 바꿔 쓸 수 있다.

14 Garcia-Fuller가 그녀의 학생들에게 말하는 교훈은 당신이 보고 있는 정보를 '한 번 더 신중하게' 확인해 보라는 것과 '모든 것', 심지어 그녀가 말하는 것에도 '의문을 가져 보라'는 것이다.

영역별 핵심문제 *p.41~45*

01 attack　　02 ③　　03 ④　　04 ④
05 ①　　06 fake　　07 comfortable
08 ③　　09 ⑤　　10 ④　　11 ②
12 ④　　13 ②　　14 ①that → if[whether]
15 ④　　16 ④　　17 ③
18 (1) He said to her, "What are you doing here?"
　(2) She said to him, "I met my sister yesterday."
　(3) She said, "I am very happy now."
19 ②　　20 무서운 광대들에 관한 이야기
21 They offered no hard evidence that clowns really were trying to attack students.
22 ④　　23 ②　　24 ③
25 invented　　26 ⑤　　27 ④

28 put down them → put them down

01 반의어 관계다. 지루한-흥미로운 : 방어하다-공격하다

02 (a) 이 책은 실화에 바탕을 둔다. '~에 근거하다'는 'be based on'을 사용한다. (b) 분홍 말에 관한 이야기는 꾸며낸 것이었다. '꾸며낸'은 'made up'을 사용한다.

03 ④번의 'complete'는 형용사로 '완전한'의 의미이다. 'complete'가 '완료하다'라는 의미의 동사로 사용되려면 'wasn't completed'의 수동형이 되는 것이 적절하다.

04 '당신이 어떤 것이 사실이라고 믿도록 만드는 어떤 것'의 의미로 'evidence(증거)'가 적절하다.

05 '불찬성을 표현하는 방식으로'의 의미로 'critically(비판적으로)'가 적절하다.

06 '진짜가 아니지만 진짜처럼 보이도록 만들어진'의 의미로 4글자 단어인 'fake(가짜의)'가 적절하다.

07 look의 보어로 comfort의 형용사형이 와야 한다.

08 G가 그것이 가짜라고 한 말에 대해 동의하지 않는다고 말하고 있고, TV에서 저런 종류의 원숭이를 봤다고 했으므로 빈칸에는 'real'이 적절하다.

09 ⑤번은 '이 광고에 대해 어떻게 생각해?'라는 A의 물음에 대해 B가 '훌륭하다고 생각해.'라고 말한 다음 '우리는 모든 광고를 다 믿으면 안 된다'고 말하는 것은 어색하다.

10 '문어가 나무에서 산다고 Mr. Big Mouth가 말했어.'라는 Alex의 말에 대해 Somi는 '말도 안 돼.'라고 말하는 것이 자연스럽다. 'It doesn't make sense.'로 바꿔야 한다.

11 위 대화는 Big Mouth's Show에서 보여준 사진이 사실인지 아닌지에 대한 대화이다.

12 Alex는 나무를 오르는 문어 사진이 사실이라고 생각하고 있다.

13 주어진 문장은 동사 'tells'의 목적절로 '~인지 아닌지'이다. ② '~인지 아닌지' ①, ③, ④, ⑤ 조건절. '만일 ~라면'

14 동사 'don't know'와 어울리는 접속사는 의문을 의미하는 'if'이다.

15 의문사가 주어이므로 문장의 어순은 바꾸지 않는다. 전달동사가 과거이므로 의문문의 과거동사는 과거완료로, 지시형용사 this는 that으로 바꾼다. 해석: 그는 나에게 누가 저 도마뱀붙이를 집으로 가져왔는지 물었다. *gecko: 도마뱀붙이

16 a. Do you know if it will be rainy tomorrow? b. I am not sure if he can finish his project. d. Tell me if[whether] you have the time. e. He asked me if I wanted something to eat.

17 전달동사가 과거이므로, 시제의 일치 법칙에 맞게 따옴표(" ") 안의 현재동사를 과거시제로 바꾸고 부사 tomorrow는 의미상 적절하게 the following day로 바꾼다. 또한 따옴표 속 'I'는 문장의 주어로 바꾸고 따옴표 속 'you'는 듣는 이로 바꾼다.

18 (1) 따옴표 안에서 의문문의 형태인 '의문사+동사+주어'의 어순이어야 한다. (2) 간접화법에서 과거완료시제이고, 전달동사

는 과거이므로 따옴표 안에서 과거시제로 써야 한다. (3) 간접화법에서 then은 직접화법에서 내용이 현재시제이므로 now로 쓰는 것이 적절하다.

19 그 이야기들은 10대들이 지어낸 것이고 광대들이 정말로 학생들을 공격하려고 한다는 명백한 증거를 하나도 제공하지 않았다고 했으므로, 그 이야기는 결국 '완벽한 거짓말'인 것으로 드러났다고 하는 것이 적절하다. ① 근거 있는 소문, ③ valid: 타당한, ⑤ suspicious: 의심스러운, column: 칼럼

20 'the story about scary clowns'를 가리킨다.

21 동격의 접속사 'that' 이하가 'evidence'와 동격을 이루도록 쓰는 것이 적절하다.

22 ⓐ와 ④: 이유를 나타내는 접속사, ① ~하는 대로(접속사), ② ~하다시피[~이듯이](접속사), ③ [비례] ~함에 따라, ~할수록(접속사), ⑤ ~하고 있을 때(접속사)

23 이 글은 '이야기들은 아주 빠른 속도로 퍼져 나갈 수 있고 누구나 허위 정보로 가득 찬 웹사이트를 만들어 낼 수 있기 때문에, 뉴스에서 그리고 인터넷상에서 보고 있는 정보에 관해 비판적으로 생각하는 것이 최근 더 중요해지고 있다'는 내용의 글이므로, 주제로는 ②번 '뉴스에서 그리고 인터넷상에서 보고 있는 정보에 관해 비판적으로 생각하는 것의 중요성'이 적절하다.

24 많은 미국의 10대들은 '뉴스에서 그리고 인터넷상에서' 보고 있는 정보에 관해 비판적으로 생각하는 것을 배워 나가고 있다.

25 make up: (특히 남을 속이거나 즐겁게 하기 위해 이야기 등을) 지어[만들어] 내다, be made up: ~로 꾸며지다, invent: (사실이 아닌 것을) 지어내다[날조하다]

26 이 글은 'Garcia-Fuller가 또한 때때로 현명한 뉴스 독자가 되는 것이 아주 어려울 수도 있다고 말하면서 그녀의 학생들에게 당신이 보고 있는 정보를 한 번만 더 신중하게 확인해 보고 모든 것, 심지어 그녀가 말하는 것에도 의문을 가져 보라는 교훈을 말하는' 내용의 글이므로, 제목으로는 ⑤번 '정보를 신중하게 확인하고 모든 것에 의문을 가져라'가 적절하다.

27 앞에 나오는 내용과 상반되는 내용이 뒤에 이어지므로 However가 적절하다. ② 게다가, ③ 다시 말해서, ⑤ 그러므로

28 이어동사의 목적어가 인칭대명사일 때는 목적어를 동사와 부사 사이에 쓰는 것이 적절하다.

단원별 예상문제
p.46~49

01 preform 02 ⑤

03 They were made out of a police officer's uniform., This police officer made them for the kids.

04 Is there anything special about them?

05 ② 06 ④ 07 ③ 08 ②, ⑤

09 (1) the answer of that question
(2) had been in trouble
(3) my new house now

---

(4) said to
(5) Are you hungry now

10 (1) Don't go out during class
(2) told[asked, ordered] students not to go out during class

11 I wonder if[whether] they will show us the fan dance.

12 (1) I am so tired now (2) I was right

13 ④ 14 proved

15 They were made by teenagers. 16 ②

17 many teenagers in America 18 ①

19 ②, ③, ⑤ 20 ④ 21 while → during

22 ①, ④ 23 best

01 '명사-동사'의 관계이다. 정보 – 알리다 : 공연 - 공연하다

02 '매우 중요하고 신지한'의 의미로 'major(주된, 주요한)'가 석설하다.

03 대화에서 'Teddy Bears'에 관해 알 수 있는 'Fact'는 '한 경찰관의 제복으로 만들어졌다.'는 것과 '이 경찰이 아이들을 위해 그것들을 만들어 줬다'는 두 가지다.

04 '~가 있니?'라는 의문문으로 'Is there+주어 ~?'로 시작하고, anything은 형용사가 뒤에서 수식해야 하므로 anything special로 쓴다.

05 '그것이 가짜라고 생각해.'라는 G의 말에 B가 '저런 종류의 원숭이를 TV에서 본 적이 있어.'라고 말하고 있으므로 G의 말에 동의하지 않는다는 것을 알 수 있다.

06 요새 여자아이들은 짧은 머리를 더 좋아한다는 말에 대해 '그것에 동의하지 않아.'라는 말을 한 다음 주어진 문장이 들어가는 것이 자연스럽다.

07 (a) '매우 예쁘다고 생각해.'라는 말 다음에 머리를 왜 잘랐는지 화제를 바꾸어 말하고 있으므로 'By the way'가 적절하다. (b) '여기 이 아이는 여자아이가 아니야.'라는 말 다음에 '강조, 첨가'하는 표현으로 '사실'의 의미를 가지는 'In fact'가 적절하다.

08 debate의 목적절이고 의문의 내용이므로 빈칸에 접속사 if 또는 whether를 쓴다. 해석: 팀 A와 팀 B는 십대들이 파트타임을 해야 할지에 관해 토론할 것이다.

09 (1) 직접화법에서 this는 간접화법에서 that으로 쓴다. (2) 전달동사가 과거이고 직접화법의 시제가 과거이면 간접화법에서 과거완료시제로 쓴다. (3) 간접화법에서 that절의 주어와 주절의 주어가 같다면 직접화법에서 일인칭으로 쓰고, then은 now로 쓴다. (4) 간접화법에서 전달동사 tell은 듣는 이가 있다면 직접화법에서 say to로 쓴다. (5) 간접화법에서의 듣는 이와 종속절의 주어가 같다면, 직접화법에서 you로 쓰고, 전달동사의 시제와 종속절의 시제가 과거로 같다면 직접화법에서 따옴표 안에서 현재시제로 쓴다. 부사 then은 now로 바꾸어 쓴다.

10 (1) 부정의 명령문 'Don't+동사원형'의 형태로 문장을 쓴다.

(2) 명령문으로 간접화법을 쓸 때, 전달동사는 의미에 따라 tell, ask, order 등을 쓸 수 있고, 부정의 명령문은 not to로 바꾸어 쓴다.

11 동사 wonder의 목적어 자리에 의미상 의문문을 넣어야 하므로, 명사절의 접속사 if 또는 whether를 넣어 목적절을 완성한다.

12 (1) that절의 주어와 주절의 주어가 같으면 따옴표 속에서 'I'로 쓰고, that절과 주절의 시제가 과거로 같으므로 따옴표 속에서 현재시제로 쓴다. 부사 then은 따옴표 속에서 now로 쓴다. (2) 직접화법을 간접화법으로 바꿀 때 전달동사가 과거라면 따옴표 속 현재시제는 과거로 바꾸고, 'you'는 듣는 이로 바꾼다.

13 ⓐ와 ④: 명백한(형용사), ① 단단한, 굳은(형용사), ② 열심히, 힘껏(부사), ③ (이해하거나 답하기) 어려운(형용사), ⑤ 열심히 하는(형용사)

14 turn out = prove: ~로 드러나다

15 무서운 광대들에 관한 이야기는 '10대들에 의해 지어졌다.'

16 ⓐ와 ②, ⑤: 명사적 용법, ①, ④: 부사적 용법, ③: 형용사적 용법

17 '많은 미국의 10대들'을 가리킨다.

18 주어진 문장의 the first steps에 주목한다. ①번 앞 문장의 '가짜 뉴스를 진짜 뉴스로부터 구분하는 방법'의 첫 단계를 말하는 것이므로 ①번이 적절하다.

19 ⓐ와 ①, ④: 부사적 용법, ②: 형용사적 용법, ③, ⑤: 명사적 용법

20 "의견들은 '읽을 만한' 가치가 있다."라고 15살인 McKenzie Campbell이 말했다.

21 during+기간을 나타내는 명사, while+주어+동사

22 ⓑ와 ①, ④: '~인지 아닌지'라는 뜻의 명사절을 이끄는 접속사, = whether, ②, ③, ⑤: '만약 ~한다면'이라는 조건의 의미를 지니는 부사절을 이끄는 접속사

23 비교급+than+any+other+단수명사: 최상급의 뜻

🦉 서술형 실전문제   p.50~51

01 Because an octopus can't live out of the sea.

02 (1) if these shoes fit his feet
   (2) that the baby is crying now
   (3) Whether this kid is a girl or a boy

03 (1) she liked Tony
   (2) he wanted some water
   (3) his sister looked happy

04 (1) I was living then
   (2) if I liked to study in that library

05 he had seen the cat the day before[the previous day], if she had an owner

06 about information they're seeing in the news and on the Internet

07 fake

08 (A) the right sources   (B) what is real

09 so, that, can't   10 that → if[whether]

11 We have to check if[whether] they are based on facts.

01 질문: 왜 소미는 그것이 가짜 사진이라 말했는가?

02 (1) 동사 wonder의 목적절로 접속사 if절이 적절하다. (2) 확신하는 내용이므로 목적절로 접속사 that절이 적절하다. (3) 의문의 내용이고 주절이 필요하므로 접속사 whether절이 적절하다.

03 (1), (2), (3) 직접화법을 간접화법으로 바꿀 때 따옴표 속 'I'는 문장의 주어로 바꾼다. 또한 전달동사가 과거라면, 시제의 일치 법칙에 맞게 따옴표(" ") 안의 동사가 현재시제라면 과거시제로 바꾼다.

04 의문문을 직접화법에서 간접화법으로 바꿀 때, 간접의문문의 형태로 바꾸고, 따옴표 속 'I'는 문장의 주어로, 따옴표 속 'you'는 듣는 이로 바꾼다. 전달동사가 과거라면, 시제의 일치 법칙에 맞게 따옴표(" ") 안의 동사가 현재시제라면 과거시제로 바꾼다. 지시대명사와 부사를 전달자의 입장에 맞게 바꾼다. now는 then으로, this는 that으로 바꾼다.

05 전달동사가 과거이므로 그림 속 대화의 현재는 과거시제, 과거는 과거완료시제로 바꾸고, 질문은 간접의문문으로 바꾼다. 이때, 부사를 적절히 바꾼다. (yesterday → the day before 또는 the previous day)

06 'information'과 'they're' 사이에는 목적격 관계대명사 'that[which]'이 생략되어 있다.

07 fake: 가짜의, 거짓된, 진짜가 아닌; 진짜인 물건의 모조품인

08 Patricia의 반 친구인 Ivy-Brooks에 따르면, '올바른 출처들'을 살펴보고, '무엇이 진짜이고' 무엇이 가짜인지에 주의를 기울이는 것이 정말 중요하다.

09 too ~ to = so ~ that … can't

10 접속사 'if'는 명사절을 이끌어 '~인지 아닌지'라는 뜻이다. 'whether'로 교체할 수 있다.

11 그것들이 사실에 기반을 둔 것인지를 확인해 보아야 한다.

🐰 창의사고력 서술형 문제   p.52

|모범답안|

01 (1) A: How do you feel about persimmons?
      B: I like them.
   (2) A: How do you feel about cucumbers?
      B: I hate them.
   (3) A: How do you feel about pears?
      B: I don't like them.

02 (1) if he could tell her about his day
   (2) he always gets up at 6 and goes to the

stadium at 7

  (3) how long his training hours had been that day

  (4) it had taken 5 hours and had been really hard

  (5) what he would do in his spare time that day

  (6) after that interview, he would go swimming or watch a movie

02 직접화법을 간접화법으로 바꿀 때 따옴표 속 ‘I’는 문장의 주어로 바꾸고, 따옴표 속 ’you’는 듣는 이로 바꾼다. 전달동사가 과거일 때, 시제의 일치 법칙에 맞게 따옴표(“ ”) 안의 동사가 현재시제라면 과거시제로, 과거시제라면 과거완료시제로 바꾼다. 단, 그 내용이 변하지 않는 사실 혹은 규칙적인 행위인 경우는 전달동사에 상관없이 항상 현재시제로 쓴다. this는 that으로, today는 that day로 바꾼다.

단원별 모의고사   p.53~57

01 ②   02 (p)rovide 03 ⑤ 04 ④

05 ③   06 it doesn't seem real, it's a little boring

07 ③   08 Look at those shoes the girl is wearing.

09 (1) fact (2) uniform (3) if[whether]

10 It is climbing a tree. 11 ② 12 ①

13 Mr. Kim asked his daughter if[whether] he could ask her a few questions.

14 (1) He says to her, "Where do you work now?"

  (2) She told me that she hadn't been at school the day before.

15 ③

16 (1) I wonder if she will like my present.

  (2) Do you know if she is married?

17 (A) scary (B) scared (C) offered

18 stories about scary clowns

19 ③   20 ⑤

21 opinion in the news → real news

  또는 fake news → fact

22 ① 글쓴이가 말하고 있는 것을 뒷받침하는 어떠한 증거라도 있는가?

  ② 이 정보가 어디서 온 것인가?

23 ③   24 ④

01 ②번은 ‘무엇에 관하여 생각하거나 믿고 있는 것’의 의미로 ‘opinion(의견)’에 관한 설명이다. ‘fact’는 ‘something that is known to have happened or to exist, especially something for which proof exists, or about which there is information’으로 ’어떤 일이 일어났거나 존재한다고 알려진 것, 특히 증거가 존재하거나 정보가 있는 것’이다.

02 유의어 관계이다. 찾다, 조사하다 : 제공하다

03 ‘한 도시, 국가 또는 세계의 특정 부분’의 의미로 ‘area(지역)’가

04 상대방의 의견을 묻는 질문에 ‘나는 동의하지 않아.’라고 말하는 것은 어색하다.

05 빈칸 뒤에서 ‘소년이 그의 여동생을 구하기 위해 자신의 생명을 포기했잖아.’라고 하고 있으므로 ‘감동적이라고 생각한다’는 말이 적절하다.

06 질문: 여학생은 왜 그것이 좋은 드라마가 아니라고 생각하는가?

07 요즘 여자아이들은 짧은 머리를 더 좋아한다는 B의 의견에 대해 ‘대부분의 여자아이는 짧은 머리보다 긴 머리를 좋아해.’라고 말하고 있으므로 (3)은 ‘I don't agree with that.‘이 되어야 한다.

08 명령문이므로 동사원형으로 문장을 시작한다. ‘저 여자애가 신고 있는’에 해당하는 말이 ‘shoes’를 수식하는 역할을 한다.

09 (1) 경찰관이 아이들에게 곰 인형을 사주었다는 말 다음에 ‘However’가 이어지므로, 앞 문장에 대한 역접의 의미가 온다는 것을 알 수 있다. (2) 경찰관 제복으로 인형을 만들어 주었다. (3) 기자가 그들을 직접 만났는지 어떤지 궁금하다는 의미로 접속사 ‘if나 whether’가 적절하다.

10 질문: 사진 속의 문어는 무엇을 하고 있는가?

11 보기와 ② ‘that’은 형용사를 수식하는 ‘지시부사’다. ① 지시형용사, ③ 접속사, ④ It ~ that ... 강조구문에 사용된 접속사, ⑤ 지시대명사

12 ① 동사 discuss의 목적절로 ‘~인지 아닌지’의 의미이다. ②~⑤ 조건의 접속사로 ‘만일 ~라면’의 의미이다.

13 의문문을 간접화법으로 전환할 때 전달동사 said to를 asked로 바꾸고 접속사 if 또는 whether를 쓴다. 전달동사가 과거이므로, 시제의 일치 법칙에 맞게 따옴표(“ ”) 안의 현재동사를 과거시제로 바꾼다. 또한 따옴표 속 ‘I’는 문장의 주어로 바꾸고 따옴표 속 ’you’는 듣는 이로 바꾼다.

14 (1) 듣는 이가 있을 때 직접화법의 전달동사는 say to를 쓴다. (2) 전달동사가 과거이므로 that절의 시제는 과거 또는 과거완료시제를 쓴다. 내용상 전달하기 이전의 내용이므로 과거완료시제로 쓰는 것이 적절하다.

15 의문사가 없는 의문문을 명사절로 바꿀 때 접속사 if는 사용할 수 없고, whether를 쓴다.

16 (1) 동사 wonder의 목적절로 if절을 쓴다. 이때 명사절인 if절에서는 will을 사용하는 것이 가능하다. (2) 의문문 ‘Do you know’의 목적절로 if절을 쓴다. 결혼한 상태를 나타내는 표현은 be married이다.

17 (A) ‘무서운 광대들’이라고 해야 하므로 scary가 적절하다. scary: 무서운, scared: 무서워하는, (B) ‘무서워했다’고 해야 하므로 scared가 적절하다. (C) They가 ‘그 이야기들’을 가리키고 있고, ‘그 이야기들은 증거를 하나도 제공하지 않았다’고 해야 하므로 능동태인 offered가 적절하다.

18 ‘무서운 광대들에 관한 이야기’를 가리킨다.

19 ⓐ pay attention to: ~에 주목하다, 유의하다, ⓑ on the Internet: 인터넷상에서

20 (A)와 ⑤: ~처럼(전치사), ① 비슷한(형용사), ② (예를 들어) ~과 같은(= such as)(전치사), ③ ~을 좋아하다(동사), ④ 비

숫한 것(명사)

21 Garcia-Fuller는 자신의 학생들에게 가짜 뉴스를 '진짜 뉴스'
로부터 구분하는 방법과 또한 뉴스에서 '사실'을 의견과 구분하
는 방법을 가르치고 있다

22 ① Is there any evidence that supports what the writer
says? ② Where is this coming from?

23 주어진 문장의 The site에 주목한다. ③번 앞 문장의 a
website를 받고 있으므로 ③번이 적절하다.

24 무서운 광대들의 이야기와 마찬가지로 '나무 문어'에 대한 정보
는 완전히 꾸며진 것이다.

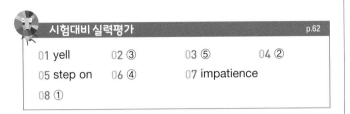

Make Peace with Others

Lesson 8

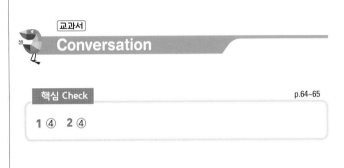

p.62

시험대비 실력평가

01 yell 02 ③ 03 ⑤ 04 ②
05 step on 06 ④ 07 impatience
08 ①

01 비록 누군가가 여러분에게 소리를 친다고 해도, 똑같이 반응해서는 안 됩니다. <영어 설명> 큰 소리로 고함지르다

02 'general'은 형용사로 '일반적인', 명사로 '장군'의 의미를 가지고 있다. • 첼로는 일반 대중에게는 여전히 낯선 악기로 여겨지고 있습니다. • 김유신은 한국 역사상 훌륭한 장군이었습니다.

03 '특히 옛날에 존재하던 매우 용감하고 싸움에 숙련된 군인 또는 투사'의 의미로 'warrior(전사)'가 적절하다.

04 '어떤 사실을 알게 되거나 이해하다'란 의미로 'realize(깨닫다)'가 적절하다.

05 '~을 밟다'는 'step on'을 사용한다.

06 (1) 이들 유권자들은 그들이 살고 있는 사회를 바꾸려고 노력하는 것에 관하여 열정적이기 때문에, 그들은 수 시간 동안 줄을 서 있다. (2) 그것은 그에게는 쉽지 않은 일이었지만, 그는 포기하지 않았습니다.

07 반의어 관계다. 전쟁-평화 : 인내심-성급함

08 나머지는 '동사 – 명사' 관계로 '사람'을 나타내고, ①번은 '동사 – 명사' 관계로 '요리하다 – 요리기구'를 의미한다. 'cook'이 명사로 사용될 때 '요리사'라는 뜻을 갖는다.

서술형 시험대비

p.63

01 (1) above (2) army (3) set, free (4) reasons
02 (1) weapon (2) pole
03 (1) look (2) situation (3) Palace
04 (1) powerful, 강력한 (2) wise, 현명한
   (3) injured, 부상당한 (4) push, 밀다
05 (1) decreasing (2) pass by (3) Sooner or later

01 (1) 그의 사진은 책상 위 선반에 놓여 있었다. (2) 내 동생은 작년에 군대에 입대했다. (3) 왕은 부하들에게 죄수를 풀어주라고 명령했다. '~을 석방하다'는 'set ~ free'다. (4) 내가 의사가 되기를 원하는 두 가지 이유가 있다. two와 어울리는 복수명사 'reasons'를 사용한다.

02 (1) 사람들은 비행기에 칼이나 총과 같은 어떤 무기도 가지고 와서는 안 된다. (2) 우리는 장대의 꼭대기에 있는 그 나라의 깃발

을 보았다. 영영 풀이: 길고 얇은 나무나 금속 조각

03 (1) look: 표정 (2) situation: 상황 (3) palace: 궁전, 궁궐

04 (1) 사람과 사건을 통제할 수 있는 많은 힘을 갖고 있는 (2) 무엇이 진실인지 또는 옳은지 제대로 판단할 수 있는 힘을 갖고 있는 (3) 신체 일부분에 물리적인 상처를 입은 (4) 손으로 누름으로써 누군가나 또는 무엇인가가 움직이게 하다

05 (1) 초등학생의 수가 계속해서 줄어들고 있다. '계속 ~하다'는 'keep -ing'를 사용한다. (2) 당신이 뭔가를 하든지 하지 않든지 방학은 시작되고, 지나갈 것이다. (3) 조만간, 그는 그녀가 정말로 그를 사랑했다는 것을 깨닫게 될 것이다.

[교과서] Conversation

핵심 Check

p.64~65

1 ④ 2 ④

교과서 대화문 익히기

Check(√) True or False

p.66

1 F 2 T 3 T 4 F

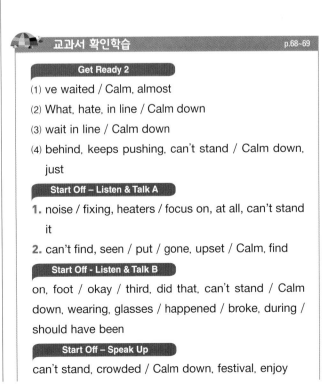

교과서 확인학습

p.68~69

Get Ready 2

(1) ve waited / Calm, almost
(2) What, hate, in line / Calm down
(3) wait in line / Calm down
(4) behind, keeps pushing, can't stand / Calm down, just

Start Off – Listen & Talk A

1. noise / fixing, heaters / focus on, at all, can't stand it
2. can't find, seen / put / gone, upset / Calm, find

Start Off - Listen & Talk B

on, foot / okay / third, did that, can't stand / Calm down, wearing, glasses / happened / broke, during / should have been

Start Off – Speak Up

can't stand, crowded / Calm down, festival, enjoy

I can use. Why didn't you, dishes / forgot to do / what, have to do, I can't stand, cleaned / busy doing / Do / finish, too difficult / m good at, Let me help / right now, the rest, finishing

1. sent / in, hundred / spend, doing nothing, can't stand it / Calm down, rule to get

2. tie me up, set me free / get free / can't stand, sign, dangerous / I'm sure, way

outside / barking / can't focus on, stand it / Calm down, quiet

---

     p.70

01 can't stand, crowded   02 ④   03 ③
04 ④

01 '~을 참을 수 없다'는 'I can't stand ~'를 사용하고, '붐비는'은 'crowded'를 쓴다.

02 화가 난 상대방에게 응대할 때, 'Calm down!(진정해!)'이라는 표현을 쓸 수 있다. 이와 같은 표현으로는 'Relax.', 'Take it easy.', 'It's going to be okay. Take a deep breath and try to relax.', 'Chill out!', 'Don't stress yourself.', 'Control yourself.' 등이 있다.

03 화난 감정을 표현하는 문장으로 'I can't stand it.(참을 수 없어.)'을 사용할 수 있다. 이외에도 'I'm very angry.', 'I'm very upset.', 'I'm very annoyed.', 'How irritating!' 등이 있다.

04 화낸 상대방에게 응대할 때, 'Calm down!(진정해!)'이라는 표현을 쓸 수 있다.

---

     p.71~72

01 ③   02 stepped on his, three   03 ③
04 ②   05 set, free
06 I can't spend a hundred days doing nothing.   07 ④
08 ⑤   09 ①   10 ④
11 The boy behind me keeps pushing me.

01 대화의 흐름상 '그 애는 더 조심했어야 했어.'라는 내용이 적절하다. '~했어야 했다'라는 과거의 유감을 나타내는 표현으로 'should have+과거분사'를 사용한다.

02 대화 속의 남자 아이가 Ben의 발을 세 번이나 밟았기 때문에 화가 났다.

03 대화의 흐름상 B가 화내는 말에 대해 '곧 끝날 거야.'라고 말하고 있는 것으로 보아 진정시키는 표현이 적절하다.

04 B가 '진정해! 이 뜨거운 우유를 마셔 봐.'라고 말하는 것으로 보아 ②번이 가장 적절하다.

05 '누군가 감옥에서 나가도록 허락하다'라는 의미로 'set+목적어+free'를 사용한다.

06 '~하면서 시간을 보내다'라는 표현으로 'spend+시간+V-ing' 구문을 이용한다.

07 대화에서 It은 'Waiting there for 100 days(100일을 거기서 기다리는 것)'를 가리키는 대명사이다.

08 민수의 누나가 가장 좋아하는 과목이 무엇인지는 대화에서 언급되어 있지 않다.

09 'forget+동명사'는 '~한 것을 잊다'라는 의미로 대화의 '설거지 할 것을 잊었다'라는 내용으로 'forgot to do'가 되어야 한다.

10 ④번의 'Chill out!'은 '침착해'라는 뜻으로 화난 상대방에게 해 주는 말이다.

11 주어인 'The boy' 뒤에서 '전치사+명사(behind me)'가 주어를 꾸며주고, 주어가 단수 명사이므로 동사는 'keeps'를 사용한다. '계속 ~하다'라는 의미로 'keep+V-ing'를 사용한다.

---

     p.73

01 He will do the dishes after he finishes his homework.

02 to do the dishes, what he has to do, difficult, help with, after

03 I can't stand it / Calm down

04 (t)ie me up, (s)et me free / can't (s)tand / (C)alm down

01 질문: 민수는 설거지를 언제 할 것인가?

02 민수와 민수의 누나는 민수가 설거지하는 것을 잊어버린 것에 대해 이야기를 나누고 있다. 민수의 누나는 그가 해야 하는 것을 항상 잊어버리기 때문에 화가 나 있다. 민수가 설거지를 하지 않은 것은 과학 숙제가 어려워서라고 변명한다. 그의 누나는 그가 숙제를 하는 것을 도와주고, 그는 숙제를 끝낸 후 설거지를 할 것이다.

03 화난 감정을 표현하는 문장으로 'I can't stand it.(참을 수 없어.)'을 사용할 수 있다. 이외에도 'I'm very angry.', 'I'm very upset.', 'I'm very annoyed.', 'How irritating!' 등을 대신 사용할 수 있다. 화낸 상대방을 진정시킬 때는, 'Calm down!(진정해!)'이라는 표현을 쓸 수 있다. 이와 같은 표현으로는 'Relax.', 'Take it easy.', 'Chill out!', 'Don't stress yourself.', 'Control yourself.' 등이 있다.

04 M1: 저를 왜 여기에 묶어 두셨습니까? 저를 풀어 주십시오.
M2: 이떻게 풀려날 수 있겠느냐? 생각해 보아라.

M1: 저는 이 푯말을 참을 수가 없습니다. 저는 위험하지도 나쁘지도 않습니다.

M2: 진정하거라. 나는 네가 방법을 찾을 것이라고 확신한다.

Grammar

핵심 Check   p.74~75

1 (1) the other   (2) the others   (3) some
2 (1) to be   (2) to go   (3) told

시험대비 기본평가   p.76

01 (1) others are playing at snowballs
　　(2) the other is sitting on the tree
　　(3) the dog to get the ball
　　(4) the boy to be careful
02 (1) another → the other
　　(2) 첫 번째 the others → others
　　(3) tell → to tell
　　(4) studying → to study
03 (1) the others are dancing
　　(2) the others are waving their hands to the singer

---

01 (1) 불특정한 다수의 일정하지 않은 몇몇과 다른 몇몇을 나타낼 때 some, others를 쓴다. (2) 두 개의 사람이나 사물 중 하나와 그 나머지 하나는 one, the other를 쓴다. (3), (4) 'order'와 'tell'은 목적격보어 자리에 to부정사가 오는 동사이다.

02 (1) 불특정한 두 사람이나 사물 중 하나와 나머지 하나를 나타낼 때 one, the other를 쓴다. (2) 불특정한 나수의 일정하지 않은 몇몇과 다른 몇몇을 나타낼 때 some, others를 쓰고 나머지 전체를 말할 때는 the others를 쓴다. (3), (4) 'want'와 'advise'는 목적격보어 자리에 to부정사가 오는 동사이다.

03 (1), (2) 불특정한 다수의 사람, 사물 중 하나와 그 나머지를 알 수 있을 때 one, the others를 쓴다.

시험대비 실력평가   p.77~79

01 ⑤　　**02** ④　　**03** ④　　**04** ⑤
05 ③　　**06** ③
07 Peace tells us to help each other.　　**08** ③
09 (1) He ordered his robot to do his homework.
　　(2) She told him to lock the door.
10 to get up　**11** ②
12 (1) the other　(2) the others　(3) the others

---

　　(4) the other　(5) Some
13 Some (shapes) are stars
14 I want him to know the truth.　　　　**15** ③
16 (1) Can you force your brothers to stop fighting?
　　(2) My parents let me buy a new tablet PC.
17 ①　　　　　　**18** Mom allowed me to go camping.
19 ①　　　　　　**20** ④

---

01 'ask, tell, order, want'는 목적격보어 자리에 'to부정사'가 오는 동사이고, 'make'는 목적격보어로 원형부정사를 쓴다.

02 'advise'는 목적격보어 자리에 to부정사가 오는 동사이다. '주어+동사+목적어+to부정사'의 어순으로 과거시제로 문장을 완성한다.

03 불특정한 다수의 일정하지 않은 수량을 나타낼 때 두 번째 언급하는 경우 one은 쓰지 않는다. other는 단독으로 쓰지 않고 'other+복수명사' 혹은 others로 써야 하고 마지막에 나머지를 나타내는 the others가 있으므로 빈칸에 또 the others를 쓸 수 없다. 그러므로 정답은 others가 적절하다.

04 'ask'는 목적격보어 자리에 to부정사가 오는 동사이다.

05 'allow, tell, order, advise'는 목적격보어 자리에 to부정사가 오는 동사이다. 'keep'은 현재분사를 목적격보어로 쓴다. ③은 'going'이 적절하다.

06 'want'는 목직격보어 자리에 to부정사가 오는 동사이다.

07 'tell'은 목적격보어 자리에 to부정사가 오는 동사이다. '주어+동사+목적어+to부정사'의 어순으로 문장을 완성한다.

08 불특정한 둘 중 하나와 나머지 하나는 one, the other로 나타내고, 불특정한 다수의 일정하지 않은 몇몇과 다른 몇몇을 나타낼 때 some, others를 쓴다.

09 (1), (2) 'order'와 'tell'은 목적격보어 자리에 to부정사가 오는 동사이다.

10 'tell'은 목적격보어 자리에 to부정사가 오는 동사이다.

11 'tell, ask, want, encourage'는 목적격보어 자리에 to부정사가 오는 동사이다. 'see'는 목적격보어 자리에 원형부정사 또는 현재분사가 오는 동사이다.

12 (1), (4) 불특정한 두 명 중 한 명과 나머지 한 명은 one, the other로 나타낸다. (2) 불특정한 다수의 사람 중 처음 여럿과 그 나머지를 알 수 있을 때 some, the others를 쓴다. (3) 불특정한 다수의 사람 중 하나와 그 나머지를 알 수 있을 때 one, the others를 쓴다. (5) 불특정한 다수의 일정하지 않은 수량을 나타내고 나머지가 불확실 할 때는 some, others를 쓴다.

13 불특정한 다수의 사람, 사물 중 일부와 그 나머지를 알 수 있을 때 some, the others를 쓴다.

14 'want'는 목적격보어 자리에 to부정사가 오는 동사이다. '주어+동사+목적어+to부정사'의 어순으로 문장을 완성한다.

15 'allow'와 'let'은 5형식 동사로 '~하는 것을 허락하다'라는 뜻이다. 'let'은 목적격보어 자리에 원형부정사가, 'allow'는 목적격보어 자리에 to부정사가 오는 동사이다.

16 (1) 'make'는 목적격보어로 원형부정사를 취하는 동사이고 'force'는 목적격보어로 to부정사가 온다. (2) 'allow'는 목적격보어로 to부정사가 오는 동사이지만, 'let'은 목적격보어로 원형부정사를 취한다.

17 불특정한 두 가지 것 중 하나와 나머지 하나는 one, the other로 나타낸다. 또한 불특정한 다수 중 두 번째 다른 하나는 another로 나타낸다.

18 'allow'는 목적격보어 자리에 to부정사가 오는 동사이다. '주어+동사+목적어+to부정사'의 어순으로 과거시제 문장을 완성한다.

19 'have'와 'get'은 둘 다 '~에게 하도록 시키다'라는 뜻이지만, 'have'는 목적격보어로 원형부정사를, 'get'은 목적격보어로 to부정사를 취한다.

20 'want', 'ask', 'get'은 목적격보어 자리에 to부정사가 오는 동사이고, 'let'은 원형부정사를, 'see'는 원형부정사 또는 현재분사를 목적격보어로 취한다.

서술형 시험대비
p.80~81

01 (1) Here are two birds. One is flying, and the other is sitting on the tree.
(2) The woman told the boy to be careful.
(3) She has a lot of pens. Some are yellow, and others are red.
(4) Jane asks me to teach math.
(5) The farmer wanted me to feed the pigs.

02 (1) My mother told me to get up early.
(2) I don't want you to tell anybody this secret.
(3) My father allowed my uncle to use his car.

03 (1) Mr. Kim allowed us to bring what we wanted to eat.
(2) Dr. Wang saw her patients work[working] out regularly during the day.

04 (1) the other has curly hair
(2) the others are boys
(3) another is rolling the snow

05 (1) The man allowed the boy to enter the grass.
(2) She has three sons. One is a singer and the others are dancers.

06 (1) He asked his people to fight peacefully.
(2) The police officer ordered the man to come out.
(3) The girl asked the boy to help her.
(4) The teacher told the boy to study hard.

07 (1) I want everyone to come here.
(2) I'd like you to listen carefully.
(3) They allow people to fish here.
(4) I advise you not to walk home alone.

(5) The dentist told Daniel to give up eating sweets.

08 (1) One (2) Some (3) the others

01 (1) 불특정한 두 개 중 하나와 나머지 하나는 one, the other로 나타낸다. (2), (4), (5) 'tell, ask, want'는 목적격보어 자리에 to부정사가 오는 동사이다. (3) 불특정한 다수의 일정하지 않은 수량을 나타내고 나머지가 불확실할 때는 some, others를 쓴다.

02 (1), (2), (3) 'tell, want, allow'는 목적격보어 자리에 to부정사가 오는 동사이다. '주어+동사+목적어+to부정사'의 어순으로 문장을 완성한다.

03 (1) 'let'은 목적격보어 자리에 원형부정사가 오는 동사이고, 'allow'는 목적격보어로 to부정사를 쓴다. (2) 'advise'는 목적격보어 자리에 to부정사가 오는 동사이고, 'see'는 목적격보어로 원형부정사 또는 현재분사를 쓸 수 있다.

04 (1) 불특정한 두 명 중 한 명과 나머지 한 명은 one, the other로 나타낸다. (2) 불특정한 다수의 사람, 사물 중 일부와 그 나머지를 알 수 있을 때 some, the others를 쓴다. (3) 불특정한 세 명 중 한 명과 또 다른 한 명, 그리고 나머지 한 명은 one, another, the other로 나타낸다.

05 (1) 'allow'는 목적격보어 자리에 to부정사가 오는 동사이다. '주어+동사+목적어+to부정사'의 어순으로 과거시제로 문장을 완성한다. (2) 셋 중 한 명과 나머지 두 명은 one, the others로 나타낸다.

06 'ask', 'order', 'tell'은 목적격보어 자리에 to부정사가 오는 동사이다. '주어+동사+목적어+to부정사'의 어순으로 문장을 완성한다.

07 (1), (2), (3) 'want, would like, allow'는 목적격보어 자리에 to부정사가 오는 동사이다. (4) to부정사의 부정은 'not to 동사원형'의 형태로 쓴다. (5) 목적어 Daniel과 목적격보어 give up은 능동 관계이므로 목적격보어로 과거분사가 아닌 to부정사를 쓰는 것이 적절하다.

08 (1) 불특정한 다수의 사람, 사물 중 하나와 그 나머지를 알 수 있을 때 one, the others를 쓴다. (2) 불특정한 다수의 일정하지 않은 몇몇을 나타낼 때 some을 쓴다. (3) 불특정한 다수의 사람, 사물 중 하나와 그 나머지를 알 수 있을 때 one, the others를 쓴다.

교과서 Reading

확인문제
p.82

1 T 2 F 3 T 4 F 5 T 6 F

교과서 확인학습 A   p.85~87

01 the Best Warrior   02 brave young

03 strongest, have much to learn

04 to go   05 In a hundred days

06 got angry   07 might be a reason

08 On the hundred and first day

09 first weapon, patience   10 to win a war

11 stand against   12 tied, to

13 that read   14 passed by

15 Some, others   16 shouted back

17 Set me free, or   18 made, worse

19 another   20 softly

21 not, but   22 kept saying

23 let him go

24 the most powerful weapon

25 stronger than   26 took, to

27 had passed   28 The first one to

29 the others   30 pushed, pulled

31 harder and harder   32 anymore

33 the injured   34 even harder

35 As   36 took good care of

37 except, following   38 to sit in it

39 standing with   40 all alone

41 the real winner

42 At that moment, my favorite

43 Sooner or later   44 returned to

45 approach, knowing, What's up

교과서 확인학습 B   p.88~90

1 Corky, the Best Warrior

2 Corky was a brave young man.

3 He wanted to be a general, but the king said, "You're the strongest man in my army, but you have much to learn."

4 He ordered Corky to go to a famous military school.

5 "Wait there. In a hundred days, your training will

start," a voice said from inside the school gate.

6 Corky got angry.

7 But then he thought there might be a reason, so he waited.

8 On the hundred and first day, the gate opened.

9 An old man said, "You have learned to use your first weapon: patience.

10 Patience is the most important thing to win a war."

11 Then, the teacher told Corky to stand against a pole.

12 Suddenly, he tied Corky to the pole.

13 Above his head, he put a sign that read "Dangerous and Bad."

14 Many people passed by.

15 Some gave Corky angry looks, and others shouted at him.

16 Corky shouted back.

17 He yelled, "Set me free, or you all will be in big trouble!"

18 That made the situation worse.

19 "I need to try another way," he thought.

20 Then, Corky began to speak softly.

21 He said he was not dangerous or bad but was a good man.

22 He kept saying this in all possible ways.

23 Finally, the people let him go.

24 "Now you control the most powerful weapon: words.

25 Soft words are stronger than sharp swords," said the teacher.

26 Next, the teacher took Corky to a large hall with a chair in the middle.

27 There were 19 other warriors who had passed their tests.

28 "The first one to sit in the chair will be the winner," the teacher said.

29 Corky and the others began fighting.

30 They pushed, pulled, ran, and jumped.

31 They fought harder and harder, so Corky became tired.

32 Finally, he said, "I will not fight anymore."

33 Instead, I will take care of the injured."

34 The other warriors saw this and fought even harder.

35 As they fought, more warriors became tired and hurt.

36 Corky took good care of them, so they followed

him.

37 Soon, all the warriors except Thunder were following Corky.

38 Thunder walked toward the chair to sit in it.

39 Then, he saw Corky standing with his 18 followers.

40 Thunder realized he was all alone.

41 "I give up. You're the real winner," Thunder said to Corky.

42 At that moment, the teacher appeared and said, "Of all the great weapons, peace is my favorite.

43 Sooner or later, everyone wants to stand on the side of peace."

44 Corky returned to the palace after his training ended.

45 When the king saw him approach, he gave Corky a wise and knowing smile and said, "What's up, General?"

 시험대비 실력평가　　　　　　　　p.91~95

01 ②　　　02 ①, ③, ⑤　03 ④　　　04 ②

05 Soft words are stronger than sharp swords

06 ④　　　07 ②　　　08 ③

09 처음에는 나머지 전사들과 격렬히 싸웠다. → 더는 싸움을 하지 않고 부상당한 자들을 돌보았다.

10 ①　　　11 ⑤　　　12 saying　　13 ④

14 Corky는 사람들에게 "나를 풀어 줘. 그렇지 않으면 모두 혼쭐날 줄 알아!"라고 소리를 질렀다. / Corky는 자신이 위험하거나 나쁘지 않고 좋은 사람이라고 계속해서 부드럽게 말하기 시작했다.

15 19 other warriors (who had passed their tests)

16 injured people[warriors]　17 ⑤

18 to stand → standing 또는 stand

19 Sooner or later, everyone wants to stand on the side of peace.

20 ②　　　21 ③　　　22 you should[must]

23 ②　　　24 that[which] 25 better → worse

26 ④　　　27 ①, ④　　28 ④

01 ②는 왕을 가리키고, 나머지는 다 Corky를 가리킨다.

02 ⓐ와 ①, ③, ⑤: 형용사적 용법, ②: 부사적 용법, ④: 명사적 용법

03 '101일째 되던 날(On the hundred and first day)', 문이 열렸다.

04 ② let(사역동사)+목적어+동사원형(목적격보어), 나머지는 다 목적격보어 자리에 to부정사를 써야 하는 동사들이다.

05 stronger than: ~보다 강한

06 Corky가 얼마나 오래 기둥에 묶여 있었는지는 대답할 수 없다. ① He told Corky to stand against a pole. ② Some gave Corky angry looks, and others shouted at him. ③ At first, he shouted back, but he realized that it made the situation worse. So he decided to try another way. ⑤ He came to control the most powerful weapon: words. come to+동사원형: ~하게 되다

07 더는 싸움을 하지 않는 '대신에' 부상당한 자들을 돌볼 것이라고 해야 하므로, Instead가 적절하다. ① 아직(도), ③ 사실, ⑤ 그러므로

08 even/much/still/far/a lot: 훨씬(비교급을 강조)

09 Corky도 처음에는 나머지 전사들과 격렬히 싸웠지만, 지치게 된 다음에는 더는 싸움을 하지 않고 부상당한 자들을 돌보았다.

10 ①은 Thunder를 가리키고, 나머지는 다 Corky를 가리킨다.

11 이 글은 'Corky가 마지막 무기인 평화를 얻고 진정한 승자가 되는' 내용의 글이므로, 교훈으로는 ⑤번 '모든 사람은 평화의 편에 서기를 원한다.'가 적절하다.

12 keep ~ing: 계속해서 ~하다

13 (A)와 ④: ~라고 적혀 있다[쓰여 있다](자동사), ① 읽다, 읽어서 알다, ② (특정한 방식으로) 이해하다, ③ (계기를) 확인[검침]하다, ⑤ (컴퓨터나 사용자가 디스크의 정보를) 읽다, 판독하다

14 Corky는 첫 번째 반응이 상황을 더 악화시키자, '다른 방법을 써야겠어.'라고 생각하며 부드럽게 말하기 시작했다.

15 '(시험에 통과한) 19명의 다른 전사들'을 가리킨다.

16 the+형용사 = 복수 보통명사

17 이 글은 '의자에 가장 먼저 앉는 사람이 승자가 될 것이라는 스승의 시험에 Corky도 처음에는 나머지 전사들과 격렬히 싸웠지만, 나중에는 더는 싸움을 하지 않고 부상당한 자들을 돌봐주었고, 그 결과 Thunder를 제외한 모든 전사들이 Corky를 따르게 되었다'는 내용의 글이므로, 주제로는 ⑤번 'Corky는 부상당한 자들을 돌봐줌으로써 많은 추종자들을 얻었다.'가 적절하다.

18 지각동사+목적어+현재분사/동사원형(목적격보어): …가 ~하는 것을 보다

19 sooner or later 조만간, 머잖아

20 이 글은 'Corky가 마지막 무기인 평화를 얻고 진정한 승자가 되어 성으로 돌아가 장군이 되는' 내용의 글이므로, 제목으로는 ②번 '진정한 승자인 Corky가 마지막 무기인 '평화'를 얻다'가 적절하다.

21 ⓐ in: (시간의 경과를 나타내어) ~ 후에[~ 만에/~ 있으면], In a hundred days: 100일 '후에', ⓑ on: (요일, 날짜, 때를 나타내어) ~에, On the hundred and first day: 101일째 되던 날

22 'to learn'은 앞에 나오는 'much'를 수식해 주는 형용사적 용법의 to부정사로, 'have much to learn'은 '배울 것이 많다'라는

뜻이다.

23 ②번 다음 문장의 he에 주목한다. 주어진 문장의 Corky를 받고 있으므로 ②번이 적절하다.

24 관계대명사 that[which]이 적절하다.

25 Corky가 "나를 풀어 줘. 그렇지 않으면 모두 혼쭐날 줄 알아!"라고 외친 것이 상황을 '더 악화시켰다'고 하는 것이 적절하다.

26 immediately: 즉시, 즉각, finally/at last/in the end/after all/eventually: 결국, 마침내

27 take care of = look after = care for: 돌보다, ② 이룩하다, ③ (특정한 상품을) 취급[거래]하다, ⑤ 찾다

28 '전사들이 얼마나 오래 싸웠는지'는 알 수 없다. ① To a large hall with a chair in the middle. ② There were 19 other warriors. ③ The first one to sit in the chair. ⑤ Because Corky took good care of them.

서술형 시험대비　　p.96~97

01 (A) the strongest man　(B) to learn
02 (A) wait here　(B) a hundred
03 (A) in front of　(B) patience
04 (1) If you don't　(2) Unless you
05 (1) 부드럽게 말하는 것
　　(2) 자신이 위험하거나 나쁘지 않고 좋은 사람이라고 계속해서 말하는 것
06 The first one to sit in the chair will be the winner
07 (A) tired　(B) injured　(C) following
08 (A) taking care of　(B) fighting
09 he gave a wise and knowing smile to Corky
10 It was 'peace'.
11 (A) real winner　(B) weapon

01 비록 Corky가 그의 군대에서 '가장 강한 전사'이지만 그는 아직도 '배울 게' 많다고 생각했기 때문이다.

02 'a reason' 뒤에는 문맥상 '그를 그곳에서 100일 동안 기다리도록 하는 것에 대한(for making him wait there for a hundred days)'이 생략되어 있다.

03 (A) "거기서 기다려라."라고 군사 학교 안에서 외치는 목소리가 들렸다고 했으므로, Corky가 기다린 곳은 군사 학교의 문 '앞'이었다고 하는 것이 적절하다. (B) Corky의 첫 번째 무기는 '인내'이다. Corky는 유명한 군사 학교에 갔지만 그 문 앞에서 100일 동안 기다려야 했다. 101일째 되던 날 한 노인이 Corky가 지난 100일 동안 그의 첫 번째 무기인 '인내'를 사용하는 법을 배운 것이라고 말했다.

04 '명령문, or'는 'If you don't'나 'Unless you'를 사용하여 고치는 것이 적절하다. 명령문+접속사 'or': …해라. 그렇지 않으면 ~할 것이다.

05 뒤에 이어지는 내용을 쓰는 것이 적절하다.

06 형용사적 용법의 to부정사 to sit이 The first one을 수식하도록 하는 것이 적절하다.

07 (A) Corky는 '지쳤다'고 해야 하므로 tired가 적절하다. tired: 피곤한, 지친, tiring: 피곤하게 만드는, (B) '부상당한 자들'을 돌볼 것이라고 해야 하므로 injured가 적절하다. the+과거분사 = 복수 보통명사, victims: 피해자들, (C) 전사들이 Corky를 '따르고 있었다'라고 해야 하므로 following이 적절하다.

08 Corky는 다른 전사들과 '싸우는' 대신에 부상당한 자들을 '돌봐 줌으로써' 많은 추종자들을 얻었다.

09 give는 전치사 'to'를 사용하여 3형식으로 고치는 것이 적절하다.

10 Corky가 얻은 마지막 무기는 '평화'였다.

11 Thunder는 Corky가 '진정한 승자'라고 말했다. 마침내 Corky는 그의 스승이 가장 좋아하는 무기이기도 한 마지막 '무기'를 얻었다. Corky는 모든 훈련을 마친 후 궁으로 돌아가 장군이 되었다.

영역별 핵심문제　　p.99~103

01 injured	02 ④	03 ①	04 ②
05 Calm down	06 ④	07 ⑤	
08 ②	09 ④	10 ④	

11 he should have been more careful　　12 ③
13 ①, ②　　14 ③　　15 ③
16 ④ be → to be
17 (1) We need two things for peace. One is love and the other is hope.
　(2) We ask you to join us for peace.
　(3) I want you to stop fighting.
18 ⑤　　19 ③　　20 ②
21 should go
22 Patience is the most important thing to win a war.
23 ③　　24 ④　　25 ②　　26 ①
27 he was not dangerous or bad but was a good man
28 ⑤　　24 the other　　25 ①, ③

01 유의어 관계이다. 전사 : 부상당한

02 (a) '조만간 당신은 결정을 내려야 할 것이다.'라는 의미로 '조만간'은 'sooner or later'를 사용한다. 'in all possible ways'는 '모든 가능한 방법으로'라는 뜻이다. (b) '그녀는 조국으로 돌아가기를 바란다.'라는 의미로 '~로 돌아가다'는 'return to'를 사용한다.

03 '어떤 일을 하라고 누군가에게 말하다'의 의미로 'order(명령하다)'가 적절하다.

04 '경쟁에서 이기는 사람'의 의미로 'winner(우승자)'가 적절하다.

05 '화나거나, 기분 나쁘거나, 흥분을 느끼지 않게 하다'라는 의미로

19

'calm down(진정해)'이 적절하다.

06 ④번의 'look'은 명사로 '표정'이라는 뜻이다.

07 문맥상 빈칸에는 '너무 붐빈다'를 나타내는 말이 적절하다.

08 (B) 밖의 소음이 무엇인지 묻자 → (C) 히터를 고치고 있다는 대답이 나오고 → (A) 공부에 집중할 수 없어 참을 수가 없다고 화내는 표현이 나오고 → (D) 화냄에 대해 '진정해'라는 답이 나오는 것이 자연스럽다.

09 ④번은 '가수들이 무엇을 하고 있니?'라는 A의 물음에 한 명은 노래를 하고 있고 '나머지 모두(the others)'는 춤을 추고 있다가 적절하다. 'another'는 '또 다른 한 명'을 뜻하고 단수 취급한다.

10 '오늘 안경을 쓰고 있지 않다'고 했으므로 잘 볼 수 '없다'는 말이 적절하다. 'can see'를 'can't see'로 바꾸어야 한다.

11 '과거의 유감이나 후회'를 나타내는 표현으로 '~했어야 했는데'의 의미를 가지는 'should have p.p.'가 적절하다.

12 A가 '내 뒤에 있는 남자아이가 자꾸 밀어. 참을 수가 없어.'라고 화를 내는 말에 대해 '진정해. 그는 아직 어린아이야.'라는 대답이 자연스럽다.

13 'make'는 목적격보어로 원형부정사를 취하고, 'help'는 목적격보어로 원형부정사와 to부정사를 취한다. 'keep', 'leave'는 목적격보어로 현재분사를 쓰고, 'allow'는 to부정사를 쓰는 것이 적절하다.

14 b. 불특정한 두 가지 것 중 하나와 나머지 하나는 one, the other로 나타낸다. c. hear의 목적격보어는 원형부정사 또는 현재분사를 쓴다. (talk 또는 talking) f. 불특정한 다수의 사람 중 하나와 그 나머지 모두를 알 수 있을 때 one, the others를 쓴다.

15 (A) 불특정한 두 가지[사람] 중 하나와 나머지 하나는 one, the other로 나타내고, (B) 'tell'은 목적격보어로 to부정사를 취한다.

16 'tell'은 목적격보어로 to부정사를 취한다.

17 (1) 불특정한 두 가지 것 중 하나와 나머지 하나는 one, the other로 나타낸다. (2), (3) 'want'와 ask'는 목적격보어 자리에 to부정사가 오는 동사이다. '주어+동사+목적어+to부정사'의 어순으로 문장을 완성한다. *stop 동명사: ~하는 것을 멈추다.

18 'had'는 목적격보어로 원형부정사를 취한다.

19 c. 복수형 others로 쓴다. d. 나머지를 알 수 있으므로 the others로 표현한다. e. 불특정한 다수 중 또 다른 하나는 another로 쓴다.

20 (B)의 he가 주어진 글의 the teacher를 가리키므로 제일 먼저 오고 (A)의 another way가 (B)에서 말한 방법이 아닌 다른 방법을 말하는 것이므로 (B) 다음에 (A)가 이어지고 (C)에서 가장 강력한 무기인 '말'을 통제하게 된 것은 (A)에서 Corky가 자신이 위험하거나 나쁘지 않고 좋은 사람이라고 계속해서 말한 결과 마침내 사람들이 그를 풀어 준 것을 보고 스승이 하는 말이므로 (A) 다음에 (C)가 와야 한다. 그러므로 (B)-(A)-(C)의 순서가 적절하다.

21 명령을 나타내는 동사 뒤에 '당위성을 나타내는 조동사 should+동사원형'으로 고치는 것이 적절하다. 이때 should는

생략 가능하다.

22 to win a war: '전쟁에서 이기기 위해', 부사적 용법(목적)

23 이 글은 '훈련은 100일 후에 시작할 것이라는 말을 듣고 100일 동안 군사 학교 문 앞에서 기다린 후에, 마침내 Corky가 자신의 첫 번째 무기인 '인내'를 사용하는 법을 배우게 되는' 내용의 글이므로, 제목으로는 ③번 '마침내 Corky는 첫 번째 무기인 '인내'를 얻다!'가 적절하다.

24 주어진 문장의 them에 주목한다. ④번 앞 문장의 more warriors를 받고 있으므로 ④번이 적절하다.

25 ⓐ와 ②: (비교급을 강조하여) 훨씬(부사), ① 짝수의(형용사), ③ 평평한, 반반한(형용사), ④ (예상 밖이나 놀라운 일을 나타내어) ~도[조차](부사), ⑤ (무엇의 양, 득점 등이) 균등한, 동일한(형용사)

26 ⓐ tie A to B: A를 B에 묶다, ⓑ be in trouble: 어려움에 처하다

27 '자신이 위험하거나 나쁘지 않고 좋은 사람이라는 것'을 가리킨다.

28 가장 '강력한(powerful)' 무기는 '말'이다.

29 두 사람 중에 나머지 한 명을 가리키므로 'the other'가 적절하다.

30 ⓑ와 ①, ③: 현재분사, ②, ④, ⑤: 동명사

단원별 예상문제
p.104~107

01 untie   02 ⑤   03 ③

04 This is the third time he did that today.

05 ③   06 ③   07 ④

08 You always forget what you have to do.

09 ④   10 ⑤

11 told her students to listen to the dialog

12 (1) She told him to lock the door.
   (2) She wouldn't allow him to use her phone.
   (3) The grapes on the dish look very delicious. Some are green, and the others are purple.
   (4) Many children are big fans of animals. Some like monkeys, and others like lions.
   (5) I bought two pens. One is for me, and the other is for you.

13 He asked his people to fight peacefully against England.

14 On the hundred and first day, the gate opened.

15 ②

16 Patience is the most important thing to win a war.

17 ⑤   18 ③   19 (A) control (B) words

20 ①, ②, ⑤

21 Corky가 더 이상 싸움을 하지 않고 대신 부상당한 사람들을 돌볼 것이라고 말한 것

01 반의어 관계다. 밀다 - 당기다 : 묶다 - 풀다

02 '어떤 일이 왜 일어나는지 설명하는 사실이나 상황'이라는 의미로 'reason(이유)'이 적절하다.

03 빈칸 다음의 G의 말이 (A)의 물음에 대한 답이므로 안경이 어떻게 되었는지 묻는 말이 적절하다.

04 주어는 'This(이번)'가 되고 'he did that today'가 'time'을 수식하는 구조다.

05 필통이 사라졌다는 말로 보아 빈칸에는 화내는 표현이 적절하다. ③번은 '상쾌하다'라는 의미로 적절하지 않다.

06 '저 사람은 여기서 일하는 사람이야.'라는 B의 답으로 보아 불만을 표시하는 내용 중 ③번이 가장 적절하다.

07 그의 머리가 계속 내 어깨에 부딪힌다는 A의 말에 '진정해. 그는 나이가 들어서 잘 들을 수 없어.'라고 말하는 것은 자연스럽지 못하다.

08 빈도부사 'always'는 일반동사 앞에 위치하고 동사 'forget'의 목적어 자리에 'what+주어+동사' 어순을 사용한다.

09 Minsu는 과학 숙제가 그에게 어렵다고 생각한다.

10 불특정한 다수의 사람 중 하나와 그 나머지 모두를 알 수 있을 때 one, the others를 쓴다.

11 'tell'은 목적격보어 자리에 to부정사가 오는 동사이다. '주어+동사+목적어+to부정사'의 어순으로 과거시제로 문장을 완성한다. 동사 listen은 전치사 to와 함께 쓴다.

12 (1), (2) 'tell'과 'allow'는 목적격보어 자리에 to부정사가 오는 동사이다. (3) 불특정한 다수의 사물 중 일부와 그 나머지를 알 수 있을 때 some, the others를 쓴다. (4) 불특정한 다수의 일정하지 않은 수량을 나타내고 나머지가 불확실 할 때는 some, others를 쓴다. (5) 불특정한 두 사물 중 처음 하나와 나머지 하나는 one, the other로 나타낸다.

13 'ask'는 목적격보어 자리에 to부정사가 오는 동사이다. '주어+동사+목적어+to부정사'의 어순으로 배열한다.

14 on: (요일, 날짜, 때를 나타내어) ~에, on the hundred and first day: 101일째 되던 날

15 위 글은 '단편 소설'이라고 하는 것이 적절하다. ① 수필, ③ (신문, 잡지의) 글, 기사, ④ (책, 연극, 영화 등에 대한) 논평[비평], 감상문, ⑤ 독후감

16 '인내'가 전쟁에서 이기기 위해 가장 중요한 것이다.

17 주어진 문장의 That에 주목한다. ⑤번 앞 문장의 내용을 받고 있으므로 ⑤번이 적절하다.

18 이 글은 'Corky가 갑자기 기둥에 묶이고 그의 머리 위에 '위험하고 나쁨'이라는 푯말이 붙여진 상황에 대처하는 과정을 통해 가장 강력한 무기인 '말'을 통제하게 되는' 내용이다. 따라서, 주제로는 ③번 'Corky는 가장 강력한 무기인 '말'을 통제하게 되었다.'가 적절하다.

19 스승은 Corky에게 가장 강력한 무기인 '말'을 '통제하는 법'을 가르치기 위하여 Corky를 기둥에 묶고 그의 머리 위에는 '위험하고 나쁜'이라는 푯말을 붙였다.

20 ⓐ와 ③, ④: 형용사적 용법, ①, ⑤: 부사적 용법, ②: 명사적 용법

21 Corky가 "I will not fight anymore. Instead, I will take care of the injured."라고 말한 것을 가리킨다.

01 (A) I can't stand it.   (B) Take it easy.

02 he should have been more careful

03 he was busy doing his homework

04 (1) Three of six people came to the party. The others didn't.

　 (2) Amy wants Brian to tell her about his problem.

05 (1) Some of them are red

　 (2) If you want me to stay

06 (1) He ordered his dog to get down on the ground.

　 (2) She told him not to close the door.

　 (3) My mom won't allow me to go there.

07 (A) Some　(B) others　(C) another

08 He yelled, "Set me free, or you all will be in big trouble!"

09 (A) worse　(B) told them　(C) free　(D) weapon

01 (A) 늦었다는 말 다음에 화냄을 표현하는 말이 자연스럽다. (B)는 화내는 상대방에게 진정하라고 말하는 표현이 적절하다.

02 '과거의 유감이나 후회'를 나타내는 표현으로 '~했어야 했는데'의 의미를 가지는 'should have p.p.'가 적절하다.

03 설거지 할 것을 잊어버린 것에 대한 민수의 변명은 무엇인가?

04 (1) 나머지가 모두 3명이므로, 'The others'로 쓴다. (2) 'want'는 목적격보어 자리에 to부정사가 오는 동사이다.

05 (1) 불특정한 다수의 일정하지 않은 몇몇과 다른 몇몇을 나타낼 때 some, others를 쓴다. (2) 'want'는 목적격보어 자리에 to부정사가 오는 동사이다. '주어+동사+목적어+to부정사'의 어순으로 문장을 완성한다.

06 (1), (3) 'order'와 'tell'은 목적격보어 자리에 to부정사가 오는 동사이다. '주어+동사+목적어+to부정사'의 어순으로 문장을 완성한다. (2) to부정사의 부정은 'not to 동사원형'으로 쓴다.

07 (A) 지나가는 많은 사람들 중 '몇몇은'이라고 해야 하므로 Some이 적절하다. 'Some'은 불특정 다수의 여러 사람 중 '몇몇 사람들'이라는 뜻, (B) 지나가는 많은 사람들 중 '다른 몇몇은'이라고 해야 하므로 others가 적절하다. 'others'는 '(그 밖의) 다른 사람들', the other: 둘 중 나머지 하나, (C) 여러 방법들 중 '또 다른' 방법이라고 해야 하므로 another가 적절하다. the other: 둘 중 나머지 하나

08 앞 문장 전체를 가리킨다.

09 (A) 그는 "나를 풀어 줘. 그렇지 않으면 모두 혼쭐날 줄 알아!"

라고 외침으로써 상황을 더 '악화'시켰다. (B) Corky가 자신이 위험하거나 나쁘지 않고 좋은 사람이라고 '말했을 때' 그는 풀려 났다.

|모범답안|

01 (1) A: She is talking too loudly on the phone. I can't stand it.
　　 B: Calm down! She is talking to her baby.
　(2) A: His head keeps hitting me on my shoulder. I can't stand it.
　　 B: Calm down! He must be very tired.
　(3) A: She is eating something. I can't stand it.
　　 B: Calm down! She looks so hungry.
　(4) A: Children are running around. I can't stand it.
　　 B: Calm down! They are just kids.
02 (A) warriors　(B) the teacher　(C) standing
　(D) to sit in the chair

01 ③　　　02 powerful　03 ①　　　04 ⑤
05 (n)oise / (f)ixing / (f)ocus on / (s)tand it / (C)alm down
06 ④　　　　07 ⑤
08 I hate standing in line in cold weather.
09 (A) to do　(B) doing
10 (that) Minsu always forgets what he has to do
11 ②　　　12 ②　　　13 ②　　　14 ①
15 (1) Mina to use his pen
　(2) the man not to say anything to the police
16 (1) Some (friends) are kind
　(2) the other (bag) is brown
17 유명한 군사 학교 문 앞에서 18 ③
19 Set me free, or you all will be in big trouble
20 not as[so] strong as
21 had passed　　　22 ④

01 ③번은 '화내지 않고 침착하게 있을 수 있는 것'의 의미로 'patience(인내심)'에 관한 설명이다. 'impatience'는 '성급함' 이란 뜻이다.
02 유의어 관계이다. 지나가다 : 강력한
03 '울타리나 벽 밖에 있는 문'의 의미로 'gate(정문, 대문)'가 적절 하다.
04 ⑤번은 상대방이 화를 내는 말에 대해 'That's great!'라고 답 하는 것은 어색하다.
06 '~ 동안'의 이미로 전치사 'for'는 뒤에 숫자가 있는 기간이 나올

때 사용 가능하다.
07 100일 뒤에 문이 열리기 때문에 기다리는 것이 이 학교에 들어 가는 중요한 규칙이라는 내용의 대화. ⑤의 '하지만, 어떻게 풀려날 수 있겠느냐? 생각해 보아라.'는 글의 흐름에 어울리지 않는 문장이다.
08 동사 'hate'의 목적어 자리에 동명사 standing을 사용하고, '줄 을 서다'는 'stand in line'을 사용한다.
09 (A): '~할 것을 잊다'라는 의미로 'forget to+동사원형'을 사용 한다. (B): '~하느라 바쁘다'라는 의미로 'be busy+-ing'를 사 용한다.
10 질문: 민수의 누나는 민수에게 왜 화가 났는가?
11 (C)와 ②는 '나머지'라는 뜻이고 ①, ④, ⑤는 '휴식', ③은 '휴 식하다'라는 뜻이다.
12 (A) 불특정한 여럿 중 처음 하나는 one으로 나타내고, (B) 또 다른 하나는 another로 나타낸다. (C) 나머지가 무엇인지 알 수 있고 복수일 때 the others를 쓴다.
13 'ask'는 목적격보어 자리에 to부정사가 오는 동사이다.
14 'tell'은 목적격보어 자리에 to부정사가 오는 동사이고, 'make' 는 목적격보어 자리에 원형부정사가 오는 동사이다.
15 (1) 'allow'는 목적격보어 자리에 to부정사가 오는 동사이다.
　(2) to부정사의 부정은 'not to 동사원형'으로 쓴다.
16 (1) 불특정한 다수의 일정하지 않은 몇몇과 다른 몇몇을 나타낼 때 some, others를 쓴다. (2) 불특정한 두 사물 중 처음 하나와 나머지 하나는 one, the other로 나타낸다.
17 'in front of a famous military school'을 가리킨다.
18 ⓑ와 ①, ④: 명사적 용법, ②, ⑤: 부사적 용법, ③: 형용사적 용법
19 or를 보충하면 된다. 명령문+접속사 'or': …해라, 그러지 않으 면 ~할 것이다.
20 A 비교급 than B를 'B not as[so] 원급 as A'를 사용하여 바 꿔 쓰는 것이 적절하다.
21 '시험에 통과한' 것이 먼저 일어난 일이므로, 과거완료 시제인 'had passed'로 쓰는 것이 적절하다.
22 ⓐ와 ④: ~함에 따라(접속사), ① (자격·기능 등이) ~로(서)(전 치사), ② ~한 대로(접속사), ③ ~이기 때문에(접속사), ⑤ ~하다시 피[~이듯이](접속사)

Teen's Magazine

교과서 확인학습 A   p.122~124

01 Teens'	02 Make, Better
03 something nice	04 Say hello to
05 to say	06 on a rainy day
07 Laugh out loud	08 for
09 behind you	10 Invite, to
11 make, better	12 Peace
13 put, on	14 having friends
15 I'd rather	16 fighting, shouting
17 smile	18 inside
19 LAUGH	20 a day
21 keeps, away	22 what they say
23 just broke	24 Be Kind
25 what books hate, Why	26 bookmark
27 folding	28 It is, that

29 The more, the happier, How about

30 Facts, Fake	31 have ever lived
32 have ever been born	33 more, than
34 largest	35 bigger than

36 covers, the size of, covering

37 were invented	38 are cut into, pieces
39 Jobs	40 the greatest movie
41 what he does	42 with, Helping Judy
43 solves many cases	44 Everyone

45 anyone

46 named, Controlling, ends up becoming

47 with

48 what these emojis mean

49 Once in a, A piece of

51 The louder, the happier	52 Secret
53 no one else can read	54 Backward
55 easy to solve, backward	56 Every
57 starting with	59 easier than it looks

60 to send to, Make sure, send along

교과서 확인학습 B   p.125~127

1 Teens' Magazine

2 Ways to Make Your Town Better

3 Doing something nice for your neighbors can change your town. Start small. Here are some tips.

4 1. Say hello to your neighbors and smile.

5 2. Don't forget to say, "Thank you."

6 3. Share your umbrella on a rainy day.

7 4. Laugh out loud when your neighbor tells a joke.

8 5. Make something for your neighbors.

9 6. Hold the door for the person behind you.

10 7. Invite your neighbors to your party.

11 If you just do one thing each day, you can make your town better.

12 Messages for Peace

13 On World Peace Day, we put our peace messages on the board.

14 Peace means having friends around the world. - Kim Jimin

15 I'd rather have peace on Earth than pieces of Earth. - Seo Eunji

16 I want peace every place I go because there is always someone fighting or shouting. - Park Hansol

17 Peace makes everyone smile.- Yang Miran

18 Peace is inside all of us. We just need to share it. - Jang Jaehee

19 LET'S LAUGH

20 An apple a day

21 Jake came in to see his dad. "Dad!" he said, "Is it true that an apple a day keeps the doctor away?"

22 "That's what they say," said his dad.

23 "Well, give me an apple quickly! I just broke the doctor's window!"

24 Be Kind to Books!

25 Do you know what books hate? They hate water, the sun, and dog ears. Why dog ears?

26 Water is bad for WITCHES and BOOKS! / The SUN also TURNs Books YELLOW / Don't DOG-EAR! Use a bookmark! / Be Kind to Books!

27 Stop folding dog ears in books. Use a bookmark instead.

28 It is a bookmark that can save your books. Be kind to your books.

29 The more you love your books, the happier your books will be. How about making your own?

30 Facts That Sound Fake

31 1. About 7% of all people who have ever lived are living on the Earth today.

32 About 108,200 million people have ever been born in the history of the world. And about 7,442 million are living on the Earth today.

33 2. Bangladesh has more people than Russia.

34 Russia is the world's largest country, but tiny Bangladesh has 166.3 million people in 2018. Russia has 143.9 million people.

35 3. A banyan tree near Kolkata, India, is bigger than the average Walmart.

36 The average Walmart store covers about 104,000 square feet. The Great Banyan Tree in Kolkata, India, is about the size of a forest, covering 155,000 square feet.

37 4. Baby carrots were invented in 1986.

38 Baby carrots are not actually baby carrots. Big ugly carrots are cut into small pieces that have the shape of a baby carrot. Farmer Mike Yurosek invented them in 1986 as a way to use ugly carrots that weren't sold.

39 Jobs in the Movies

40 Zootopia (2016) It's the greatest movie ever!

41 Flash is a public officer. He is very slow but works hard. You will be surprised to see what he does in his free time. It's driving a race car!

42 Nick is a fox with a big mouth. Helping Judy, he gets closer to her. He later becomes a police officer like Judy.

43 Judy is a small rabbit, but she's smart and strong. After a lot of effort, she becomes a police officer and solves many cases.

44 Ratatouille (2007) Everyone will love this movie.

45 Anton Ego is a food critic. After he eats the food Remy cooked, he realizes that anyone can cook.

46 Remy, a little mouse, dreams of becoming a cook. He goes into a restaurant and meets a boy named Linguini. Controlling Linguini, he makes delicious food and ends up becoming a great cook.

47 Say It with Emojis

48 Do you know what these emojis mean?

49 Killing two birds with one stone. / The apple of your eyes. / Don't play games with fire. / Once in a blue moon. / Let's call it a day. / Money does not grow on trees. / It's raining cats and dogs. / A piece of cake.

50 Emoji Song

51 Now, let's sing a Christmas song together! The louder, the happier!

52 Secret Messages

53 Imagine you can send messages to your friend that no one else can read! It's not so difficult for you to learn how to read and write your own secret messages.

54 1. Read Backward

55 This is easy to solve. Just read the words backward! It seems simple once you know the secret, but it can be a hard one when you don't.

56 2. Read Every Second Letter

57 Read every second letter starting with the first letter, and when you finish, start again on the letters you missed.

58 3. Pig-pen

59 The Pig-pen is easier than it looks. The lines around each letter mean the letter inside the lines.

60 Now create your own set of secret letters and write secret messages to send to your friends. Make sure you send along a key so your friends can understand your messages!

서술형 실전문제 p.128~129

01 (1) case   (2) case

02 (1) had better   (2) keeps, away   (3) making sure

03 (1) end up arguing   (2) stop hiccupping
    (3) rained cats and dogs

04 (1) said (that) he had just broken the doctor's window
    (2) told his dad to give him an apple quickly

05 You will be surprised to see what he does in his free time.

06 (1) cut → are cut / Big ugly carrots가 작은 조각으로 잘리는 것이므로 수동태로 쓰는 것이 적절하다.
    (2) has → have / 주격 관계대명사 다음의 동사는 선행사에 수를 맞춘다. 선행사가 small pieces 이므로 동사는 have로 쓰는 것이 적절하다.

07 Why do books hate dog ears?

08 to fold → folding

09 more, happier

10 YOU LOOK GREAT TODAY.

11 every second letter

12 WHEN SHALL WE MEET? – LET'S MEET AT FIVE.

01 (1) 어떤 경우에는 사람들이 예약을 하기 위해 몇 주를 기다려야
했다. (2) 경찰이 그 사건 수사를 재개하기로 결정했다.

02 (1) 너는 외출하기 전에 설거지를 하는 것이 좋겠다. had
better+동사원형: ~하는 게 낫다 (2) 하루에 사과 한 알이면 의
사가 필요 없다. '~을 멀리하게 하다'라는 의미로 'keep+목적
어+away'를 사용한다. 주어가 'an apple'로 3인칭 단수이므로
'keeps'를 사용한다. (3) 학교는 학생들이 배우고 있는 것을 확
실히 하는 데에 집중해야 합니다. '~을 확실히 하다'라는 의미로
'make sure'를 사용하고, 전치사 on 뒤에는 '동명사'가 적절하
므로 'make'를 'making'으로 바꾸어 준다.

03 (1) '결국 ~가 되다'라는 의미로 'end up –ing'를 사용한다.
(2) '~을 멈추다'는 'stop+V-ing'를 사용한다. (3) '비가 억수
같이 내리다'는 'It rains cats and dogs.'를 사용하고 시제가
과거이므로 'raincd'를 쓴다. 여기서 'it'은 날씨를 나타내는 비
인칭 주어이다.

04 (1) 전달동사가 과거이므로, 시제의 일치 법칙에 맞게 따옴표
(" ") 안의 과거동사를 과거완료로 바꾼다. (just broke → had
just broken), 또한 따옴표 속 'I'는 문장의 주어로 바꾼다. (I →
he) (2) 전달동사 'said to'는 'told'로 바꿔야 하고 명령문의 간
접화법이므로 명령문의 동사원형을 to부정사로 쓴다. 또한 따옴
표 속 'me'는 문장의 주어인 'him'으로 바꾼다.

05 'What does he do in his free time?'이 간접의문문으로 이
어지면서 '의문사+주어+동사'의 순으로 쓴다.

06 (1) Big ugly carrots가 작은 조각으로 잘리는 것이므로 수동
태를 쓰는 것이 적절하다. (2) 주격 관계대명사 다음의 동사는
선행사에 수를 맞춘다. 선행사가 small pieces이므로 동사는
그에 맞게 have로 쓰는 것이 적절하다.

07 '왜 책들이 강아지 귀를 싫어할까요?'라고 해야 하므로 Why 다
음에 'do books hate'가 생략되어 있다.

08 '강아지 귀 모양으로 책을 접는 것을 멈춰 주세요.'라고 해야 하
므로 동명사로 고치는 것이 적절하다, stop+~ing: ~을 그만 두
다, stop+to부정사: ~을 하기 위해 멈추다

09 'the+비교급 …, the+비교급 ~' 구문을 접속사 As를 사용하여
고칠 때는, 비교급 앞의 the를 생략한 다음에 비교급을 As 뒤의
적절한 자리를 찾아 옮겨 쓰는 것이 적절하다. the+비교급 …,
the+비교급 ~: …하면 할수록, 더 ~하다

10 첫 번째 글자에서 시작해서 매 두 번째 글자를 읽고, 끝나면 여
러분이 빠뜨린 글자로 다시 시작하라고 했으므로, 비밀 메시지
의 내용은 'YOU LOOK GREAT TODAY.(너는 오늘 멋져
보인다.)'이다.

11 every second letter: 매 두 번째 글자

12 각 글자 주변의 선들은 그 선들 안에 있는 글자를 의미한다고 했으
므로, 비밀 메시지의 내용은 'WHEN SHALL WE MEET? –

LET'S MEET AT FIVE.(우리 언제 만날까? – 5시에 만나자.)'
이다.

단원별 예상문제

p.130~134

01 ③　　　02 shout　　　03 ①　　　04 realize
05 I would rather stay home than go there.
06 ④　　　07 ⑤
08 (1) instead, 대신에　(2) share, 공유하다
　(3) fold, 접다　(4) realize, 깨닫다
09 ⑤
10 (1) The more you love your books, the happier
　your books will be.
　(2) The more you work out, the harder you can
　study.
　(3) The hotter it gets, the shorter our pants get.
11 ②　　　12 ④　　　13 ③, ⑤　　　14 ③
15 ⑤　　　16 becoming　17 critic　　18 Remy
19 ④　　　20 saying → to say　　21 ①
22 It is a bookmark that can save your books.
23 ①, ③, ⑤　24 ②
25 Imagine you can send messages to your friend
　that no one else can read! 또는 Imagine you can
　send messages that no one else can read to your
　friend!
26 COME TO MY HOUSE AT TEN.　　27 ②
28 What he does in his free time
29 ①, ②, ④　30 ②, ⑤

01 ③번은 '책, 연극, 영화 등에 대한 의견을 말하는 것이 직업인
사람'의 뜻을 가지고 있는 'critic(비평가)'에 대한 설명이다.
'playwriter'는 '극작가'로 영어 풀이는 'a person who writes
plays'가 적절하다.

02 유의어 관계이다. 구하다 : 외치다, 소리치다

03 '누군가에게 당신의 집이나 파티에 오라고 부탁하다'라는 의미로
'초대하다'가 적절하다.

04 • 나는 오늘 처음으로 에너지의 소중함을 깨달았어. • 그는 최근
에 그의 꿈을 실현했습니다.

05 would rather A(동사원형) than B(동사원형) = prefer A(동
명사/명사) to B(동명사/명사) = prefer A(to V) rather than
B(to V): B보다 A하는 게 낫다

06 • 많은 배우들이 뉴욕의 브로드웨이 무대에서 공연하기를 꿈꿉
니다. '~에 관해 꿈꾸다'는 'dream of'를 사용한다. • 저는 친구
들과 더욱 많은 대화를 할 수 있고 그들에게 더욱 가까이 다가
갈 수 있습니다. '~에 다가가다'는 'get closer to'를 사용한다.

- 그러니, 누가 알겠어? 너는 놀랄만한 요리사가 될 수도 있어! '결국 ~가 되다'는 'end up -ing'를 사용한다.

07 모두 반의어 관계이고, ⑤번은 '상상하다'는 유의어 관계다.

08 (1) 다른 사람 또는 다른 어떤 것을 대신하여 (2) 다른 사람과 동시에 무언가를 가지거나 사용하는 것 (3) 어떤 것의 일부분이 다른 부분 위에 평평하게 놓이도록 어떤 것을 구부리다 (4) 이전에는 알아차리지 못하거나 이해하지 못했던 것을 알아차리거나 이해하다

09 ①~④는 'It ~ that ...' 강조구문이다. ⑤는 원인과 결과를 나타내는 'so ~ that' 구문이다.

10 '…하면 할수록 더 ~하다'라는 의미로 'The+비교급+주어+동사, the+비교급+주어+동사' 구문으로 문장을 쓴다.

11 'Do you know' 뒤에 목적어로 의문문 'what do books hate?'를 간접의문문으로 바꾸어 '의문사+주어+동사'의 순으로 나옴에 유의한다. 동사 'know'는 의문사를 문장 맨 앞에 쓰지 않는다.

12 ④ '의문사+to부정사'를 써야 하므로 'to read'로 쓰는 것이 적절하다. ① be동사의 보어가 필요하므로 형용사를 쓴다. ② 부정사의 의미상 주어에 of를 쓸 때는 술부에 사람의 성격을 나타내는 단어가 쓰일 때이다. ③ 가주어, 진주어 구문이므로 'to동사원형'을 쓴다. ⑤ 뒤에 명사가 이어지므로 소유대명사가 아닌 소유격을 쓴다.

13 '…하면 할수록 더 ~하다'라는 의미로 'The+비교급+주어+동사, the+비교급+주어+동사' 구문으로 문장을 쓰고, 이 문장을 'As 주어+동사+비교급, 주어+동사+비교급'으로도 쓸 수 있다. 이때 비교급은 동사에 맞게 형용사와 부사를 골라서 쓴다.

14 ①. ②. ④. ⑤는 가주어이고, ③은 비인칭 주어이다.

15 ①~④는 '열쇠도 함께 보낼 것을 명심하라.'는 뜻으로 앞으로 할 일을 나타낸다. ⑤ remember의 동명사 목적어는 이미 한 일을 나타내므로 '열쇠도 함께 보낸 것을 기억하라.'는 뜻이 되므로 나머지 문장과 다른 뜻이 된다.

16 end up ~ing: 결국 ~하게 되다

17 critic: 비평가, 책, 영화, 음악, 또는 예술과 같은 것들에 대해 글을 쓰거나 의견을 표현하는 사람

18 '작은 쥐 Remy'를 가리킨다.

19 ⓐ for: ~을 위해, ⓑ invite A to B: A를 B에 초대하다

20 '잊지 말고 말해라'라고 해야 하므로 to부정사로 고치는 것이 적절하다. forget+~ing: (과거에) ~한 것을 잊다, forget+to부정사: (미래에) ~해야 할 것을 잊다

21 '작은' 것부터 시작하라고 했다.

22 'A bookmark can save your books'에서 주어인 'A bookmark'를 강조하기 위해 'It is ... that ~' 강조 구문으로 영작하는 것이 적절하다.

23 ⓑ와 ①, ③, ⑤: ~하는 게 어때?, ② How do you like ~?: ~은 어떻습니까?, ~이 마음에 드십니까?, ④ Why don't we ~?: 우리 ~하는 게 어때?

24 '강아지 귀 모양으로 책을 접는 것' 대신에 '책갈피'를 이용해야 한다.

25 선행사 'messages'를 수식하는 관계대명사절은 'your friend' 다음에 써도 상관없다.

26 그냥 단어들을 거꾸로 읽으라고 했으므로, 비밀 메시지의 내용은 'COME TO MY HOUSE AT TEN.(10시에 우리 집에 오세요.)'이다.

27 ⓒ와 ②, ⑤: 부사적 용법, ①: 형용사적 용법, ③, ④: 명사적 용법

28 '그가 여가 시간에 하는 것'을 가리킨다.

29 ⓑ와 ①, ②, ④: 동명사, ③, ⑤ 현재분사

30 'Helping Judy'는 동시동작을 나타내는 분사구문으로 'Judy를 도우면서'의 뜻이다. 동시동작을 나타내는 분사구문은 접속사 As나 While을 사용하여 고치는 것이 적절하다. He helps Judy, and (he) gets closer to her.

교과서 파헤치기

단어 TEST Step 1   p.02

01 제공하다	02 최근에	03 건강한
04 찾다, 검색하다	05 증거	06 거짓의, 잘못된
07 근원, 출처	08 실제로, 사실	09 예술 작품
10 지지하다, 후원하다		11 ~인 것 같다
12 전적으로	13 가라앉다	14 비판적으로
15 우스운	16 가벼운	17 주요한, 주된
18 문어	19 감동적인	20 장소
21 공격하다	22 광대	23 제공하다
24 독특한	25 편안한	26 사실이 아닌
27 세제, 청소기	28 완벽한	29 공연, 수행
30 퍼진; 퍼지다	31 불확실한	32 완전한
33 뱀	34 선호하다	35 판명되다
36 포기하다	37 A와 B를 구별하다	
38 의미가 통하다	39 ~에 바탕을 두다	
40 돌아가시다	41 ~에 주의를 기울이다	
42 꾸며낸, 지어낸	43 큰 소리로 웃다	

단어 TEST Step 2   p.03

01 save	02 perfect	03 sink
04 prefer	05 cleaner	06 critically
07 attack	08 recently	09 false
10 performance	11 comfortable	12 actually
13 totally	14 source	15 evidence
16 support	17 complete	18 provide
19 scary	20 site	21 clown
22 spread	23 healthy	24 cheer
25 untrue	26 light	27 major
28 touching	29 octopus	30 artwork
31 unique	32 wear	33 boring
34 search	35 give up	36 pass away
37 be based on	38 make sense	39 laugh out loud
40 be made out of		41 turn out
42 pay attention to		43 tell A from B

단어 TEST Step 3   p.04

1 totally, 전적으로 2 lie, 거짓말 3 touching, 감동적인
4 major, 주된, 주요한 5 false, 거짓의, 잘못된
6 cheer, 환호하다 7 opinion, 의견 8 provide, 제공하다
9 critically, 비판적으로 10 sink, 가라앉다
11 octopus, 문어 12 evidence, 증거
13 spread, 퍼지다 14 attack, 공격하다
15 support, 지지하다 16 clown, 광대

대화문 TEST Step 1   p.05~06

Get Ready 2

(1) like, I think, fake / agree, kind, real
(2) sharp teeth. What do you think of, real / let's search, check
(3) What, think of / look like, strange / too
(4) This, real / Let's, fact sites, check, together

Start Off – Listen & Talk A

1. How do you feel about / light, comfortable / to buy, school field trip
2. is wearing, warm, light / agree with. Actually, much heavier / believe

Start Off - Listen & Talk B

How, feel / touching, gave up, to save, the best drama / don't agree / Why, think so / seem real, a little boring

Start Off – Speak Up

How, about, ad / shows / should not believe

Step Up – Real-life Scene

cool, How do you feel about / that / makes, laugh out loud / everything, says / octopus / make sense / when, climbing, lying / agree with, fake, out of

Express Yourself A

1. How, feel about / get along, with / these two, enjoying, together
2. How, feel / By the way / guess / prefer / with, better than, In fact / to help
3. feel about / anything special / were made out, uniform / passed away recently / touching

대화문 TEST Step 2   p.07~08

Get Ready 2

(1) G: There's no monkey like this in the world. Its nose is too big. I think it's fake.
   B: I don't agree. I saw that kind of monkey on TV. It's real.
(2) G: This animal has a long nose and two long, sharp teeth. What do you think of it? Is it real?
   B: Well, let's search the Internet and check it together.
   G: That's a good idea.

(3) B: What do you think of this animal?

G: It doesn't have legs, but it doesn't look like a snake. It's very strange.

B: I think so, too.

(4) B: This monkey is very small. Is it real?

G: I don't know. Let's visit some animal fact sites and check it together.

B: That's a good idea.

Start Off – Listen & Talk A

1. G: Look at those shoes the girl is wearing. I think they're great. How do you feel about them?

B: I think they look light and comfortable.

G: Right. I want to buy them for the school field trip.

2. G: I like the coat the boy is wearing. I think it's warm and light.

B: Well, I don't agree with you. Actually, I bought one last week. It's not so warm, and it's much heavier than it looks.

G: Really? I don't believe it.

Start Off - Listen & Talk B

G: How do you feel about this drama?

B: I think it's very touching. The boy gave up his life to save his sister. It's the best drama of this year.

G: I don't agree. It's not a good drama.

B: Come on. Why do you think so?

G: It doesn't seem real. And it's a little boring.

Start Off – Speak Up

A: How do you feel about this ad?

B: I think it's great. It shows the phone is strong.

A: I don't agree. We should not believe every ad.

Step Up – Real-life Scene

Alex: Big Mouth's show is really cool. How do you feel about it?

Somi: Well, I don't think it's that great.

Alex: Come on. I love Mr. Big Mouth. He always makes me laugh out loud.

Somi: He's funny, but don't believe everything he says.

Alex: All right. Oh, look at his photo of an octopus. He said it lives in a tree.

Somi: It doesn't make sense.

Alex: He took the photo when it was climbing the tree. I don't think he's lying. It's a great photo.

Somi: I don't agree with you. It's a fake photo. An octopus can't live out of the sea.

Express Yourself A

1. G: How do you feel about these animals?

B: They are very cute, but I think cats don't get along well with dogs.

G: I don't agree. And these two are good friends. They are enjoying the trip together.

2. G: How do you feel about this kid here?

B: I think she is very pretty. By the way, why did she cut her hair?

G: Can you guess?

B: Well, girls these days prefer short hair.

G: I don't agree with that. Most girls like long hair better than short hair. And this kid here is not a girl. In fact, he is a boy.

B: Really?

G: Yes. He grew his hair to help sick children.

3. G: How do you feel about the teddy bears?

B: They are cute. Is there anything special about them?

G: They were made out of a police officer's uniform.

B: Oh, I see.

G: This police officer made them for the kids. Their dad was a police officer, and he passed away recently.

B: That's very touching.

본문 TEST Step 1   p.09~10

01 Smart News Reader

02 scary, shook, across, bit

03 getting scared, things, one

04 checked up on, saying

05 actually made by, stations

06 hard evidence, trying, attack

07 turned out, complete lie

08 lot, at, thing, true

09 right sources, real, fake

10 Like, teenagers, think critically

11 getting, spread, full, false

12 how to tell, from

13 One, steps, slow down   14 too, to, true, think

15 evidence, supports what, says

16 where, coming from

17 tell fact from opinion   18 check, based on facts

19 hard, smart news reader

20 appears, provide, called, octopus

21 site, full, along, unclear

22 scary clowns, made up

23 once, carefully, everything, even

01 How to, Smart News Reader
02 shook schools across, didn't believe, a bit
03 getting scared, one of
04 checked up on, was saying
05 were actually made by, major newspapers
06 no hard evidence, trying to attack
07 turned out to be, complete lie
08 just look at one thing
09 to look at the right sources, pay attention to what is real, what is fake
10 Like, to think critically, on the Internet
11 getting more important, spread, full of false information
12 how to tell, from real news
13 One of the first steps, slow down
14 too good to be true
15 evidence, what the writer says
16 coming from   17 how to tell, from
18 have to, if, are based on facts
19 a smart news reader   20 appears to provide
21 is full of, along with, unclear photos
22 like, scary clowns, made up
23 once more carefully, question everything

1 현명한 뉴스 독자가 되는 방법
2 2016년 10월, 무서운 광대들에 관한 이야기가 워싱턴 지역 전역의 학교에 충격을 안겼지만, Danina Garcia-Fuller의 학생들은 조금도 그 이야기들을 믿지 않았다.
3 "몇몇 사람들은 그들이 소셜 미디어에 올라온 것들을 봤기 때문에 무서워했어요."라고 Garcia-Fuller의 학생 중 한 명인 Patricia Visoso가 말했다.
4 "하지만 그들은 이것을 누가 말하고 있는지를 전혀 확인하지 않았어요."
5 그 이야기들은 실제로 주요 신문사나 TV 방송국이 아닌 10대들이 지어냈다.
6 그들은 광대들이 정말로 학생들을 공격하려고 한다는 명백한 증거를 하나도 제공하지 않았다.
7 그 이야기는 결국 완벽한 거짓말인 것으로 드러났다.
8 "많은 사람이 단지 한 가지만을 보고 그것이 사실이라고 믿는 것 같아요."라고 Patricia의 반 친구인 Ivy-Brooks가 말했다.
9 올바른 출처를 살펴보고, 무엇이 진짜이고 무엇이 가짜인지에 주의를 기울이는 것은 정말 중요해요."
10 Garcia-Fuller의 학생들처럼, 많은 미국의 10대들은 뉴스 속 그리고 인터넷상에서 보고 있는 정보에 관해 비판적으로

생각하는 것을 배워 나가고 있다.
11 이 기능은 최근 더 중요해지고 있는데, 이야기들은 아주 빠른 속도로 퍼져 나갈 수 있고 누구나 허위 정보로 가득 찬 웹사이트를 만들어 낼 수 있기 때문이다.
12 Garcia-Fuller는 그녀가 자신의 학생들에게 가짜 뉴스를 진짜 뉴스로부터 구분하는 방법을 가르치고 있다고 말했다.
13 "첫 단계 중 하나는 속도를 늦추는 것(천천히 생각하는 것)입니다.
14 만약 어떤 이야기나 어떤 사진이 진짜라고 하기엔 너무 좋아 보인다면, 멈춰서 생각해 보세요.
15 글쓴이가 말하고 있는 것을 뒷받침하는 어떠한 증거라도 있나요?
16 그리고 이 정보가 어디서 온 것인가요?"
17 Garcia-Fuller의 학생들은 또한 뉴스에서 사실을 의견과 구분하는 방법에 대해서도 배운다.
18 "의견들은 읽을 만한 가치가 있습니다."라고 15실인 McKenzie Campbell이 말했다. "하지만 여러분은 그것들이 사실에 기반을 둔 것인지를 확인해 보아야 합니다."
19 Garcia-Fuller는 또한 때때로 현명한 뉴스 독자가 되는 것이 아주 어려울 수도 있다고 말했다.
20 그녀는 자신의 학생들을 '나무 문어'라는 이름의 동물에 대한 정보를 제공하는 것처럼 보이는 웹사이트로 시험한다.
21 그 사이트는 나무 위에 있는 문어들의 몇몇 불확실한 사진과 함께, 이 동물에 대한 정보로 가득 차 있다.
22 하지만 무서운 광대들의 이야기와 마찬가지로, 그것은 완전히 꾸며진 것이다.
23 Garcia-Fuller가 그녀의 학생들에게 말하는 교훈은 '당신이 보고 있는 정보를 한 번만 더 신중하게 확인해 보라'는 것과 '모든 것, 심지어 내가 말하는 것에도 의문을 가져 보라'는 것이다.

1 How to Be a Smart News Reader
2 In October 2016, stories about scary clowns shook schools across the Washington area, but Danina Garcia-Fuller's students didn't believe them a bit.
3 "Some people were getting scared because they saw things on social media," said Patricia Visoso, one of Garcia-Fuller's students.
4 "But they never checked up on who was saying this."
5 The stories were actually made by teenagers, not by major newspapers or TV stations.
6 They offered no hard evidence that clowns really were trying to attack students.
7 The story turned out to be a complete lie.
8 "I think a lot of people just look at one thing and

believe it's true," Patricia's classmate Ivy-Brooks said.

9 "It's really important to look at the right sources and to pay attention to what is real and what is fake."

10 Like Garcia-Fuller's students, many teenagers in America are learning to think critically about information they're seeing in the news and on the Internet.

11 This skill is getting more important these days as stories can spread very fast, and anyone can make a website full of false information.

12 Garcia-Fuller said she was teaching her students how to tell fake news from real news.

13 "One of the first steps is to slow down.

14 If a story or a photo seems too good to be true, stop and think.

15 Is there any evidence that supports what the writer says?

16 And where is this coming from?"

17 Garcia-Fuller's students also learn how to tell fact from opinion in the news.

18 "Opinions are good to read," said 15-year-old McKenzie Campbell, "but you also have to check if they are based on facts."

19 Garcia-Fuller also said sometimes it can be very hard to be a smart news reader.

20 She tests her students with a website that appears to provide information on an animal called a tree octopus.

21 The site is full of information on this animal, along with a few unclear photos of octopuses in trees.

22 But like the story of scary clowns, it's totally made up.

23 The lesson, Garcia-Fuller tells her students, is to "check the information you're seeing once more carefully" and to "question everything, even things that I say."

구석구석지문 TEST Step 1   p.19

After You Read A

1. shook, across the Washington area
2. how to tell fact from opinion
3. is full of, along with, unclear photos of octopuses

Do It Yourself

1. danced on the stage during

---

2. wondered if, would like their dancing
3. much better than any other
4. stood up, cheered loudly
5. the performance of the year

Link to the World

1. one of Picasso's works
2. drew, with, against a white background
3. if, brave, looks very tired, hungry
4. needs some food, water
5. artwork shows the most interesting part

구석구석지문 TEST Step 2   p.20

After You Read A

1. In October 2016, stories about scary clowns shook schools across the Washington area.
2. Garcia-Fuller's students also learn how to tell fact from opinion in the news.
3. The site is full of information on this animal, along with a few unclear photos of octopuses in trees.

Do It Yourself

1. Team NW danced on the stage during the school festival.
2. They wondered if the students and teachers would like their dancing.
3. But they performed much better than any other team.
4. A lot of students stood up and cheered loudly when the team danced.
5. Ms. Yu, the P.E. teacher, said it was the performance of the year.

Link to the World

1. This drawing, *Don Quixote*, is one of Picasso's works.
2. Picasso drew it in 1955 with black lines against a white background.
3. I don't know if the man on the horse is brave, but he looks very tired and hungry.
4. I think he needs some food and water.
5. I think this artwork shows the most interesting part of Cervantes' novel *Don Quixote*.

14 look, 표정 15 reason, 이유 16 warrior, 전사

단어 TEST Step 1   p.21

01 기둥, 막대, 장대	02 수리하다	03 무기
04 이유	05 상황	06 대신에
07 다 안다는 듯한	08 다가가다	09 군대; 군대의
10 전사	11 부상당한	
12 (사람들이 조직적으로 벌이는) 운동		13 인내심, 참을성
14 따르다, 따라가다	15 참다, 견디다	16 갑자기
17 장군	18 ~보다 위에	19 더 이상
20 일어나다, 발생하다		21 소리 지르다
22 표정	23 난방기, 히터	24 명령하다
25 궁, 궁전	26 군대, 육군	27 (개가) 짖다
28 강력한	29 정문, 대문	30 밀다
31 검, 칼	32 묶다	33 마침내
34 소음	35 포기하다	36 ~에 기대다
37 ~을 풀어주다, 석방하다		38 ~에 집중하다
39 진정하다	40 조만간, 머지않아	41 줄을 서다
42 그 순간에	43 모든 가능한 방법으로	

단어 TEST Step 2   p.22

01 gate	02 military	03 above
04 sword	05 patience	06 fix
07 situation	08 order	09 finally
10 anymore	11 injured	12 general
13 pole	14 happen	15 instead
16 approach	17 stand	18 fast
19 follow	20 warrior	21 army
22 palace	23 bark	24 knowing
25 look	26 winner	27 reason
28 movement	29 noise	30 weapon
31 yell	32 powerful	33 suddenly
34 tie	35 be in trouble	36 focus on
37 sooner or later	38 let ~ go	39 at that moment
40 calm down	41 give up	42 take care of
43 on the side of		

단어 TEST Step 3   p.23

1 yell, 소리 지르다 2 fix, 수리하다 3 general, 장군

4 fast, 단식하다 5 military, 군대 6 finally, 결국, 마침내

7 order, 명령하다 8 realize, 깨닫다 9 injured, 부상당한

10 patience, 인내심 11 powerful, 강력한

12 winner, 승리자, 우승자 13 bark, (개가) 짖다

대화문 TEST Step 1   p.24~25

Get Ready 2

(1) ve waited for more than / Calm, almost

(2) What, hate, in line, cold weather / Calm down, hot milk

(3) wait in line / Calm down, works

(4) behind, keeps pushing, can't stand / Calm down, just

Start Off – Listen & Talk A

1. noise outside / fixing, heaters / focus on, at all, can't stand it / down

2. can't find, seen / haven't, put / gone, upset / Calm, find

Start Off - Listen & Talk B

stepped on, foot / okay / third, did that, can't stand / Calm down, wearing, glasses / happened to / broke, during / should have been

Start Off – Speak Up

can't stand, crowded / Calm down, festival, enjoy

Step Up – Real-life Scene

I can use. Why didn't you, dishes / forgot to do / what, have to do, I can't stand, cleaned / busy doing / Do, dishes / finish, too difficult / m good at, Let me help / right now, the rest, after finishing

Express Yourself A

1. sent / in, hundred / spend, doing nothing, can't stand it / Calm down, It, rule to get

2. tie me up, set me free / get free / can't stand, sign, dangerous / I'm sure, way

Check yourself

noise outside / barking / can't focus on, stand it / Calm down, quiet

대화문 TEST Step 2   p.26~27

Get Ready 2

(1) M: We've waited for more than one hour, and we're still waiting.

   W: Calm down! We're almost there.

(2) G: Brrr.... What a cold day! I hate standing in line in cold weather.

   B: Calm down! Drink this hot milk.

   G: Oh, thank you so much.

(3) G: Look! That man didn't wait in line! I'm very angry.

B: Calm down! He works here.

(4) B: The boy behind me keeps pushing me. I can't stand it.

G: Calm down. He's just a child.

Start Off – Listen & Talk A

1. B: What's that noise outside?

G: They're fixing the heaters.

B: I can't focus on my studies at all. I can't stand it.

G: Calm down! They will finish it soon.

2. G: I can't find my pencil case. Have you seen it?

B: No, I haven't. Where did you put it?

G: I put it on my desk, but now it's gone. I'm really upset.

B: Calm down! I'll help you find it.

Start Off - Listen & Talk B

B: Ouch! He stepped on my foot again.

G: Are you okay?

B: No. This is the third time he did that today. I can't stand it. I'll go and talk to him.

G: Calm down! He's not wearing his glasses today, so he can't see well.

B: What happened to his glasses?

G: He broke his glasses during a soccer game this morning.

B: I see, but he should have been more careful.

Start Off – Speak Up

A: I can't stand this place. It's too crowded.

B: Calm down! We're at the festival. Let's enjoy it.

Step Up – Real-life Scene

Minji: Minsu, there is no cup I can use. Why didn't you do the dishes?

Minho: Sorry, but I forgot to do them.

Minji: What? You always forget what you have to do. I can't stand it. I cleaned the living room all morning.

Minho: Calm down! I'm busy doing my homework.

Minji: Do the dishes first, and then do your homework.

Minho: I can't. I don't think I can finish my homework today. Science is too difficult for me.

Minji: Science? You know I'm goot at science. Let me help you.

Minho: Great. Thanks. I'll wash your cup right now and I'll do the rest of the dishes after finishing this.

Express Yourself A

1. M1: The king sent me here. Open the door.

M2: Wait there. The door will open in a hundred days.

M1: What? A hundred days? I can't spend a hundred days doing nothing. I can't stand it.

M2: Calm down! It is an important rule to get in this school.

2. M1: Why did you tie me up here? Please set me free.

M2: How can you get free? Think.

M1: I can't stand this sign. I'm not dangerous or bad.

M2: Calm down. I'm sure you'll find a way.

Check yourself

G: What's that noise outside?

B: A dog is barking.

G: I can't focus on my studies at all. I can't stand it.

B: Calm down! He will be quiet soon.

본문 TEST Step 1   p.28~30

01 the Best Warrior   02 brave young man

03 general, strongest, army, much

04 ordered, to, famous military

05 hundred, training, voice, gate

06 got angry

07 thought, might, reason, waited

08 hundred, first, gate opened

09 learned, use, weapon, patience

10 Patience, most, thing, win

11 Then, stand against, pole

12 Suddenly, tied, to, pole

13 Above, put, read, Dangerous

14 passed by

15 Some, looks, others shouted

16 shouted back

17 yelled, Set, free, trouble   18 made, situation worse

19 try another way, thought

20 Then, speak softly

21 not dangerous, bad but

22 kept saying, possible ways

23 let him go

24 the most powerful weapon

25 words, stronger than, swords

26 took, to, with, middle

27 other warriors, had passed

28 first one to sit　　　29 the others, fighting

30 pushed, pulled, jumped

31 fought, harder, became tired

32 Finally, fight anymore

33 Instead, take care, injured

34 other warriors, even harder

35 As, fought, warriors, hurt

36 care of, so, followed

37 all, warriors except, following

38 walked toward, sit in

39 saw, standing with, followers

40 realized, all alone　　　41 give up, real winner

42 moment, appeared, weapons, favorite

43 Sooner, later, side, peace

44 returned, palace, training ended

45 approach, wise, knowing, up

---

35 As, became tired, hurt　　36 took good care of

37 except, following

38 walked toward, to sit in it

39 standing with　　　　40 all alone

41 give up, the real winner

42 At that moment, appeared, my favorite

43 Sooner or later, on the side of

44 returned to

45 approach, knowing, What's up

---

01 the Best Warrior　　　　02 brave young man

03 strongest, the strongest man, have much to learn

04 ordered, to go

05 In a hundred days, voice said

06 got angry

07 might be a reason so, waited

08 On the hundred and first day

09 have learned, first weapon, patience

10 to win a war　　　11 to stand against

12 Suddenly, tied, to　　　13 Above, that read

14 passed by

15 Some, angry looks, others

16 shouted back

17 Set me free, or, in big trouble

18 made, worse　　　19 another, thought

20 began to speak softly　21 not, but

22 kept saying, all possible ways

23 Finally, let him go

24 the most powerful weapon

25 stronger than sharp swords

26 took, to, in the middle　27 other, had passed

28 The first one to, winner

29 the others began fighting

30 pushed, pulled, jumped

31 harder and harder, became tired

32 anymore

33 take care of the injured

34 other warriors, even harder

---

1 최고의 전사, Corky

2 Corky는 용감한 청년이었다.

3 그는 장군이 되기를 원했지만 왕은 이렇게 말했다. "자네는 우리 군대에서 가장 강한 전사이네. 하지만 자네는 아직도 배울 게 많아."

4 왕은 Corky에게 유명한 군사 학교에 갈 것을 명령했다.

5 "거기서 기다려라. 훈련은 100일 후에 시작할 것이다." 군사 학교 안에서 이렇게 외치는 목소리가 들렸다.

6 Corky는 화가 났다.

7 하지만 이유가 있을 것으로 생각하고 기다렸다.

8 101일째 되던 날, 문이 열렸다.

9 한 노인이 이렇게 말했다. "너는 첫 번째 무기인 '인내'를 사용하는 법을 배운 것이다.

10 인내는 전쟁에서 이기기 위해 가장 중요한 것이다."

11 그리고 난 뒤, 스승은 Corky에게 기둥 앞에 서라고 말했다.

12 갑자기 그는 Corky를 기둥에 묶었다.

13 그의 머리 위에는 '위험하고 나쁨'이라는 푯말을 붙였다.

14 많은 사람이 지나갔다.

15 몇몇은 Corky를 화난 표정으로 쳐다봤고, 다른 몇몇은 그에게 소리를 질렀다.

16 Corky도 그들에게 소리를 질렀다.

17 그는 "나를 풀어 줘. 그러지 않으면 모두 혼쭐날 줄 알아!"라고 외쳤다.

18 그것은 상황을 더 악화시켰다.

19 그는 '다른 방법을 써야겠어.'라고 생각했다.

20 그리고 나서 Corky는 부드럽게 말하기 시작했다.

21 그는 자신이 위험하거나 나쁘지 않고 좋은 사람이라고 말했다.

22 그는 모든 방법을 동원해 계속해서 이렇게 말했다.

23 마침내 사람들은 그를 풀어 주었다.

24 "이제 너는 가장 강력한 무기인 '말'을 통제하게 되었다.

25 부드러운 말은 날카로운 칼보다 강하니라."라고 스승은 말했다.

26 다음 단계로 스승은 Corky를 중앙에 의자가 놓여 있는 커다란 홀로 데리고 갔다.

27 그곳에는 시험에 통과한 19명의 다른 전사들이 있었다.

28 "저 의자에 가장 먼저 앉는 사람이 승자가 될 것이다."라고 스승이 말했다.

29 Corky와 나머지 전사들은 싸우기 시작했다.

30 그들은 밀고 당기고 달리고 뛰어올랐다.

31 그들은 점점 더 격렬히 싸웠고, Corky는 지쳤다.

32 마침내 그가 말했다. "나는 더는 싸움을 하지 않겠다.

33 대신에 부상당한 자들을 돌볼 것이다."

34 나머지 전사들은 이것을 보고 더 심하게 싸움을 했다.

35 그들이 싸움을 할수록 더 많은 전사들이 지치고 다쳤다.

36 Corky는 그들을 잘 돌봐 주었고, 그들은 Corky를 따르게 되었다.

37 곧 Thunder를 제외한 모든 전사들이 Corky를 따르고 있었다.

38 Thunder는 의자로 걸어가 그곳에 앉으려 했다.

39 그러다 그는 Corky가 18명의 추종자들과 함께 서 있는 것을 봤다.

40 Thunder는 자신이 혼자라는 사실을 깨달았다.

41 "나는 포기하겠다. 네가 진정한 승자다."라고 Thunder가 Corky에게 말했다.

42 그때 스승이 나타나 말했다. "모든 훌륭한 무기 중에서 평화는 내가 가장 좋아하는 것이다.

43 조만간 모든 사람은 평화의 편에 서기를 원한다."

44 Corky는 훈련을 마친 후 성으로 돌아갔다.

45 Corky가 다가오는 것을 본 왕은 그에게 이미 모든 것을 알고 있다는 듯한 현명한 미소를 띠며 말했다. "안녕하시오, 장군?"

---

1 Corky, the Best Warrior

2 Corky was a brave young man.

3 He wanted to be a general, but the king said, "You're the strongest man in my army, but you have much to learn."

4 He ordered Corky to go to a famous military school.

5 "Wait there. In a hundred days, your training will start," a voice said from inside the school gate.

6 Corky got angry.

7 But then he thought there might be a reason, so he waited.

8 On the hundred and first day, the gate opened.

9 An old man said, "You have learned to use your first weapon: patience.

10 Patience is the most important thing to win a war."

11 Then, the teacher told Corky to stand against a pole.

12 Suddenly, he tied Corky to the pole.

13 Above his head, he put a sign that read "Dangerous and Bad."

14 Many people passed by.

15 Some gave Corky angry looks, and others shouted at him.

16 Corky shouted back.

17 He yelled, "Set me free, or you all will be in big trouble!"

18 That made the situation worse.

19 "I need to try another way," he thought.

20 Then, Corky began to speak softly.

21 He said he was not dangerous or bad but was a good man.

22 He kept saying this in all possible ways.

23 Finally, the people let him go.

24 "Now you control the most powerful weapon: words.

25 Soft words are stronger than sharp swords," said the teacher.

26 Next, the teacher took Corky to a large hall with a chair in the middle.

27 There were 19 other warriors who had passed their tests.

28 "The first one to sit in the chair will be the winner," the teacher said.

29 Corky and the others began fighting.

30 They pushed, pulled, ran, and jumped.

31 They fought harder and harder, so Corky became tired.

32 Finally, he said, "I will not fight anymore.

33 Instead, I will take care of the injured."

34 The other warriors saw this and fought even harder.

35 As they fought, more warriors became tired and hurt.

36 Corky took good care of them, so they followed him.

37 Soon, all the warriors except Thunder were following Corky.

38 Thunder walked toward the chair to sit in it.

39 Then, he saw Corky standing with his 18 followers.

40 Thunder realized he was all alone.

41 "I give up. You're the real winner," Thunder said to Corky.

42 At that moment, the teacher appeared and said, "Of all the great weapons, peace is my favorite.

43 Sooner or later, everyone wants to stand on the side of peace."

44 Corky returned to the palace after his training

---

ended.

45 When the king saw him approach, he gave Corky a wise and knowing smile and said, "What's up, General?"

After You Read A

1. wanted to be a general
2. the military school, for a hundred days
3. kept saying, dangerous[bad], set, free
4. stopped fighting, the injured

Inside the Story

1. are talking, One, the other
2. orders, to go to the military school
3. One, the others are listening
4. tells Corky to be quiet, stay
5. One, sword, the other is holding a stick
6. The man holding a sword, to wait
7. Some, the others are kneeling
8. to keep fighting to sit in

Link to the World

1. peaceful movement to free India
2. asked, to fight peacefully against
3. fasted, instead of fighting
4. An eye for an eye, make, blind

After You Read A

1. Corky wanted to be a general in the army.
2. Corky went to the military school and waited for a hundred days.
3. Corky kept saying he was not dangerous[bad], so people finally set him free.
4. Corky stopped fighting and took care of the injured.

Inside the Story

1. Two people are talking in the hall. One is the king, and the other is Corky.
2. The king orders Corky to go to the military school.
3. Many people are standing around Corky. One is talking to Corky, the others are listening.
4. The teacher tells Corky to be quiet and stay there.
5. Two men are standing inside the gate. One is holding a sword, and the other is holding a stick.
6. The man holding a sword tells Corky to wait there for 100 days.

7. Many warriors are listening to the teacher. Some are standing, and the others are kneeling.
8. The teacher wants them to keep fighting to sit in the chair.

Link to the World

1. Mahatma Gandhi led a peaceful movement to free India.
2. He asked his people to fight peacefully against England.
3. He fasted for a long time instead of fighting with weapons.
4. "An eye for an eye will only make the whole world blind," he said.

Lesson S

단어 TEST Step 1   p.45

01 대신에	02 평균; 평균의	03 통제하다, 조종하다
04 조언, 도움말	05 비평가	06 노력
07 공공의	08 깨닫다	09 대략
10 가짜의	11 접다	12 숲
13 모양, 형태	14 백만	
15 뒤에서부터, 역방향으로		16 사건
17 잡다	18 상상하다	19 공유하다, 나누다
20 작은	21 농담	22 이웃, 옆집 사람
23 소리치다	24 일단 ~하기만 하면	
25 (주로 소유격 뒤에서) ~ 자신의		26 평화
27 공무원	28 구하다	29 싫어하다
30 책갈피	31 관리, 관료	32 조각
33 해결하다	34 경주용 차	35 결국 ~가 되다
36 B하느니 A하겠다	37 ~와 가까워지다	38 ~를 멀리하게 하다
39 큰 소리로 웃다	40 ~를 잘게 썰다	41 ~하는 것을 멈추다
42 ~에게 인사하다	43 비가 억수같이 오다	

단어 TEST Step 2   p.46

01 critic	02 effort	03 average
04 fake	05 tip	06 fold
07 control	08 share	09 about
10 joke	11 public	12 forest
13 solve	14 once	15 race car
16 realize	17 save	18 shout
19 tiny	20 backward	21 own
22 peace	23 case	24 million
25 create	26 shape	27 bookmark
28 public officer	29 hold	30 neighbor
31 officer	32 instead	33 piece
34 imagine	35 laugh out loud	36 stop+-ing
37 make sure	28 would rather A than B	
39 end up -ing	40 get closer to	41 keep ~ away
42 say hello to	43 rain cats and dogs	

단어 TEST Step 3   p.47

1 effort, 노력   2 neighbor, 이웃 사람

3 backward, 뒤에서부터   4 delicious, 맛있는

5 forest, 숲   6 rain cats and dogs, 비가 억수같이 오다

7 instead, 대신에   8 invite, 초대하다

9 imagine, 상상하다   10 peace, 평화

---

11 share, 공유하다   12 fold, 접다   13 save, 구하다

14 critic, 비평가   15 realize, 깨닫다

16 make sure, 틀림없이 ~하다

본문 TEST Step 1   p.48~51

01 Teens' Magazine   02 Ways, Make, Better

03 something nice, change, tips

04 Say hello, neighbors, smile

05 forget to say   06 on a rainy day

07 Laugh out loud, joke

08 something for, neighbors

09 Hold, door, person behind

10 Invite, neighbors to

11 each, make, town better 12 Messages. Peace

13 put, messages on, board

14 having friends around

15 rather, peace, than pieces

16 place, because, fighting, shouting

17 makes everyone smile   18 inside, need to share

19 LET'S LAUGH   20 An, a day

21 true that, keeps, away   22 what they say

23 apple, just broke, window

24 Be Kind to

25 what books hate, Why

26 bad, WITCHES, TURNs, bookmark

27 Stop folding, bookmark instead

28 It, that, save, Be

29 more, happier, How about

30 Facts, Fake   31 About, have ever lived

32 have ever been born   33 has more people than

34 largest country, tiny, in

35 near, bigger than, average

36 covers, square, size, covering

37 were invented in

38 into, pieces, shape, sold

39 Jobs in, Movies

40 the greatest movie ever

41 public, surprised, what, free

42 with, gets closer, later

43 lot, effort, solves, cases 44 will love this

45 critic, cooked, realizes, anyone

46 named, Controlling, ends, becoming

47 Say It with

48 what these emojis mean

49 stone, grow, cats, piece 50 Emoji Song

51 let's sing, louder, happier

52 Secret Messages

53 Imagine, else, difficult, secret

54 Read Backward

55 solve, backward, simple, hard

56 Every Second Letter

57 every, starting, finish, missed

59 easier, looks, around, inside

60 Make sure, send along

49 Once in a, cats, dogs, A piece of

51 let's sing, The louder, the happier

52 Secret   53 no one else can read

54 Backward

55 easy to solve, backward, once

56 Every   57 starting with, missed

59 easier than it looks, each letter

60 secret letters, to send to, Make sure, send along

---

01 Teens'   02 Ways to Make, Better

03 something nice, some tips

04 Say hello to, smile   05 forget to say

06 on a rainy day   07 Laugh out loud

08 for   09 Hold, behind you

10 Invite, to

11 each day, make, better   12 Peace

13 put, on   14 having friends

15 I'd rather, than pieces

16 every place, fighting, shouting

17 makes, smile   18 inside

19 LAUGH   20 a day

21 it, that, keeps, away   22 what they say

23 just broke   24 Be Kind

25 what books hate, Why

26 WITCHES, TURNs, Don't, bookmark, Be Kind

27 folding, instead   28 It is, that can save

29 The more, the happier, How about, your own

30 Facts, Sound Fake

31 have ever lived, living on

32 have ever been born, about

33 more, than   34 largest

35 bigger than, average

36 covers, the size of, covering

37 were invented in

38 are cut into, pieces, way to use, weren't sold

39 Jobs   40 the greatest movie

41 public officer, surprised to see what he does

42 with, Helping Judy, later

43 a lot of effort, solves many cases

44 Everyone will love

45 food critic, realizes, anyone

46 dreams of becoming, named, Controlling, ends up becoming

47 with

48 what these emojis mean

1 십대들의 잡지

2 마을을 더 좋게 만드는 방법들

3 이웃들을 위해 뭔가 좋은 일을 하면 여러분의 마을을 변화시킬 수 있다. 작은 것부터 시작하라. 여기 몇 가지 도움말이 있다.

4 1. 이웃들에게 인사를 하고 미소를 지어라.

5 2. 잊지 말고 "고맙습니다."라고 말하라.

6 3. 비 오는 날에 당신의 우산을 함께 써라.

7 4. 이웃이 농담하면 크게 소리 내어 웃어라.

8 5. 이웃들을 위해 뭔가를 만들어라.

9 6. 뒤에 오는 사람을 위해 문을 잡아 줘라.

10 7. 이웃을 당신의 파티에 초대해라.

11 만약 당신이 매일 한 가지씩 하기만 하면, 당신의 마을을 더 좋게 만들 수 있다.

12 평화 메시지

13 우리는 세계 평화의 날에 게시판에 평화 메시지를 붙였다.

14 평화는 세상 어디에서나 친구가 있다는 것을 의미한다. – 김지민

15 나는 지구의 조각들을 갖니 지구 위의 평화를 갖겠다. – 서은지

16 항상 싸우거나 소리치는 누군가가 있으므로 I는 I내가 가는 모든 곳에서 평화를 원한다. – 박한솔

17 평화는 모든 사람을 미소 짓게 만든다. – 양미란

18 평화는 우리 모두의 내면에 있다. 우리는 단지 그것을 공유할 필요가 있을 뿐이다. – 장재희

19 웃읍시다

20 하루에 사과 한 개

21 Jake가 아빠를 보러 들어왔다. "아빠!" 그는 "하루에 사과 한 개가 의사를 멀리하게 만든다는 것이 사실이에요?"라고 말했다.

22 "사람들이 그렇게 말하지." 아빠가 말했다.

23 "자, 저에게 빨리 사과 한 개를 주세요! 제가 방금 의사 선생님의 유리창을 깨뜨렸어요!"

24 책들을 친절하게 대해 주세요!

25 여러분은 책들이 무엇을 싫어하는지 아나요? 그들은 물, 햇빛, 그리고 강아지 귀를 싫어합니다. 왜 강아지 귀일까요?

26 물은 마녀와 책에 해롭다! / 햇빛도 책을 누룽게 뜨게 한다. /

강아지 귀처럼 책을 접지 마라! 책갈피를 사용해라! / 책들을 친절하게 대해 주세요!

27 강아지 귀 모양으로 책을 접는 것을 멈춰 주세요. 대신에 책갈피를 이용하세요.

28 여러분의 책을 구해 주는 것은 바로 책갈피입니다. 여러분의 책들을 친절하게 대해 주세요.

29 여러분이 책을 더 많이 사랑하면 할수록 여러분의 책들은 더 행복해질 겁니다. 여러분 자신의 책갈피를 만들어 보는 게 어떨까요?

30 가짜 같은 사실

31 1. 지금까지 살아온 모든 사람의 약 7%가 오늘날 지구상에 살고 있다.

32 세계 역사에서 약 1천8십2억 명의 사람들이 지금까지 태어났다. 그리고 약 7십4억 4천2백만 명이 오늘날 지구상에 살고 있다.

33 2. 방글라데시는 러시아보다 인구가 더 많다.

34 러시아는 세계에서 가장 큰 나라이지만, 아주 작은 방글라데시에는 2018년 기준으로 1억 6천6백3십만 명의 인구가 있다. 러시아는 1억 4천3백9십만 명의 인구가 있다.

35 3. 인도 Kolkata 부근의 한 바니안(banyan) 나무는 평균적인 월마트보다 크다.

36 평균적인 월마트 상점은 약 10만4천 평방피트의 넓이이다. 인도 Kolkata에 있는 그레이트 바니안 나무는 대략 숲 하나의 크기로 15만5천 평방피트를 차지한다.

37 4. 베이비 당근은 1986년 발명되었다.

38 베이비 당근은 실제로 아기처럼 작은 당근이 아니다. 크고 못생긴 당근들이 베이비 당근 모양을 가진 작은 조각으로 잘린다. 농부 Mike Yurosek이 팔리지 않는 못생긴 당근을 사용할 하나의 방편으로 1986년에 그것을 발명하였다.

39 영화 속 직업들

40 주토피아(2016) 그것은 이제까지 가장 대단한 영화이다!

41 Flash는 공무원이다. 그는 아주 느리지만 열심히 일한다. 여러분은 그가 여가 시간에 무엇을 하는지 알게 되면 놀랄 것이다. 그것은 경주용 자동차를 운전하는 것이다!

42 Nick은 커다란 입을 가진 여우이다. Judy를 도우면서 그녀와 가까워진다. 나중에 Judy처럼 경찰관이 된다.

43 Judy는 작은 토끼지만, 영리하고 강하다. 많은 노력을 한 후에, 그녀는 경찰관이 되었고 많은 사건을 해결한다.

44 라따뚜이(2007) 누구라도 이 영화를 사랑할 것이다.

45 Anton Ego는 음식 비평가이다. Remy가 요리한 음식을 먹은 후에, 그는 "누구라도 요리할 수 있다."라는 것을 깨닫는다.

46 작은 쥐 Remy는 요리사가 되기를 꿈꾼다. 그는 식당에 들어가서 Linguini라는 이름의 소년을 만난다. Linguini를 통제하면서 그는 맛있는 음식을 만들고 결국에는 훌륭한 요리사가 된다.

47 이모지로 말하자

48 이 이모지들이 무엇을 의미하는지 아니?

49 돌 하나로 새 두 마리 잡기. (일석이조.) / 당신이 가장 사랑하는

사람. (눈에 넣어도 안 아플 사람.) / 불을 가지고 장난치지 마라. / 극히 드물게. / 오늘은 이만하자. / 돈이 나무에서 자라는 것은 아니다. (돈이 그냥 생기는 건 아니다.) / 비가 억수같이 온다. / 케이크 한 조각. (누워서 떡 먹기.)

50 이모지 노래

51 자, 함께 크리스마스 노래를 불러 봅시다! 더 크게 부를수록, 더 행복해집니다!

52 비밀 메시지

53 다른 어떤 사람도 읽을 수 없는 메시지를 친구에게 보낼 수 있다고 상상해 봐! 여러분 자신의 비밀 메시지를 읽고 쓰는 법을 배우는 것이 그렇게 어렵지는 않다.

54 1. 거꾸로 읽어라

55 이것은 풀기 쉽다 – 그냥 단어들을 거꾸로 읽어라! 일단 여러분이 비밀을 알면 간단하지만, 그렇지 못하면 어려울 수 있다.

56 2. 두 번째 글자마다 읽어라

57 첫 번째 글자에서 시작해서 두 번째 글자마다 읽어라. 그리고 끝나면 여러분이 빠뜨린 글자로 다시 시작하라.

58 3. 피그펜

59 피그펜(돼지우리)은 보기보다 쉽다. 각 글자 주변의 선들은 그 선들 안에 있는 글자를 의미한다.

60 이제 여러분은 자신만의 비밀 문자 세트를 만들어서 친구들에게 보낼 비밀 메시지를 써 보아라. 친구들이 메시지를 이해할 수 있도록 해결의 열쇠도 함께 보내도록 해라.

본문 TEST Step 4~Step 5   p.58~64

1 Teens' Magazine

2 Ways to Make Your Town Better

3 Doing something nice for your neighbors can change your town. Start small. Here are some tips.

4 1. Say hello to your neighbors and smile.

5 2. Don't forget to say, "Thank you."

6 3. Share your umbrella on a rainy day.

7 4. Laugh out loud when your neighbor tells a joke.

8 5. Make something for your neighbors.

9 6. Hold the door for the person behind you.

10 7. Invite your neighbors to your party.

11 If you just do one thing each day, you can make your town better.

12 Messages for Peace

13 On World Peace Day, we put our peace messages on the board.

14 Peace means having friends around the world. - Kim Jimin

15 I'd rather have peace on Earth than pieces of Earth. - Seo Eunji

16 I want peace every place I go because there is always someone fighting or shouting. - Park Hansol

17 Peace makes everyone smile.- Yang Miran

18 Peace is inside all of us. We just need to share it. - Jang Jaehee

19 LET'S LAUGH

20 An apple a day

21 Jake came in to see his dad. "Dad!" he said, "Is it true that an apple a day keeps the doctor away?"

22 "That's what they say," said his dad.

23 "Well, give me an apple quickly! I just broke the doctor's window!"

24 Be Kind to Books!

25 Do you know what books hate? They hate water, the sun, and dog ears. Why dog ears?

26 Water is bad for WITCHES and BOOKS! / The SUN also TURNs Books YELLOW / Don't DOG-EAR! Use a bookmark! / Be Kind to Books!

27 Stop folding dog ears in books. Use a bookmark instead.

28 It is a bookmark that can save your books. Be kind to your books.

29 The more you love your books, the happier your books will be. How about making your own?

30 Facts That Sound Fake

31 1. About 7% of all people who have ever lived are living on the Earth today.

32 About 108,200 million people have ever been born in the history of the world. And about 7,442 million are living on the Earth today.

33 2. Bangladesh has more people than Russia.

34 Russia is the world's largest country, but tiny Bangladesh has 166.3 million people in 2018. Russia has 143.9 million people.

35 3. A banyan tree near Kolkata, India, is bigger than the average Walmart.

36 The average Walmart store covers about 104,000 square feet. The Great Banyan Tree in Kolkata, India, is about the size of a forest, covering 155,000 square feet.

37 4. Baby carrots were invented in 1986.

38 Baby carrots are not actually baby carrots. Big ugly carrots are cut into small pieces that have the shape of a baby carrot. Farmer Mike Yurosek invented them in 1986 as a way to use ugly carrots that weren't sold.

39 Jobs in the Movies

40 Zootopia (2016) It's the greatest movie ever!

41 Flash is a public officer. He is very slow but works hard. You will be surprised to see what he does in his free time. It's driving a race car!

42 Nick is a fox with a big mouth. Helping Judy, he gets closer to her. He later becomes a police officer like Judy.

43 Judy is a small rabbit, but she's smart and strong. After a lot of effort, she becomes a police officer and solves many cases.

44 Ratatouille (2007) Everyone will love this movie.

45 Anton Ego is a food critic. After he eats the food Remy cooked, he realizes that anyone can cook.

46 Remy, a little mouse, dreams of becoming a cook. He goes into a restaurant and meets a boy named Linguini. Controlling Linguini, he makes delicious food and ends up becoming a great cook.

47 Say It with Emojis

48 Do you know what these emojis mean?

49 Killing two birds with one stone. / The apple of your eyes. / Don't play games with fire. / Once in a blue moon. / Let's call it a day. / Money does not grow on trees. / It's raining cats and dogs. / A piece of cake.

50 Emoji Song

51 Now, let's sing a Christmas song together! The louder, the happier!

52 Secret Messages

53 Imagine you can send messages to your friend that no one else can read! It's not so difficult for you to learn how to read and write your own secret messages.

54 1. Read Backward

55 This is easy to solve. Just read the words backward! It seems simple once you know the secret, but it can be a hard one when you don't.

56 2. Read Every Second Letter

57 Read every second letter starting with the first letter, and when you finish, start again on the letters you missed.

58 3. Pig-pen

59 The Pig-pen is easier than it looks. The lines around each letter mean the letter inside the lines.

60 Now create your own set of secret letters and write secret messages to send to your friends. Make sure you send along a key so your friends can understand your messages!

적중 100

영어 기출 문제집

정답 및 해설

천재 | 정사열